PSSA

Particularly Sensitive Sea Areas

2017 Edition

*Compilation of official guidance documents
and PSSAs adopted since 1990*

London, 2017

First published in 2007 by the
INTERNATIONAL MARITIME ORGANIZATION
4 Albert Embankment, London SE1 7SR
www.imo.org

Second edition 2017

Printed by CPI Colour

ISBN 978-92-801-1604-5

Picture credits: annex 6, Kyle Taylor (wrasse) and Taro Taylor (reef); annex 7, Steve Jurvetson (pelicans); annex 8, Joanne Goldby (Nazca booby) and Barry Peters (hammerhead shark); annex 9, BDJ238 (mangroves) and A.M.Anderson (grey angelfish); annex 10, Jerry Kirkhart (*Salicornia*); annex 13, Ingo Ronner (dolphins); annex 14, Brian Gratwicke (Magnificent frigate bird) and Rein Ketelaars (guineafowl pufferfish); annex 15, Mindaugas Danys (cormorant); annex 16, Gregory Moine (butterfly fish) and Troy McKaskle (Muana Lani); annex 17, Arnaud Abadie (white seabream, fan mussel); annex 18, F. Mazeas (corals); annex 19, Steve Raaymakers.

IMO PUBLICATION
Sales number: IA545E

This publication has been prepared from official documents of IMO, and every effort has been made to eliminate errors and reproduce the original text(s) faithfully. Readers should be aware that, in case of inconsistency, the official IMO text will prevail.

Contents

Contents

Foreword

A Particularly Sensitive Sea Area (PSSA) is an area of the marine environment that needs special protection through action by the International Maritime Organization (IMO) because of its significance for recognized ecological, socio-economic, or scientific attributes where such attributes may be vulnerable to damage by international shipping activities. At the time of designation of a PSSA, an associated protective measure (APM), which meets the requirements of the appropriate legal instrument establishing such measure, must have been approved or adopted by IMO to prevent, reduce, or eliminate the threat or identified vulnerability.

IMO is the only international body responsible for assessing proposals for and designating areas as PSSAs and adopting measures applicable to international shipping.

This publication provides the reader with an overview of all PSSAs designated by the MEPC since 1990[*] and includes all key "administrative documents" as follows:

.1 Revised PSSA Guidelines;

.2 Revised Guidelines to submit a PSSA Proposal to IMO;

.3 PSSA Proposal Review Form; and

.4 Uniform PSSA Resolution Format.

These texts were designed by the Marine Environment Protection Committee (MEPC) to assist Member Governments in the preparation, identification and submission of PSSAs and to provide the MEPC with the information for a robust review method of a PSSA proposal to ensure that the revised PSSA Guidelines are fulfilled.

It is also hoped that this publication will also assist mariners world-wide to approach and navigate near or through these PSSAs with caution and to act as recommended by the APMs.

---

[*] Some items of information contained in this book have been subject to amendment, and some associated protective measures have been added, renamed or revoked after the original documents were released. This is a consolidated text in which superseded texts have been replaced by the more recent ones; some details have been omitted but are in other publications that are available from IMO.

Worldwide Particularly Sensitive Sea Areas

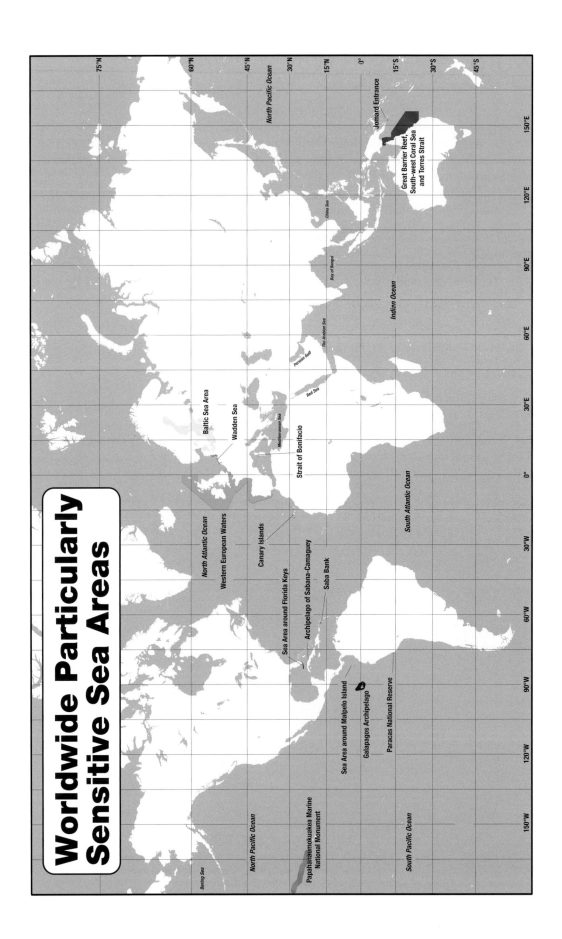

1 Introduction

Background

1.1   The Marine Environment Protection Committee (MEPC) of the International Maritime Organization (IMO) began its study of the question of Particularly Sensitive Sea Areas (PSSAs) in response to resolution 9 of the International Conference on Tanker Safety and Pollution Prevention, 1978 concerning the protection of particularly valuable sea areas. This resolution invited the then Inter-Governmental Maritime Consultative Organization (the original name of IMCO was changed in 1982 to IMO) to incorporate any necessary provisions within MARPOL for the protection of such areas against marine pollution from ships and dumping. These areas would be identified through an inventory of sea areas around the world which were in need of protection against marine pollution from ships and dumping, on account of the areas' particular value in respect of renewable resources or in respect of their importance for scientific purposes.

1.2   As a result, MEPC, recognizing the importance of this issue, consequently adopted the concept of PSSAs and identified a PSSA as an area that needs special protection through action by IMO because of its significance for recognized ecological, socio-economic, or scientific attributes where such attributes may be vulnerable to damage by international shipping activities.

1.3   In general, to be identified as a PSSA, three elements must be present: (1) the area must have certain attributes (ecological, socio-economic, or scientific); (2) it must be vulnerable to damage by international shipping activities; and (3) there must be a measure[*] with an identified legal basis that can be adopted by IMO to prevent, reduce, or eliminate risks from these activities. If approved by IMO, the end result will be an area designated as a "Particularly Sensitive Sea Area" and one or more IMO-adopted measures for ships to follow. It is noteworthy that such sea areas may include the territorial sea of States, and sea areas beyond national jurisdiction. Proposals must be submitted in accordance with IMO rules and procedures for the submission of documents. Governments[†] may check with the IMO Secretariat for the precise submission deadline as well as other administrative rules.

1.4   Another way of protecting sensitive sea areas is by establishing Marine Protected Areas. These are established for marine nature conservation reasons outside the IMO forum and, whilst they are an effective management tool, it is important to note that they do not protect areas from international shipping activities. Marine Protected Areas which require protection from international shipping should be brought to the attention of IMO for them to be proposed as PSSAs (or Special Areas under MARPOL), depending on the type of protection measure that is needed. Note that PSSAs can encompass both Special Areas and Marine Protected Areas and vice versa.

1.5   It is important to note that IMO is the only international body responsible for assessing proposals for and designating areas as PSSAs and adopting measures applicable to international shipping.

1.6   Discussions on the PSSA concept continued from 1986 to 1991 and culminated in the adoption of Guidelines for the Designation of Special Areas and the Identification of Particularly Sensitive Sea Areas by Assembly resolution A.720(17) in 1991 (the PSSA Guidelines). The PSSA Guidelines were designed to assist

---

[*] The reference to "measure" or "associated protective measure" is used both in the singular and plural throughout this guidance document. It is important to recognize that an identified vulnerability may be addressed by only one or by more than one measure or associated protective measure, and that therefore the use of this terminology in the singular or plural should not be taken as any indication to the contrary.

[†] The word "Government" is used both in the singular and plural throughout the text of this guidance document. It is clear, however, that the PSSA Guidelines recognize that an application for designation of a PSSA may be submitted by one or more Governments, and therefore the use of this terminology in the singular or plural should not be taken as an indication to the contrary.

---

in providing guidance to IMO Member Governments in the formulation and submission of applications for designation of PSSAs and in general aim to:

.1 ensure that, in the process, all interests – those of the coastal State, flag State, and the environmental shipping communities – are thoroughly considered on the basis of relevant scientific, technical, economic and environmental information regarding the area at risk of damage from international shipping activities and the protective measures to minimize the risk; and

.2 provide for the assessment of such applications by IMO.

PSSA Guidelines

1.7   In a continuing effort to provide a clearer understanding of the concepts set out in the PSSA Guidelines, and, where appropriate, strengthening certain aspects and procedures for the identification and designation of PSSAs and the adoption of associated protective measures (APMs), the IMO Assembly adopted subsequent sets of revisions of the PSSA Guidelines (A.720(17)) as resolution A.885(21) in 1999 and resolution A.927(22) in 2001. In 2005 MEPC finalized a comprehensive revision of the PSSA Guidelines, as contained in annex 2 of Assembly resolution A.927(22). The Assembly adopted the current set of PSSA Guidelines as A.982(24) in 2005 and revoked annex 2 of A.927(22). Resolution A.982(24) has been amended by resolution MEPC.267(68), adopted on 15 May 2015.

1.8   The 2005 PSSA Guidelines (A.982(24)) contain key differences in comparison with earlier versions, including:

.1 at the time of designation of a PSSA, an APM which meets the requirements of the appropriate legal instrument establishing such measure must have been approved or adopted by IMO to prevent, reduce, or eliminate the ship-related threat or identified vulnerability. Therefore all PSSA applications should identify proposals for at least one APM; however, proponents will be allowed to propose additional APMs at a later stage. The term "designation in principle" is now only to be used by the Committee after it reviews a proposal and is awaiting approval or adoption of the APM by the appropriate body;

.2 in order to be identified as a PSSA, the area should meet at least one of the criteria listed in section 4 (of the PSSA Guidelines) and supporting documentation should be provided to establish that at least one of the criteria exists throughout the entire proposed area, though the same criterion need not be present throughout the entire area. Terminology in some criteria listed in section 4 has also been strengthened and clarified;

.3 Member Governments wishing to have IMO designate a PSSA must submit an application to MEPC based on the criteria outlined in section 4 of the PSSA Guidelines, must provide information pertaining to the vulnerability of this area to damage from international shipping activities, and must include the proposed associated protective measures to prevent, reduce or eliminate the identified vulnerability. Applications must be submitted in accordance with the procedures set forth in the Guidelines and the rules adopted by IMO for submission of papers;

.4 there are no references to compulsory pilotage or vessel traffic management systems; and there are appropriate references to the fact that the Guidelines are to be implemented in accordance with international law; and

.5 in preparing its submission for a PSSA proposal, a Member Government which requires technical assistance to facilitate the development of robust and complete PSSA proposals is encouraged to request such assistance from IMO. The IMO should take into account the technical and financial resources available to developing Member Governments and those with economies in transition when considering PSSA proposals.

Revised supporting PSSA documentation

1.9   In 2005 and 2006, MEPC, having noted that substantial changes had taken place in the revised PSSA Guidelines, finalized a review of the Guidance Document for Submission of PSSA Proposals to IMO (MEPC.1/Circ.510, which replaced an earlier version, MEPC.1/Circ.398), developed a uniform format of the MEPC resolutions to designate PSSAs (MEPC 54/21 annex 11) and concluded a review of the PSSA Proposal Review Form (MEPC 55/23 annex 20). Full copies of the PSSA Guidelines and all supporting documents are contained in annexes 1, 2, 3 and 4 respectively.

Existing PSSAs

1.10   Since 1990, MEPC has reviewed and designated 16 PSSAs, including the Torres Strait extension and the Coral Sea extension to the Great Barrier Reef PSSA, which, incidentally, was the first PSSA designated in 1990 through MEPC resolutions MEPC.44(30) and MEPC.45(30). The details of every PSSA designated since 1990 have been brought together in this publication and are found in annexes 6–19. A useful overview of key information is set out in section 3 of this publication.

1.11   After designation takes place, information about the PSSA and the APM(s) is broadly disseminated to mariners operating in the designated area through identification on charts through the International Hydrographic Organization (IHO). They have also been brought to the attention of the shipping community through Notices to Mariners in a range of countries.

Compliance and enforcement

1.12   The PSSA Guidelines place an obligation on all IMO Member Governments to ensure that ships flying their flag comply with the APMs adopted to protect the designated PSSA. Nevertheless, in submitting proposals for APMs as part of a PSSA submission, proposing Member Governments need to give careful consideration to strategies for ensuring compliance by international shipping. While such strategies will depend largely on the applicable legal system, common concerns include jurisdiction, presentation of evidence, standards of proof of violation, whether sanctions are administrative, civil or penal, and the rights of the accused. IMO suggest that an effective compliance programme should incorporate all of the following elements:

-   Compliance monitoring through routine inspections, surveys, and/or examinations;

-   Detection and policing "patrols";

-   Reporting procedures and incentives, including incentives for self-reporting;

-   Adequate investigations of violations reported or otherwise detected;

-   A system of adequate sanctions in respect of violations;

-   Education and public awareness programmes; and

-   Co-operation and co-ordination with other States parties.

2 Summary of administrative documents

PSSA Guidelines

2.1   The 2005 PSSA Guidelines (Assembly resolution A.982(24)) set out the detailed requirements to be included in an application for designation of a PSSA. Its requirements should be followed in preparing a PSSA proposal. To assist Member Governments in meeting the requirements of resolution A.982(24), the document provides guidance for the development, drafting, and submission of proposals to IMO for the designation of a PSSA. The document also sets out the issues that should be included in such a proposal to facilitate its assessment and approval by IMO's MEPC; however, the assessment and determination of whether a PSSA should be designated are ultimately controlled by whether the proposal meets the provisions of resolution A.982(24).

2.2   A copy of the 2005 PSSA Guidelines, as amended by resolution MEPC.267(78), is set out in annex 1.

Guidance Document for Submission of PSSA Proposals to IMO

2.3   The MEPC, at its forty-eighth session, with a view to ensuring the proper development, drafting, and submission of proposals for the designation of Particularly Sensitive Sea Areas in accordance with the PSSA Guidelines, approved a guidance document for submission of PSSA proposals to IMO, which was circulated as MEPC/Circ.398.

2.4   Since the revised PSSA Guidelines were substantially amended, MEPC, at its fifty-fourth session, adopted a revised guidance document and issued it as MEPC.1/Circ.510. The revised guidance document supersedes the guidance document contained in MEPC/Circ.398.

2.5   It is important to note that MEPC, at its forty-sixth session, agreed that the Florida Keys PSSA proposal (MEPC 46/6/2) should serve as a model for Member States when proposing their PSSAs, and Member Governments should use the revised PSSA Guidelines (resolution A.982(24)) in preparing submissions of PSSA proposals. This guidance document for submission of PSSA proposals to IMO in no way supersedes the PSSA Guidelines, and any PSSA application must fulfil the provisions of those Guidelines. Member Governments are therefore invited to use the guidance document in the development, drafting, and submission of proposals for the designation of PSSAs.

2.6   A copy of the guidance document for submission of PSSA proposals to IMO (MEPC.1/Circ.510) is set out in annex 2.

PSSA Proposal Review Form

2.7   The PSSA Proposal Review was developed by the Technical Group on PSSAs as a tool to assist in assessing a PSSA proposal. At the time, a review form for Special Areas under MARPOL was also developed; however, this is outside the current mandate and is not reproduced herewith. It was recognized, however, that this form was only being used as a checklist and tended to promote only a "yes" or "no" reply rather than a thorough discussion of the proposed area in relation to the criteria set out in the PSSA Guidelines.

2.8   Given the length of the revised PSSA Guidelines, the importance of ensuring that all elements within the Guidelines are met, and that a robust review of proposals be conducted, a significantly revised review form was adopted by the Committee that would be more helpful in reviewing PSSA submissions. The form is structured in such a manner so as to promote a thorough discussion of all the elements of a submission. The review form also clearly alerts those Member Governments seeking PSSA designation of the questions they must address in their submissions.

2.9   A copy of the PSSA proposal review form (MEPC 55/23, annex 20) is set out in annex 3 of this publication.

Uniform format of the MEPC resolution for the designation of PSSAs

2.10   MEPC, having noted that existing PSSAs had been designated using a diverse range of resolutions, adopted a uniform format of the MEPC resolution to designate PSSAs.

2.11   A copy of the uniform format of the MEPC resolution for the designation of Particularly Sensitive Sea Areas is set out in annex 4 of this publication.

3 PSSAs designated by the Committee since 1990

Area	Proposing State(s)	Associated Protective Measures	MEPC endorsement
Great Barrier Reef	Australia	IMO-recommended Australia's system of pilotage; Mandatory ship reporting system; Area to be avoided [revoked 2015]	MEPC 30, September 1990 Resolution MEPC.44(30)
Torres Strait as an extension to the Great Barrier Reef	Australia and Papua New Guinea	IMO-recommended Australia's system of pilotage; Two-way route	MEPC 53, July 2005 Resolution MEPC.133(53)
South-west Coral Sea as an extension of the Great Barrier Reef and Torres Strait	Australia	Area to be avoided; Two-way routes	MEPC 68, May 2015 Resolution MEPC.268(68)
Archipelago of Sabana-Camagüey	Cuba	Traffic separation schemes; Areas to be avoided; Discharge prohibitions	MEPC 40, September 1997 Resolution MEPC.74(40)
Sea area around Malpelo Island	Colombia	Area to be avoided	MEPC 47, March 2002 Resolution MEPC.97(47)
Sea area around the Florida Keys	United States	Areas to be avoided; Mandatory no anchoring areas	MEPC 47, March 2002 Resolution MEPC.98(47)
Wadden Sea	Netherlands, Denmark, Germany	Existing protective measures – mandatory ship reporting systems; Recommended and mandatory pilotage; MARPOL Special Area	MEPC 48, October 2002 Resolution MEPC.101(48)
Paracas National Reserve	Peru	Area to be avoided (by ships > 200 gt carrying hydrocarbons in bulk)	MEPC 49, July 2003 Resolution MEPC.106(49)
Western European Waters	Belgium, France, Ireland, Portugal, Spain, UK	Reporting obligations for single-hull tankers carrying heavy grades of fuel oil	MEPC 52, October 2004 Resolution MEPC.121(52)
Canary Islands	Spain	Areas to be avoided; Traffic separation schemes; Mandatory ship reporting system	MEPC 53, July 2005 Resolution MEPC.134(53)
Galapagos Archipelago	Ecuador	Area to be avoided; Mandatory ship reporting system	MEPC 53, July 2005 Resolution MEPC.135(53)

Area	Proposing State(s)	Associated Protective Measures	MEPC endorsement
Baltic Sea	Denmark, Estonia, Finland, Germany, Latvia, Lithuania, Poland, Sweden	Traffic separation schemes; Deep-water routes; Areas to be avoided, in addition to existing routeing and pilotage systems; Mandatory ship reporting systems; MARPOL Special Area; MARPOL Special Area: SO_x Emission Control Area	MEPC 53, July 2005 Resolution MEPC.136(53)
Papahānaumokuākea Marine National Monument	United States	Areas to be avoided; Mandatory ship reporting system	MEPC 57, April 2008 Resolution MEPC.171(57)
Strait of Bonifacio	France and Italy	Recommendation on navigation; Routeing measures; Mandatory ship reporting system	MEPC 62, July 2011 Resolution MEPC.204(62)
Saba Bank, in the North-eastern Caribbean area of the Kingdom of the Netherlands	Netherlands	Existing Special Area according to Annex V (garbage); Mandatory no anchoring area for all ships; Area to be avoided (by ships > 300 gt)	MEPC 64, October 2012 Resolution MEPC.226(64)
Jomard Entrance	Papua New Guinea	Two-way routes; Precautionary area	MEPC 70, July 2016 Resolution MEPC.283(70)

4 Annexes

The following annexes contain copies of Assembly resolutions and associated MEPC resolutions designed to assist MEPC in the identification and designation of PSSAs and for Member Governments to prepare submissions to MEPC regarding PSSA proposals.

This section also contains full details about the PSSAs designated by IMO since 1990. For each PSSA, the MEPC resolution designating the area as a PSSA usually contains a succinct description of the area, a chartlet to identify where the PSSA is located, the co-ordinates and a description of the associated protective measures. The documents have been supplemented with additional information about associated protective measures or updated to incorporate amendments that have been made since their original adoption.

Annex 1 – PSSA Guidelines

Resolution A.982(24)

adopted on 1 December 2005
as amended by resolution MEPC.267(68), adopted on 15 May 2015

Revised guidelines for the identification and designation of Particularly Sensitive Sea Areas

THE ASSEMBLY,

RECALLING Article 15(j) of the Convention on the International Maritime Organization concerning the functions of the Assembly in relation to regulations and guidelines concerning maritime safety, the prevention and control of marine pollution from ships and other matters concerning the effect of shipping on the marine environment,

RECALLING ALSO resolution A.720(17) by which the Assembly adopted the Guidelines for the Designation of Special Areas and the Identification of Particularly Sensitive Sea Areas and requested the Marine Environment Protection Committee and the Maritime Safety Committee to keep the Guidelines under review,

RECALLING FURTHER resolution A.885(21), by which the Assembly adopted "Procedures for the Identification of Particularly Sensitive Sea Areas and the Adoption of Associated Protective Measures" and "Amendments to the Guidelines Contained in Resolution A.720(17)" and also requested the Marine Environment Protection Committee and the Maritime Safety Committee to keep those Procedures and Guidelines under review,

NOTING resolution A.927(22), by which it adopted: (a) new "Guidelines for the Designation of Special Areas under MARPOL 73/78", as set out in annex 1 to that resolution, which superseded chapter 2 of the annex to resolution A.720(17) and (b) new "Guidelines for the Identification and Designation of Particularly Sensitive Sea Areas", as set out in annex 2 to that resolution, which superseded chapter 3 of the annex to resolutions A.720(17) and A.885(21); and by which it also revoked resolutions A.720(17) and A.885(21) and requested the Marine Environment Protection Committee and the Maritime Safety Committee to keep the new Guidelines under review,

REAFFIRMING that these Guidelines are to be implemented in accordance with international law,

RECOGNIZING the need to clarify and, where appropriate, strengthen certain aspects and procedures for the identification and subsequent designation of Particularly Sensitive Sea Areas and the adoption of associated protective measures through amendments to the Guidelines for the Identification and Designation of Particularly Sensitive Sea Areas,

HAVING CONSIDERED the recommendations made by the Marine Environment Protection Committee at its fifty-third session:

1   ADOPTS the revised Guidelines for the Identification and Designation of Particularly Sensitive Sea Areas as set out in the annex, which supersede those in annex 2 of resolution A.927(22);

2   REQUESTS both the Marine Environment Protection Committee and the Maritime Safety Committee to keep the revised Guidelines under review;

3   REVOKES annex 2 of resolution A.927(22).

Annex
Revised Guidelines for the Identification and Designation
of Particularly Sensitive Sea Areas

1   Introduction

1.1   The Marine Environment Protection Committee (MEPC) of the International Maritime Organization (IMO) began its study of the question of Particularly Sensitive Sea Areas (PSSAs) in response to a resolution of the International Conference on Tanker Safety and Pollution Prevention of 1978. The discussions of this concept from 1986 to 1991 culminated in the adoption of Guidelines for the Designation of Special Areas and the Identification of Particularly Sensitive Sea Areas by Assembly resolution A.720(17) in 1991. In a continuing effort to provide a clearer understanding of the concepts set forth in the guidelines, the Assembly adopted resolutions A.885(21), A.927(22) and A.982(24). This document is intended to clarify and, where appropriate, strengthen certain aspects and procedures for the identification and designation of PSSAs and the adoption of associated protective measures. It sets forth revised Guidelines for the Identification and Designation of Particularly Sensitive Sea Areas (the Guidelines or PSSA Guidelines).

1.2   A PSSA is an area that needs special protection through action by IMO because of its significance for recognized ecological, socio-economic, or scientific attributes where such attributes may be vulnerable to damage by international shipping activities. At the time of designation of a PSSA, an associated protective measure,[*] which meets the requirements of the appropriate legal instrument establishing such measure, must have been approved or adopted by IMO to prevent, reduce, or eliminate the threat or identified vulnerability. Information on each of the PSSAs that has been designated by IMO is available at www.imo.org.

1.3   Many international and regional instruments encourage the protection of areas important for the conservation of biological diversity as well as other areas with high ecological, cultural, historical/ archaeological, socio-economic or scientific significance. These instruments further call upon their Parties to protect such vulnerable areas from damage or degradation, including from shipping activities.

1.4   The purpose of these Guidelines is to:

    .1   provide guidance to IMO Member Governments in the formulation and submission of applications for designation of PSSAs;

    .2   ensure that, in the process, all interests – those of the coastal State, flag State, and the environmental and shipping communities – are thoroughly considered on the basis of relevant scientific, technical, economic, and environmental information regarding the area at risk of damage from international shipping activities and the associated protective measures to prevent, reduce, or eliminate that risk; and

    .3   provide for the assessment of such applications by IMO.

1.5   Identification and designation of any PSSA and the adoption of associated protective measures require consideration of three integral components: the particular attributes of the proposed area, the vulnerability of such an area to damage by international shipping activities, and the availability of associated protective measures within the competence of IMO to prevent, reduce, or eliminate risks from these shipping activities.

2   International shipping activities and the marine environment

2.1   Shipping activity can constitute an environmental hazard to the marine environment in general and consequently even more so to environmentally and/or ecologically sensitive areas. Environmental hazards associated with shipping include:

    .1   operational discharges;

---

[*] The term "associated protective measure" or "measure" is used both in the singular and plural throughout these Guidelines. It is important to recognize that an identified vulnerability may be addressed by only one or by more than one associated protective measure and that therefore the use of this terminology in the singular or plural should not be taken as any indication to the contrary.

.2   accidental or intentional pollution; and

.3   physical damage to marine habitats or organisms.

2.2   Adverse effects and damage may occur to the marine environment and the living resources of the sea as a result of shipping activities. With the increase in global trade, shipping activities are also increasing, thus including greater potential for adverse effects and damage. In the course of routine operations, accidents, and wilful acts of pollution, ships may release a wide variety of substances either directly into the marine environment or indirectly through the atmosphere. Such releases include oil and oily mixtures, noxious liquid substances, sewage, garbage, noxious solid substances, anti-fouling systems, harmful aquatic organisms and pathogens, and even noise. In addition, ships may cause harm to marine organisms and their habitats through physical impact. These impacts may include the smothering of habitats, contamination by anti-fouling systems or other substances through groundings, and ship strikes of marine mammals.

3   Process for the designation of Particularly Sensitive Sea Areas

3.1   The IMO is the only international body responsible for designating areas as Particularly Sensitive Sea Areas and adopting associated protective measures. An application to IMO for designation of a PSSA and the adoption of associated protective measures, or an amendment thereto, may be submitted only by a Member Government. Where two or more Governments have a common interest in a particular area, they should formulate a co-ordinated proposal.* The proposal should contain integrated measures and procedures for co-operation between the jurisdictions of the proposing Member Governments.

3.2   Member Governments wishing to have IMO designate a PSSA should submit an application to MEPC based on the criteria outlined in section 4, provide information pertaining to the vulnerability of this area to damage from international shipping activities as called for in section 5, and include the proposed associated protective measures as outlined in section 6 to prevent, reduce or eliminate the identified vulnerability. Applications should be submitted in accordance with the procedures set forth in section 7 and the rules adopted by IMO for submission of documents.

3.3   If, in preparing its submission for a PSSA proposal, a Member Government requires technical assistance, that Government is encouraged to request such assistance from IMO.

4   Ecological, socio-economic, or scientific criteria for the identification of a Particularly Sensitive Sea Area

4.1   The following criteria apply to the identification of PSSAs only with respect to the adoption of measures to protect such areas against damage, or the identified threat of damage, from international shipping activities.

4.2   These criteria do not, therefore, apply to the identification of such areas for the purpose of establishing whether they should be protected from dumping activities, since that is implicitly covered by the London Convention 1972 (the Convention on the Prevention of Marine Pollution by Dumping of Wastes and Other Matter, 1972) and the 1996 Protocol to that Convention.

4.3   The criteria relate to PSSAs within and beyond the limits of the territorial sea. They can be used by IMO to designate PSSAs beyond the territorial sea with a view to the adoption of international protective measures regarding pollution and other damage caused by ships. They may also be used by national administrations to identify areas within their territorial seas that may have certain attributes reflected in the criteria and be vulnerable to damage by shipping activities.

4.4   In order to be identified as a PSSA, the area should meet at least one of the criteria listed below and information and supporting documentation should be provided to establish that at least one of the criteria exists throughout the entire proposed area, though the same criterion need not be present throughout the entire

---

* It is clear that the Guidelines recognize that an application for designation of a PSSA may be submitted by one or more Governments. For ease of drafting, however, the use of the word "Government" will be used throughout the text and it should be recognized that this term applies equally to applications where there is more than one Government involved.

area. These criteria can be divided into three categories: ecological criteria; social, cultural, and economic criteria; and scientific and educational criteria.

Ecological criteria

4.4.1 *Uniqueness or rarity* – An area or ecosystem is unique if it is "the only one of its kind". Habitats of rare, threatened, or endangered species that occur only in one area are an example. An area or ecosystem is rare if it only occurs in a few locations or has been seriously depleted across its range. An ecosystem may extend beyond country borders, assuming regional or international significance. Nurseries or certain feeding, breeding, or spawning areas may also be rare or unique.

4.4.2 *Critical habitat* – A sea area that may be essential for the survival, function, or recovery of fish stocks or rare or endangered marine species, or for the support of large marine ecosystems.

4.4.3 *Dependency* – An area where ecological processes are highly dependent on biotically structured systems (e.g. coral reefs, kelp forests, mangrove forests, seagrass beds). Such ecosystems often have high diversity, which is dependent on the structuring organisms. Dependency also embraces the migratory routes of fish, reptiles, birds, mammals, and invertebrates.

4.4.4 *Representativeness* – An area that is an outstanding and illustrative example of specific biodiversity, ecosystems, ecological or physiographic processes, or community or habitat types or other natural characteristics.

4.4.5 *Diversity* – An area that may have an exceptional variety of species or genetic diversity or includes highly varied ecosystems, habitats, and communities.

4.4.6 *Productivity* – An area that has a particularly high rate of natural biological production. Such productivity is the net result of biological and physical processes which result in an increase in biomass in areas such as oceanic fronts, upwelling areas and some gyres.

4.4.7 *Spawning or breeding grounds* – An area that may be a critical spawning or breeding ground or nursery area for marine species which may spend the rest of their life-cycle elsewhere, or is recognized as migratory routes for fish, reptiles, birds, mammals, or invertebrates.

4.4.8 *Naturalness* – An area that has experienced a relative lack of human-induced disturbance or degradation.

4.4.9 *Integrity* – An area that is a biologically functional unit, an effective, self-sustaining ecological entity.

4.4.10 *Fragility* – An area that is highly susceptible to degradation by natural events or by the activities of people. Biotic communities associated with coastal habitats may have a low tolerance to changes in environmental conditions, or they may exist close to the limits of their tolerance (e.g. water temperature, salinity, turbidity or depth). Such communities may suffer natural stresses such as storms or other natural conditions (e.g. circulation patterns) that concentrate harmful substances in water or sediments, low flushing rates, and/or oxygen depletion. Additional stress may be caused by human influences such as pollution and changes in salinity. Thus, an area already subject to stress from natural and/or human factors may be in need of special protection from further stress, including that arising from international shipping activities.

4.4.11 *Bio-geographic importance* – An area that either contains rare bio-geographic qualities or is representative of a bio-geographic "type" or types, or contains unique or unusual biological, chemical, physical, or geological features.

Social, cultural and economic criteria

4.4.12 *Social or economic dependency* – An area where the environmental quality and the use of living marine resources are of particular social or economic importance, including fishing, recreation, tourism, and the livelihoods of people who depend on access to the area.

4.4.13 *Human dependency –* An area that is of particular importance for the support of traditional subsistence or food production activities or for the protection of the cultural resources of the local human populations.

4.4.14 *Cultural heritage –* An area that is of particular importance because of the presence of significant historical and archaeological sites.

Scientific and educational criteria

4.4.15 *Research –* An area that has high scientific interest.

4.4.16 *Baseline for monitoring studies –* An area that provides suitable baseline conditions with regard to biota or environmental characteristics, because it has not had substantial perturbations or has been in such a state for a long period of time such that it is considered to be in a natural or near-natural condition.

4.4.17 *Education –* An area that offers an exceptional opportunity to demonstrate particular natural phenomena.

4.5 In some cases a PSSA may be identified within a Special Area and vice versa. It should be noted that the criteria with respect to the identification of PSSAs and the criteria for the designation of Special Areas are not mutually exclusive.

5 Vulnerability to impacts from international shipping

5.1 In addition to meeting at least one of the criteria listed in 4.4, the recognized attributes of the area should be at risk from international shipping activities. This involves consideration of the following factors:

Vessel traffic characteristics

5.1.1 *Operational factors –* Types of maritime activities (e.g. small fishing boats, small pleasure craft, oil and gas rigs) in the proposed area that by their presence may reduce the safety of navigation.

5.1.2 *Vessel types –* Types of vessels passing through or adjacent to the area (e.g. high-speed vessels, large tankers, or bulk carriers with small under-keel clearance).

5.1.3 *Traffic characteristics –* Volume or concentration of traffic, vessel interaction, distance offshore or other dangers to navigation are such as to involve greater risk of collision or grounding.

5.1.4 *Harmful substances carried –* Type and quantity of substances on board, whether cargo, fuel or stores, that would be harmful if released into the sea.

Natural factors

5.1.5 *Hydrographical –* Water depth, bottom and coastline topography, lack of proximate safe anchorages and other factors which call for increased navigational caution.

5.1.6 *Meteorological –* Prevailing weather, wind strength and direction, atmospheric visibility and other factors which increase the risk of collision and grounding and also the risk of damage to the sea area from discharges.

5.1.7 *Oceanographic –* Tidal streams, ocean currents, ice, and other factors which increase the risk of collision and grounding and also the risk of damage to the sea area from discharges.

5.2 In proposing an area as a PSSA and in considering the associated protective measures to prevent, reduce, or eliminate the identified vulnerability, other information that might be helpful includes the following:

    .1 any evidence that international shipping activities are causing or may cause damage to the attributes of the proposed area, including the significance or risk of the potential damage, the degree of harm that may be expected to cause damage, and whether such damage is reasonably foreseeable, as well as whether damage is of a recurring or cumulative nature;

.2   any history of groundings, collisions, or spills in the area and any consequences of such incidents;

.3   any adverse impacts to the environment outside the proposed PSSA expected to be caused by changes to international shipping activities as a result of PSSA designation;

.4   stresses from other environmental sources; and

.5   any measures already in effect and their actual or anticipated beneficial impact.

6   Associated Protective Measures

6.1   In the context of these Guidelines, associated protective measures for PSSAs are limited to actions that are to be, or have been, approved or adopted by IMO and include the following options:

6.1.1   designation of an area as a Special Area under MARPOL Annexes I, II, IV or V, or an emission control area under MARPOL Annex VI, or application of special discharge restrictions to vessels operating in a PSSA. Procedures and criteria for the designation of Special Areas are contained in the 2013 *Guidelines for the Designation of Special Areas under MARPOL*, set forth in the annex to resolution A.1087(28). Criteria and procedures for the designation of emission control areas are contained in appendix 3 to MARPOL Annex VI;

6.1.2   adoption of ships' routeing and reporting systems near or in the area, under the International Convention for the Safety of Life at Sea (SOLAS) and in accordance with the General Provisions on Ships' Routeing and the Guidelines and Criteria for Ship Reporting Systems. For example, a PSSA may be designated as an area to be avoided or it may be protected by other ships' routeing or reporting systems; and

6.1.3   development and adoption of other measures aimed at protecting specific sea areas against environmental damage from ships, provided that they have an identified legal basis.

6.2   Consideration should also be given to the potential for the area to be listed on the World Heritage List, declared a Biosphere Reserve, or included on a list of areas of international, regional, or national importance, or if the area is already the subject of such international, regional, or national conservation action or agreements.

6.3   In some circumstances, a proposed PSSA may include within its boundaries a buffer zone; in other words, an area contiguous to the site-specific feature (core area) for which specific protection from shipping is sought. However, the need for such a buffer zone should be justified in terms of how it would directly contribute to the adequate protection of the core area.

7   Procedure for the designation of Particularly Sensitive Sea Areas and the adoption of associated protective measures

7.1   An application for PSSA designation should contain a proposal for an associated protective measure that the proposing Member Government intends to submit to the appropriate IMO body. If the measure is not already available under an IMO instrument, the proposal should set forth the steps that the proposing Member Government has taken or will take to have the measure approved or adopted by IMO pursuant to an identified legal basis (see paragraph 7.5.2.3).

7.2   Alternatively, if no new associated protective measure is being proposed because IMO measures are already associated with the area to protect it, then the application should identify the threat of damage or damage being caused to the area by international shipping activities and show how the area is already being protected from such identified vulnerability by the associated protective measures. Amendments to existing measures may be introduced to address identified vulnerabilities.

7.3   In the future, additional associated protective measures may also be introduced to address identified vulnerabilities.

7.4   The application should first clearly set forth a summary of the objectives of the proposed PSSA designation, the location of the area, the need for protection, the associated protective measures, and demonstrate how the identified vulnerability will be addressed by existing or proposed associated protective measures. The summary should include the reasons why the associated protective measures are the preferred method for providing protection for the area to be identified as a PSSA.

7.5 Each application should then consist of two parts.

7.5.1 *Part I – Description, significance of the area and vulnerability*

.1 *Description* – a detailed description of the location of the proposed area, along with a nautical chart on which the location of the area and any associated protective measures are clearly marked, should be submitted with the application.

.2 *Significance of the area* – the application should state the significance of the area on the basis of recognized ecological, socio-economic, or scientific attributes and should explicitly refer to the criteria listed above in section 4.

.3 *Vulnerability of the area to damage by international shipping activities* – the application should provide an explanation of the nature and extent of the risks that international shipping activities pose to the environment of the proposed area, noting the factors listed in section 5. The application should describe the particular current or future international shipping activities that are causing or may be expected to cause damage to the proposed area, including the significance of the damage and degree of harm that may result from such activities, either from such activity alone or in combination with other threats.

7.5.2 *Part II – Appropriate associated protective measures and IMO's competence to approve or adopt such measures*

.1 The application should identify the existing and/or proposed associated protective measures and describe how they provide the needed protection from the threats of damage posed by international maritime activities occurring in and around the area. The application should specifically describe how the associated protective measures protect the area from the identified vulnerability.

.2 If the application identifies a new associated protective measure, then the proposing Member Government must append a draft of the proposal which is intended to be submitted to the appropriate Sub-Committee or Committee or, if the measures are not already available in an IMO instrument, information must be provided with regard to its legal basis and/or the steps that the proposing Member Government has taken or will take to establish the legal basis.

.3 The application should identify the legal basis for each measure. The legal bases for such measures are:

(i) any measure that is already available under an existing IMO instrument; or

(ii) any measure that does not yet exist but could become available through amendment of an IMO instrument or adoption of a new IMO instrument. The legal basis for any such measure would only be available after the IMO instrument was amended or adopted, as appropriate; or

(iii) any measure proposed for adoption in the territorial sea,[*] or pursuant to Article 211(6) of the United Nations Convention on the Law of the Sea where existing measures or a generally applicable measure (as set forth in subparagraph (ii) above) would not adequately address the particularized need of the proposed area.

.4 These measures may include ships' routeing measures; reporting requirements discharge restrictions; operational criteria; and prohibited activities, and should be specifically tailored to meet the need of the area to prevent, reduce, or eliminate the identified vulnerability of the area from international shipping activities.

---

[*] This provision does not derogate from the rights and duties of coastal States in the territorial sea as provided for in the United Nations Convention on the Law of the Sea.

.5 The application should clearly specify the category or categories of ships to which the proposed associated protective measures would apply, consistent with the provisions of the United Nations Convention on the Law of the Sea, including those related to vessels entitled to sovereign immunity, and other pertinent instruments.

7.6 The application should indicate the possible impact of any proposed measures on the safety and efficiency of navigation, taking into account the area of the ocean in which the proposed measures are to be implemented. The application should set forth such information as:

.1 consistency with the legal instrument under which the associated protective measure is being proposed;

.2 implications for vessel safety; and

.3 impact on vessel operations, such as existing traffic patterns or usage of the proposed area.

7.7 An application for PSSA designation should address all relevant considerations and criteria in these Guidelines, and should include relevant supporting information for each such item.

7.8 The application should contain a summary of steps taken, if any, by the proposing Member Government to date to protect the proposed area.

7.9 The proposing Member Government should also include in the application the details of action to be taken pursuant to domestic law for the failure of a ship to comply with the requirements of the associated protective measures. Any action taken should be consistent with international law as reflected in the United Nations Convention on the Law of the Sea.

7.10 The proposing Member Government should submit a separate proposal to the appropriate Sub-Committee or Committee to obtain the approval of any new associated protective measure. Such a proposal must comply with the requirements of the legal instrument relied upon to establish the measure.

8 Criteria for assessment of applications for designation of Particularly Sensitive Sea Areas and the adoption of associated protective measures

8.1 IMO should consider each application, or amendment thereto, submitted to it by a proposing Member Government on a case-by-case basis to determine whether the area fulfils at least one of the criteria set forth in section 4, the attributes of the area meeting section 4 criteria are vulnerable to damage by international shipping activities as set forth in section 5, and associated protective measures exist or are proposed to prevent, reduce, or eliminate the identified vulnerability.

8.2 In assessing each proposal, IMO should in particular consider:

.1 the full range of protective measures available and determine whether the proposed or existing associated protective measures are appropriate to prevent, reduce, or eliminate the identified vulnerability of the area from international shipping activities;

.2 whether such measures might result in an increased potential for significant adverse effects by international shipping activities on the environment outside the proposed PSSA; and

.3 the linkage between the recognized attributes, the identified vulnerability, the associated protective measure to prevent, reduce, or eliminate that vulnerability, and the overall size of the area, including whether the size is commensurate with that necessary to address the identified need.

8.3 The procedure for considering a PSSA application by IMO is as follows:

.1 the MEPC should bear primary responsibility within IMO for considering PSSA applications and all applications should first be submitted to the MEPC:

.1 the Committee should assess the elements of the proposal against the Guidelines and, as appropriate, should establish a technical group, comprising representatives with appropriate environmental, scientific, maritime, and legal expertise;

.2 the proposing Member Government is encouraged to make a presentation of the proposal, along with nautical charts and other supporting information on the required elements for PSSA designation;

.3 any technical group formed should prepare a brief report to the Committee summarizing their findings and the outcome of its assessment; and

.4 the outcome of the assessment of a PSSA application should be duly reflected in the report of the MEPC;

.2 if appropriate following its assessment, the MEPC should designate the area "in principle" and inform the appropriate Sub-Committee, Committee (which could be the MEPC itself), or the Assembly that is responsible for addressing the particular associated protective measures proposed for the area of the outcome of this assessment;

.3 the appropriate Sub-Committee or Committee which has received a submission by a proposing Member Government for an associated protective measure should review the proposal to determine whether it meets the procedures, criteria, and other requirements of the legal instrument under which the measure is proposed. The Sub-Committee may seek the advice of the MEPC on issues pertinent to the application;

.4 the MEPC should not designate a PSSA until after the associated protective measures are considered and approved by the pertinent Sub-Committee, Committee, or Assembly. If the associated protective measures are not approved by the pertinent IMO body, then the MEPC may reject the PSSA application entirely or request that the proposing Member Government submit new proposals for associated protective measures. A proper record of the proceedings should be included in the report of the MEPC;

.5 for measures that require approval by the Maritime Safety Committee (MSC), the Sub-Committee should forward its recommendation for approval of the associated protective measures to the MSC or, if the Sub-Committee rejects the measures, it should inform the MSC and MEPC and provide a statement of reasons for its decision. The MSC should consider any such recommendations and, if the measures are to be adopted, it should notify the MEPC of its decision;

.6 if the application is rejected, the MEPC shall notify the proposing Member Government, provide a statement of reasons for its decision and, if appropriate, request the Member Government to submit additional information; and

.7 after approval by the appropriate Sub-Committee, Committee, or, where necessary, the Assembly of the associated protective measures, the MEPC may designate the area as a PSSA.

8.4 IMO should provide a forum for the review and re-evaluation of any associated protective measure adopted, as necessary, taking into account pertinent comments, reports, and observations of the associated protective measures. Member Governments which have ships operating in the area of the designated PSSA are encouraged to bring any concerns with the associated protective measures to IMO so that any necessary adjustments may be made. Member Governments that originally submitted the application for designation with the associated protective measures should also bring any concerns and proposals for additional measures or modifications to any associated protective measure or the PSSA itself to IMO.

8.5 After the designation of a PSSA and its associated protective measures, IMO should ensure that the effective date of implementation is as soon as possible, based on the rules of IMO and consistent with international law.

8.6 IMO should, in assessing applications for designation of PSSAs and their associated protective measures, take into account the technical and financial resources available to developing Member Governments and those with economies in transition.

9 Implementation of designated PSSAs and the associated protective measures

9.1   When a PSSA receives final designation, all associated protective measures should be identified on charts in accordance with the symbols and methods of the International Hydrographic Organization (IHO).

9.2   A proposing Member Government should ensure that any associated protective measure is implemented in accordance with international law as reflected in the United Nations Convention on the Law of the Sea.

9.3   Member Governments should take all appropriate steps to ensure that ships flying their flag comply with the associated protective measures adopted to protect the designated PSSA. Those Member Governments which have received information of an alleged violation of an associated protective measure by a ship flying their flag should provide the Government which has reported the offence with the details of any appropriate action taken.

Annex 2 – Guidance document for submission of PSSA proposals to IMO

MEPC.1/Circ.510
10 May 2006

1   The Marine Environment Protection Committee, at its forty-eighth session, with a view to ensuring the proper development, drafting, and submission of proposals for the designation of Particularly Sensitive Sea Areas in accordance with the Guidelines for the Identification and Designation of Particularly Sensitive Sea Areas (the PSSA Guidelines), approved a Guidance Document for Submission of PSSA Proposals to IMO, which was circulated as MEPC/Circ.398. Since the revised PSSA Guidelines were adopted by the twenty-fourth Assembly in December 2005, the Committee, at its fifty-fourth session, adopted this revised Guidance Document. It is also important to note that the Committee, at its forty-sixth session, agreed that the Florida Keys PSSA proposal (MEPC 46/6/2) should serve as a model by Member States when proposing their PSSAs, and Member Governments should use the revised PSSA Guidelines (resolution A.982(24)) in preparing submissions of PSSA proposals.

2   The Guidance Document, as set out at annex to this circular, is complementary to the revised Guidelines for the Identification and Designation of Particularly Sensitive Sea Areas, contained in Assembly resolution A.982(24). This document in no way supersedes the PSSA Guidelines and any PSSA application must fulfil the provisions of those Guidelines.

3   Member Governments are invited to use the annexed Guidance Document in the development, drafting, and submission of proposals for the designation of Particularly Sensitive Sea Areas. Member Governments are also invited to bring this annexed Guidance Document to the attention of all interested entities.

4   This Guidance Document supersedes the Guidance Document contained in MEPC/Circ.398.

Annex

Guidance document for submission of PSSA proposals to IMO

1   Background

1.1   In December 2005, the International Maritime Organization (IMO) Assembly adopted resolution A.982(24), which sets forth the detailed requirements to be included in an application for designation of a Particularly Sensitive Sea Area (PSSA). This resolution supersedes annex 2 of Assembly resolution A.927(22). Its requirements should be followed in preparing a PSSA proposal. To assist Member Governments in meeting the requirements of resolution A.982(24), this document provides guidance for the development, drafting, and submission of proposals to IMO for the designation of a PSSA. This document sets forth the issues that should be included in such a proposal to facilitate its assessment and approval by IMO's Marine Environment Protection Committee (MEPC); however, the assessment and determination of whether a PSSA should be designated are ultimately controlled by whether the proposal meets the provisions of resolution A.982(24).

1.2   A PSSA is a comprehensive management tool at the international level that provides a mechanism for reviewing an area that is vulnerable to damage by international shipping and determining the most appropriate way to address that vulnerability. In general, to be identified as a PSSA, three elements must be present: (1) the area must have certain attributes (ecological, socio-economic, or scientific); (2) it must be vulnerable to damage by international shipping activities; and (3) there must be a measure[*] with an identified legal basis that can be adopted by IMO to prevent, reduce, or eliminate risks from these activities. If approved by IMO, the end result will be an area designated as a "Particularly Sensitive Sea Area" and one or more IMO-adopted measures for ships to follow. Information on each of the PSSAs that has been designated by IMO is available at www.imo.org.

1.3   Proposals must be submitted in accordance with the IMO rules and procedures for the submission of documents. Governments[†] may check with the IMO Secretariat for the precise submission deadline as well as other administrative rules.

2   Initial considerations

2.1   Before proceeding to IMO, a determination must be made that there is a threat to the attributes of an area from international shipping. If the threat is primarily being caused by shipping registered domestically, it may be more appropriate to address such a threat as a matter of domestic law. After the threat is identified, a decision can be made as to the most appropriate means to address it. Threats to the marine environment from international shipping can generally be separated into three categories: (1) impacts from accidents (e.g. groundings, spills, collisions); (2) operational discharges (i.e. oil, noxious liquid substances, sewage, garbage, air emissions, introduction of harmful aquatic organisms and pathogens through ships' ballast water); and (3) physical damage to marine habitats or organisms (i.e. anchor damage, ship strikes of marine animals, smothering of species/habitats, harmful effects from anti-fouling systems). Damage may also be caused from intentional violations of existing rules and regulations.

2.2   A proposal for PSSA designation may only be submitted by an IMO Member Government. To successfully develop a PSSA proposal, it may be necessary to assemble a small team of national experts in the country concerned. The team should include members who can describe and document the attributes of the area as well as the damage that has been or could be caused to the area. It should also include members who are familiar with the vessel operations in the area and the IMO measures that can be proposed to address the

---

[*] The reference to "measure" or "Associated Protective Measure" is used both in the singular and plural throughout this Guidance Document. It is important to recognize that an identified vulnerability may be addressed by only one or by more than one measure or Associated Protective Measure and that therefore the use of this terminology in the singular or plural should not be taken as any indication to the contrary.

[†] The word "Government" is used both in the singular and plural throughout the text of this Guidance Document. It is clear, however, that the PSSA Guidelines recognize that an application for designation of a PSSA may be submitted by one or more Governments and therefore the use of this terminology in the singular or plural should not be taken as an indication to the contrary.

damage. The proposing Member Government's representative(s) to IMO should also participate to facilitate submission and presentation of the proposal.

3   Required elements for a PSSA application

3.1   Summary of the proposal

3.1.1   The application should first clearly set forth a summary of the objectives of the proposed PSSA designation, the location of the area, the need for protection, the proposed associated protective measure, and demonstrate how the identified vulnerability will be addressed by the existing or proposed associated protective measure (APM). The summary should also include the reasons why the proposed associated protective measure is the preferred method for providing protection for the area to be identified as a PSSA.

3.2   Description of the area

3.2.1   The application must contain the location of the proposed area, including the geographic co-ordinates and a chart on which the area is marked. A buffer zone, which is an area contiguous to the site-specific or core feature of the proposed PSSA, may be included within the boundaries of the PSSA; however, the need for such a zone should be justified as to how it contributes to the protection of the core area.

3.3   Significance of the area: ecological, socio-economic, or scientific criteria

3.3.1   An area being proposed for PSSA identification must satisfy one or more of the economic, socio-economic, or scientific criteria, and information and supporting documentation should be provided to support that at least one criterion exists throughout the proposed area, although the same criterion need not be present throughout the entire area.

3.3.2   Proposing Member Governments should review the section of the PSSA Guidelines for a complete description of each criterion; however, the titles of the criteria are as follows:

 .1 *Ecological criteria*

  .1 Uniqueness or rarity

  .2 Critical habitat

  .3 Dependency

  .4 Representativeness

  .5 Diversity

  .6 Productivity

  .7 Spawning or breeding grounds

  .8 Naturalness

  .9 Integrity

  .10 Fragility

  .11 Bio-geographic importance

 .2 *Social, cultural and economic criteria*

  .1 Social or economic dependency

  .2 Human dependency

  .3 Cultural heritage

 .3 *Scientific and educational criteria*

  .1 Research

  .2 Baseline for monitoring studies

  .3 Education

3.4   Vulnerability to impacts by international shipping activities

3.4.1   In addition to meeting at least one of the criteria listed above, the recognized attributes of the area should be at risk from international shipping activities. Proposing Member Governments should review section 5 of the PSSA Guidelines for a complete description of such factors:

> **.1**   *Vessel traffic characteristics*
>
>> **.1**   Operational factors
>>
>> **.2**   Vessel types
>>
>> **.3**   Traffic characteristics
>>
>> **.4**   Harmful substances carried
>
> **.2**   *Natural factors*
>
>> **.1**   Hydrographical
>>
>> **.2**   Meteorological
>>
>> **.3**   Oceanographic
>
> **.3**   Other helpful information as suggested in paragraph 5.2 of the PSSA Guidelines.

3.5   Associated Protective Measures

3.5.1   The application should propose the APMs available through IMO and show how they provide the needed protection from the threats of damage posed by the international shipping activities occurring in and around the area. If the application identifies a new APM, then the proposing Member Government must append a draft of the proposal which is intended to be submitted to the appropriate Sub-Committee or Committee to its application. If the measure is not already available under an IMO instrument, the proposal should set forth its legal basis and/or the steps that the proposing Member Government has taken or will take to have the measure approved and adopted by IMO pursuant to an identified legal basis. If a protective measure already exists to protect the area, then the application should show how the area is being protected by this measure. Additional APMs may be introduced in the future to address identified vulnerabilities and, as with APMs that are proposed at the time of the initial application for PSSA designation, such measures must comply with the Guidelines.

> **.1**   *Types of measures* – The possible measures may include ships' routeing or reporting measures; discharge restrictions; operational criteria; and prohibited activities, and should be specifically tailored to meet the need of the area at risk.

> **.2**   *Legal basis* – Each APM must have an identified legal basis and the application should set forth the information on the consistency of the APM with the legal instrument under which the APM is proposed. (Guidelines, paragraphs 7.5.2.3 and 7.6.) The legal bases for APMs are: (i) any measure that is already available under an existing IMO instrument; or (ii) any measure that does not yet exist but could become available through the amendment of an IMO instrument or adoption of a new IMO instrument. The legal basis for any such measure would only be available after the IMO instrument was amended or adopted, as appropriate; or (iii) any measures proposed for adoption in the territorial sea[*] or pursuant to Article 211(6) of the United Nations Convention on the Law of the Sea where existing measures or a generally applicable measure (as set forth in (ii)) would not adequately address the particularized need of the proposed area. If the country is proceeding under a measure that is not yet available under an IMO instrument, the application should contain the steps that the Government is pursuing to have the measure approved or adopted by IMO pursuant to an identified legal basis.

---

[*] This provision does not derogate from the rights and duties of coastal States in the territorial sea as provided for in the United Nations Convention on the Law of the Sea.

.3   *Categories of ships* – The application should clearly specify the category or categories of ships to which the proposed associated protective measures would apply, consistent with the provisions of the United Nations Convention on the Law of the Sea – including those related to vessels entitled to sovereign immunity – and other pertinent instruments.

.4   *Impact on navigation* – The application should indicate the possible impact of any proposed measures on the safety and efficiency of navigation, taking into account the area of the ocean in which the proposed measures are to be implemented. The application should set forth such information as implications for ship safety and the impact on ship operations.

3.6 Miscellaneous issues

3.6.1   *Area* – The application should include a nautical chartlet on which the location of the area and the existing or proposed associated protective measure are clearly marked. The size of the area should be commensurate with that necessary to address the identified need.

3.6.2   *Summary of measures* – The application should contain a summary of steps taken, if any, to protect the proposed area. This would include any domestic regulations, any previously adopted IMO measures, and measures taken to address the adverse effects from activities other than shipping. It would also be useful to include whether the area has received any international designation, such as listed on the World Heritage List or declared a Biosphere Reserve.

3.6.3   *Enforcement* – The details of action to be taken pursuant to domestic law for the failure of a ship to comply with the requirements of the associated protective measures should also be provided as well as a statement that such action shall be consistent with international law as reflected in the United Nations Convention on the Law of the Sea.

3.6.4   *Joint proposals* – Where two or more Governments have a common interest in a particular area, they should formulate a co-ordinated proposal. The proposal should contain integrated measures and procedures for co operation between the jurisdictions of the proposing Governments.

3.6.5   *Implementation after designation* – Proposing Governments should ensure that any associated protective measure is implemented in accordance with international law as reflected in the United Nations Convention on the Law of the Sea. Information regarding such measures should be broadly disseminated to mariners operating in the designated area. All associated protective measures should be identified on charts in accordance with the symbols and methods of the International Hydrographic Office (IHO). A designated PSSA may also be charted with appropriate symbology.

3.6.6   *Technical assistance* – If, in preparing its PSSA application, a Member Government requires technical assistance, that Government is encouraged to request such assistance from IMO.

Annex 3 – PSSA proposal review form

MEPC 55/23, annex 20

The Technical Group will ask that the proposing Member Government provide a response to the issues raised below, including the appropriate citations to its submission. This, in combination with comments and information offered by other Member Governments regarding the proposed PSSA, will enable a thorough discussion and assessment of the proposal by the Technical Group.[*]

1 General

1.1 Name of area proposed to be designated as a PSSA: . . . .

1.2 Proposing Member Government(s): . . . .

1.3 Document containing proposal: . . . .

1.4 Related documents: . . . .

1.5 Navigational chart number which depicts area: . . . .

2 Summary of the proposal and other necessary background information

2.1 What are the objectives of the proposed designation? *(paragraph 7.4)*[†]

2.2 Is the description of the area complete and is it, and the existing or proposed associated protective measure (APM), clearly depicted on a chart or chartlet? *(paragraph 7.5.1.1)*

2.3 Does the application provide an adequate summary of the need for protection, including a demonstration of the identified vulnerability to international shipping? *(paragraph 7.4)*

2.4 Is the APM adequately described, including how it will address the identified vulnerability? *(paragraph 7.4)*

2.5 Are the reasons included as to why the APM is the preferred method for providing protection? *(paragraph 7.4)*

2.6 Are there other Member States that have a common interest in the proposed area? *(paragraph 3.1)*

2.7 If the answer to 2.6 is yes, have they been consulted to formulate a coordinated proposal, with integrated measures and procedures for cooperation? *(paragraph 3.1)*

3 Ecological, socio-economic, or scientific criteria
(Guidelines, section 4)

Do the supporting documentation and references establish that the area is vulnerable to damage or the identified threat of damage from international shipping activities for at least one of the following reasons? *(paragraph 4.1)*

---

[*] As with the PSSA Guidelines, references to "Member Government" and "measure" are in the singular and it is intended that such usage encompasses both the singular and plural of these terms.

[†] The paragraphs are citations to the appropriate paragraphs in the Revised PSSA Guidelines.

(In addressing this point, at least one of the criteria needs to exist throughout the entire proposed area, though the same criterion need not be present throughout the entire area.) *(paragraph 4.4)*

Ecological criteria *(beginning at paragraph 4.4.1)*

3.1 *Uniqueness or rarity:* Is the proposal based on this criterion? If so, is the criterion met, why, and based on what information?

3.2 *Critical habitat:* Is the proposal based on this criterion? If so, is the criterion met, why, and based on what information?

3.3 *Dependency:* Is the proposal based on this criterion? If so, is the criterion met, why, and based on what information?

3.4 *Representativeness:* Is the proposal based on this criterion? If so, is the criterion met, why, and based on what information?

3.5 *Diversity:* Is the proposal based on this criterion? If so, is the criterion met, why, and based on what information?

3.6 *Productivity:* Is the proposal based on this criterion? If so, is the criterion met, why, and based on what information?

3.7 *Spawning or breeding grounds:* Is the proposal based on this criterion? If so, is the criterion met, why, and based on what information?

3.8 *Naturalness:* Is the proposal based on this criterion? If so, is the criterion met, why, and based on what information?

3.9 *Integrity:* Is the proposal based on this criterion? If so, is the criterion met, why, and based on what information?

3.10 *Fragility:* Is the proposal based on this criterion? If so, is the criterion met, why, and based on what information?

3.11 *Bio-geographic importance:* Is the proposal based on this criterion? If so, is the criterion met, why, and based on what information?

Social, cultural, and economic criteria *(beginning at paragraph 4.4.12)*

3.12 *Social or economic dependency:* Is the proposal based on this criterion? If so, is the criterion met, why, and based on what information?

3.13 *Human dependency:* Is the proposal based on this criterion? If so, is the criterion met, why, and based on what information?

3.14 *Cultural heritage:* Is the proposal based on this criterion? If so, is the criterion met, why, and based on what information?

Scientific and educational criteria *(beginning at paragraph 4.4.15)*

3.15 *Research:* Is the proposal based on this criterion? If so, is the criterion met, why, and based on what information?

3.16 *Baseline for monitoring studies:* Is the proposal based on this criterion? If so, is the criterion met, why, and based on what information?

3.17 *Education:* Is the proposal based on this criterion? If so, is the criterion met, why, and based on what information?

Conclusion: Does the proposed area fulfil at least one of the above criteria in section 3 throughout the entire proposed area? If so, which criterion, why, and based on what information? The Technical Group should provide a brief summary of this element in its report to the Committee.

4 Vulnerability to impacts from international shipping
(Guidelines, section 5)

Do the supporting documentation and references support that the area is vulnerable to damage or the identified threat of damage from international shipping? In addressing this question, the following factors, as well as the time for which the information applies, should be considered:

Vessel traffic characteristics

4.1 *Operational factors:* What types of maritime activities exist in the area that may reduce the safety of navigation? (paragraph 5.1.1)

4.2 *Vessel types:* What types of vessels pass through or adjacent to the area? (paragraph 5.1.2)

4.3 *Traffic characteristics:* What are the data provided on the vessel traffic characteristics (e.g. volume or concentration of traffic, vessel interactions, distance offshore, other dangers to navigation)? (paragraph 5.1.3)

4.4 *Harmful substances:* What information is there on harmful substances being carried? (paragraph 5.1.4)

Natural factors

4.5 *Hydrographic conditions:* What information is provided on the hydrographical conditions? *(paragraph 5.1.5)*

4.6 *Meteorological conditions:* What information is provided on the meteorological conditions? *(paragraph 5.1.6)*

4.7 *Oceanographic conditions:* What information is provided on the oceanographic conditions? *(paragraph 5.1.7)*

Conclusion: Are there factors relating to vessel traffic characteristics and natural conditions that result in the attributes of the proposed area being vulnerable to damage from international shipping and if so, what are they and based on what information? The Technical Group should provide a short summary of the information provided and its assessment.

5 Associated Protective Measure proposed to protect the area from the identified vulnerability
(Guidelines, sections 6 and 7)

5.1 Is there an IMO measure already in place to protect the area from the identified vulnerability? *(paragraphs 7.2 and 7.5.2.1)*

5.1.1 If so, how does it protect the attributes of the area from the identified vulnerability by international shipping? *(paragraph 7.2)*

5.2 Is there a new IMO measure being proposed to protect the area? *(paragraphs 7.1 and 7.5.2)*

5.2.1 Is there a draft of the proposal for such a measure appended to the submission? *(paragraph 7.5.2.2)*

If yes, what is the measure?

5.2.2 What is its legal basis? *(paragraphs 7.1, 7.5.2.2, 7.5.2.3)*

5.2.2.1 Is it:

> **.1**   An existing IMO measure? *(paragraph 7.5.2.3(i))*

If so, under what IMO instrument is it being proposed? *(paragraph 7.6.1)*

> **.2**   A measure that does not yet exist at IMO, but could become available through amendment of an IMO instrument or adoption of a new IMO instrument? *(paragraph 7.5.2.3(ii))*

If so, what steps have been set forth in its application that the proposing Member Government has taken or will take to have the amendment or instrument approved or adopted by IMO? *(paragraphs 7.1 and 7.5.2.3(ii))* Is the measure proposed consistent with the requirements being proposed? *(paragraph 7.6.1)*

> **.3**   A measure proposed for adoption in the territorial sea or by IMO pursuant to UNCLOS Article 211(6) where generally applicable measures would not adequately address the particularized need of the proposed area? *(paragraph 7.5.2.3(iii))*

If it is a measure under Article 211(6), what steps have been set forth in its application that the proposing Member Government has taken or will take to obtain adoption of this measure? Is the measure proposed consistent with the requirements of this Article? *(paragraph 7.6.1)*

5.2.2.2 Is the proposed measure consistent with the legal instrument under which the APM is being proposed? *(paragraph 7.6.1)*

5.2.2.3 How does the associated protective measure provide the needed protection from the threats of damage to the attributes of the area posed by international shipping activities and is it specifically tailored to do so? *(paragraph 7.5.2.4)*

5.3   To what category or categories of ships does the APM apply? *(paragraph 7.5.2.5)*

5.4   Are there any possible impacts of the proposed measure on the safety and efficiency of navigation? *(paragraph 7.6)*

5.5   Is there a possibility that the existing or proposed APM might result in undesirable adverse effects by international shipping on the environment outside of the proposed PSSA? *(paragraph 8.2.2)*

5.6   After considering the full range of protective measures available and reviewing the existing or proposed associated protective measure, are there any other more appropriate APMs than that being proposed to address the identified vulnerability (e.g. more environmentally protective or having less impact on international shipping)? *(paragraph 8.2.1)*

Conclusion: Is the proposed APM the appropriate measure to address the identified vulnerability to the attributes of the area and if so, why? *(paragraph 8.2.3)* Is there an identified legal basis for this measure and what is it? The Technical Group should provide a short summary of its assessment of the APM and the linkage among the three elements of the PSSA proposal (i.e., the attributes of the area, the identified vulnerability and the APM).

6   Miscellaneous issues

6.1   Is the size of the area commensurate with that necessary to address the identified need? *(paragraph 8.2.3)*

6.2   Has the Member Government taken steps to date to protect the area (e.g. with respect to its vessels, as a condition of port entry, or intended to apply to vessels in the area, consistent with international law)? *(paragraph 7.8)*

6.3   What are the enforcement actions that may be taken pursuant to domestic law for the failure of a ship to comply with an APM? *(paragraph 7.9)*

6.4   Does the area include a buffer zone? Why is a buffer zone necessary? How were the boundaries of the buffer zone drawn? *(paragraph 6.3)*

6.5   If the answer to 6.4 is yes, how does it directly contribute to the protection of the area? *(paragraph 6.3)*

6.6   Has the area been declared a World Heritage Site, a Biosphere Reserve, or included on a list of areas of international, regional, or national importance or is the area the subject of international, regional, or national conservation action or agreements? *(paragraph 6.2)* If so, please describe.

7   Conclusion

The Technical Group's report should contain a recommendation to the Committee, based on its assessment of the proposal, regarding whether the proposed area should be designated as a PSSA "in principle", while awaiting action by the appropriate Sub-Committee or Committee on the APM. If the PSSA is based on an existing measure, the Group – again, after its assessment –may recommend to the Committee that it designate the area as a PSSA. Finally, if the Group decides to recommend against designation, it should provide the Committee with a statement of reasons for its recommendation and, if appropriate, request additional information.

Annex 4 – Uniform format of the MEPC resolution for the designation of Particularly Sensitive Sea Areas

MEPC 54/21, annex 11
Uniform format of the MEPC resolution for the designation of Particularly Sensitive Sea Areas

Resolution MEPC.xxx(xx)
adopted on [dd/mm/yyyy]
Designation of [name of sea area]
as a Particularly Sensitive Sea Area

THE MARINE ENVIRONMENT PROTECTION COMMITTEE,

BEING AWARE of the [ecological], [socio-economic], [and scientific] attributes[*] of [name of sea area] as well as its vulnerability to damage by international shipping activities and the steps taken by [name of proposing Member Government] to address that vulnerability,

NOTING the Revised Guidelines for the Identification and Designation of Particularly Sensitive Sea Areas adopted under resolution A.982(24) (PSSA Guidelines) and the Revised Guidance Document for Submission of PSSA Proposals to IMO set forth in circular MEPC/Circ.510,

HAVING CONSIDERED the proposal from [name of proposing Member Government] to designate [name of sea area] as a Particularly Sensitive Sea Area,

HAVING AGREED that the provisions for the identification and designation of a Particularly Sensitive Sea Area provided in resolution A.982(24) are fulfilled for the [name of sea area],

1   DESIGNATES [name of sea area] as defined in annex 1[†] to this resolution as a Particularly Sensitive Sea Area;

2   INVITES Member Governments to recognize the [ecological], [socio-economic], [and scientific] attributes of the area set forth in annex 2[‡] and its vulnerability to damage by international shipping activities set forth in annex 3;[§] and

3   FURTHER INVITES Member Governments to note the associated protective measure(s) established to address this vulnerability set forth in annex 4,[¶] and inform ships flying their flag that they should act in accordance with such measure(s).

---

[*] Since, under paragraph 4.4 of the PSSA Guidelines, one or more of the ecological, socio-economic, or scientific criteria needs to be fulfilled, these categories are in brackets. The appropriate terminology should be used for each PSSA. This issue is also presented in the second operative paragraph.

[†] Annex 1 should contain the coordinates of the PSSA as well as a chartlet on which the PSSA and associated protective measures are marked.

[‡] Annex 2 should contain the information submitted to address section 4 of the PSSA Guidelines.

[§] Annex 3 should be a summary that identifies the vulnerability to damage by international shipping activities.

[¶] Annex 4 should contain the APM(s) that have been adopted by the appropriate IMO body. It should also contain a notation to the related documents pertinent to the APM(s).

Annex 5 – PSSAs designated since 1990

These annexes describe the PSSAs that have been adopted, and the dates of their adoption or enlargement.

Annex	PSSA
6	The Great Barrier Reef (1990) and the Torres Strait extension (2005) and the Coral Sea extension (2015)
7	Archipelago of Sabana-Camagüey (1997)
8	Malpelo Island (2002)
9	Florida Keys (2002)
10	Wadden Sea (2002)
11	Paracas National Reserve (2003)
12	Western European Waters (2004)
13	Canary Islands (2005)
14	Galapagos Archipelago (2005)
15	Baltic Sea area (2005)
16	Papahānaumokuākea Marine National Monument (2007)
17	Strait of Bonifacio (2011)
18	Saba Bank (2012)
19	Jomard Entrance (2016)

Annex 6 – Great Barrier Reef and Torres Strait and Coral Sea Particularly Sensitive Sea Area

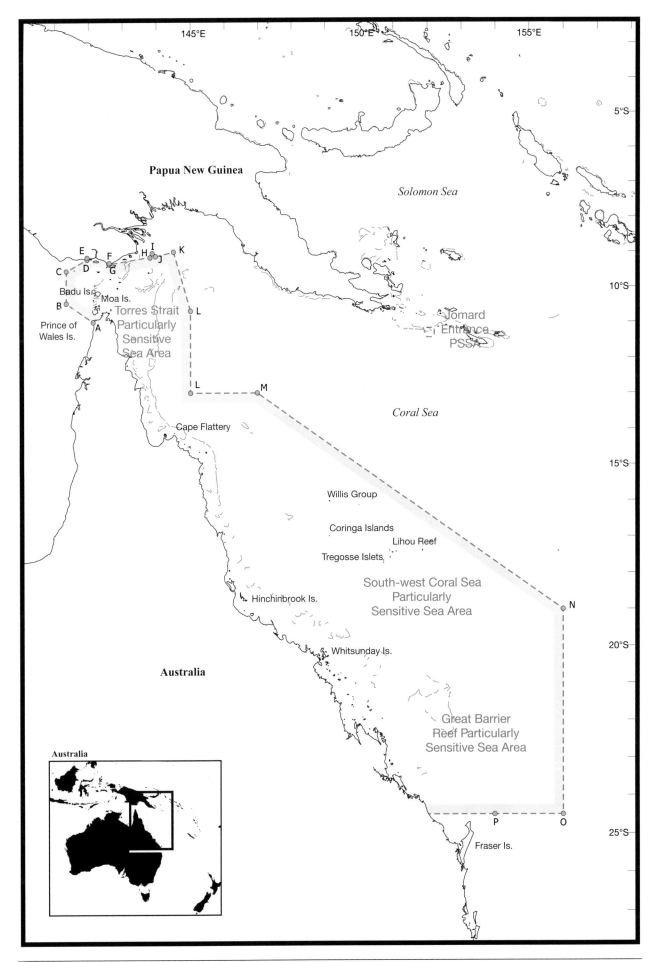

Great Barrier Reef PSSA

Resolution MEPC.44(30)

Adopted on 16 November 1990

Identification of the Great Barrier Reef Region as a Particularly Sensitive Area

THE MARINE ENVIRONMENT PROTECTION COMMITTEE,

BEING AWARE that the Great Barrier Reef region has been inscribed on the World Heritage List established pursuant to the 1972 Convention concerning the Protection of the World Cultural and Natural Heritage, the only exclusively marine area to have been so inscribed,

RECALLING that amendments to the International Convention for the Prevention of Pollution of the Sea by Oil, 1954, concerning the protection of the Great Barrier Reef, adopted on 12 October 1971, recognize the need to protect the Great Barrier Reef by defining the nearest land off the north-eastern coast of Australia as the outer edge of the Reef and prohibiting the discharge into the sea in its vicinity of oil, or oily mixtures, even in limited quantities, from ships,

RECALLING ALSO that Annexes I, II, IV and V of the International Convention for the Prevention of Pollution from Ships, 1973, as modified by the Protocol of 1978 relating thereto, recognize the need to protect the environment of the Great Barrier Reef, by defining the nearest land off the north-eastern coast of Australia as the outer edge of the Reef and prohibiting the discharge into the sea in its vicinity of various harmful substances from ships,

NOTING that article 211(6) of the United Nations Convention on the Law of the Sea is further evidence of the will of States to co-operate in defining vulnerable marine areas requiring a higher level of protection than that which generally applies,

NOTING ALSO resolution 9 of the International Conference on Tanker Safety and Pollution Prevention (TSPP) 1978 concerning the protection of Particularly Sensitive Areas,

CONFIRMING that the Great Barrier Reef fulfils the criteria for identification as a Particularly Sensitive Area, approved at the twenty-ninth session of the Marine Environment Protection Committee,

IDENTIFIES the Great Barrier Reef region as defined in the annex to this resolution as a Particularly Sensitive Area in terms of the Guidelines for the Designation of Special Areas and the Identification of Particularly Sensitive Areas approved by the thirtieth session of the Marine Environment Protection Committee.

Annex

Geographical description of the Great Barrier Reef region

The area is defined by the following boundary:

(a) commences at the point that, at low water, is the northernmost extremity of Cape York Peninsula, Queensland;

(b) runs thence easterly along the geodesic to the intersection of parallel of latitude 10°41′ S with the meridian of longitude 145°00′ E;

(c) runs thence southerly along that meridian to its intersection by the parallel of latitude 13°00′ S;

(d) runs thence south-easterly along the geodesic to a point of latitude 15°30′ S, longitude 146°00′ E;

(e) runs thence south-easterly along the geodesic to a point of latitude 17°30′ S, longitude 147°00′ E;

(f) runs thence south-easterly along the geodesic to a point of latitude 21°00′ S, longitude 152°55′ E;

(g) runs thence south-easterly along the geodesic to a point of latitude 24°30′ S, longitude 154°00′ E;

(h) runs thence westerly along the parallel of latitude 24°30′ S to its intersection by the coastline of Queensland at low water; and

(i) runs thence generally northerly along that coastline at low water to the point of commencement.

Torres Strait PSSA as an extension of the Great Barrier Reef PSSA

Resolution MEPC.133(53)

adopted on 22 July 2005

Designation of the Torres Strait as an extension
of the Great Barrier Reef Particularly Sensitive Sea Area

THE MARINE ENVIRONMENT PROTECTION COMMITTEE,

BEING AWARE of the ecological, social, economic, cultural, scientific and educational value of the Torres Strait, as well as its vulnerability to damage by shipping traffic and activities in the area and the steps taken by Australia and Papua New Guinea to address that vulnerability,

NOTING that the Guidelines for the Identification and Designation of Particularly Sensitive Sea Areas adopted under resolution A.927(22) set out procedures for the designation of Particularly Sensitive Sea Areas,

HAVING CONSIDERED the proposal from Australia and Papua New Guinea to extend the existing Great Barrier Reef Particularly Sensitive Sea Area to include the Torres Strait,

HAVING AGREED that criteria for identification of a Particularly Sensitive Sea Area provided in resolution A.927(22) are fulfilled for the Torres Strait,

1   DESIGNATES the Torres Strait, as defined in annex 1 to this resolution, as an extension of the Great Barrier Reef Particularly Sensitive Sea Area;

2   RECOGNIZES the establishment of a two-way route through the Torres Strait as defined in annex 2 to this resolution;

3   RECOMMENDS that Governments recognize the need for effective protection of the Great Barrier Reef and Torres Strait region and inform ships flying their flag that they should act in accordance with Australia's system of pilotage for merchant ships 70 m in length and over or oil tankers, chemical tankers, and gas carriers, irrespective of size, when navigating:

    (a)   the Inner Route of the Great Barrier Reef between the northern extreme of Cape York Peninsula (10°41′ S) and 16°40′ S and in Hydrographers Passage; and

    (b)   the Torres Strait and the Great North East Channel between Booby Island (latitude 10°36′ S, longitude 141°54′ E) and Bramble Cay (latitude 09°09′ S, longitude 143°53′ E).

4   REVOKES resolution MEPC.45(30).

Annex 1

Description of the Particularly Sensitive Sea Area: Torres Strait

1   Description of the area

1.1   The Torres Strait lies to the north and north-east of Cape York and separates Australia and Papua New Guinea. It is about 90 nautical miles wide and 150 nautical miles long although useable routes for larger commercial vessels are limited to the Prince of Wales Channel and the Great North East Channel. The area lies within the exclusive economic zones of Australia and Papua New Guinea and includes some areas of the territorial sea and internal waters of both countries. The recommended pilotage system that is operational in the area has pilot embarkation areas entirely within the territorial waters of Australia. The eastern boundary and part of the western boundary of the PSSA aligns with the "nearest land" definition included in Annexes I, II, IV and V of MARPOL. The northern and a large part of the western boundary aligns with the Torres Strait Protected Zone (TSPZ) established by the Torres Strait Treaty between Australia and Papua New Guinea. The coordinates of the Torres Strait PSSA extension are set out below as amendments to the existing Great Barrier Reef PSSA described in resolution MEPC.44(30). Note that the geographic positions *in italics* are those adopted in 1990 to define the Great Barrier Reef Particularly Sensitive Sea Area and are unchanged.

1.2   The area is defined by a line:

(a)   commencing at a point on the coast of Australia in latitude 11°00′ South, longitude 142°08′ East;

(b)   running thence north-westerly along the geodesic to the point of latitude 10°28′ South, longitude 141°20′ East;

(c)   thence north along the meridian of longitude 141°20′ East to its intersection by the parallel of latitude 9°33′ South;

(d)   thence north-easterly along the geodesic to the point of latitude 9°13′ South, longitude 141°57′ East;

(e)   thence north along the meridian of longitude 141°57′ East to its intersection by the southern coastline of the island of Papua New Guinea at low water;

(f)   thence generally easterly along the southern coastline of the island of Papua New Guinea, that is along the low-water line on that coast and across any river mouth and in the case of the mouth of the Mai Kussa River along the parallel of latitude 9°09′ South, thence along the southern coastline of the island of Papua New Guinea, that is along the low-water line on that coast and across any river mouth, to its intersection by the meridian of longitude 142°36′ East;

(g)   thence south along that meridian to its intersection by the parallel of latitude 9°21′ South;

(h)   thence north-easterly along the geodesic between that point of intersection and the point of latitude 9°09′ South, longitude 143°47′20″ East;

(i)   thence along the outer limit of the three-mile territorial sea of Black Rocks, so as to pass to the north-west of Black Rocks, to the point of intersection of that limit by the outer limit of the three-mile territorial sea of Bramble Cay;

(j)   thence along that outer limit, so as to pass successively to the north and east of Bramble Cay, to the point of latitude 9°08′30″ South, longitude 143°55′57″ East;

(k)   thence north-easterly to the point of latitude 9°00′ South, longitude 144°30′ East;

(l)   thence generally southerly along a line joining the following geographic positions:

(a)	*10°41′ S*	*145°00′ E*
(b)	*13°00′ S*	*145°00′ E*
(c)	*15°00′ S*	*146°00′ E*
(d)	*17°30′ S*	*147°00′ E*
(e)	*21°00′ S*	*152°55′ E*
(f).	*24°30′ S*	*154°00′ E*

(m)   thence westerly along the parallel of latitude 24°30′ South to its intersection by the coastline of Queensland at low water; and

(n)   thence generally northerly along that coastline at low water to the point of commencement.

1.3   A chartlet of the Torres Strait extension to the Great Barrier Reef PSSA is provided below.

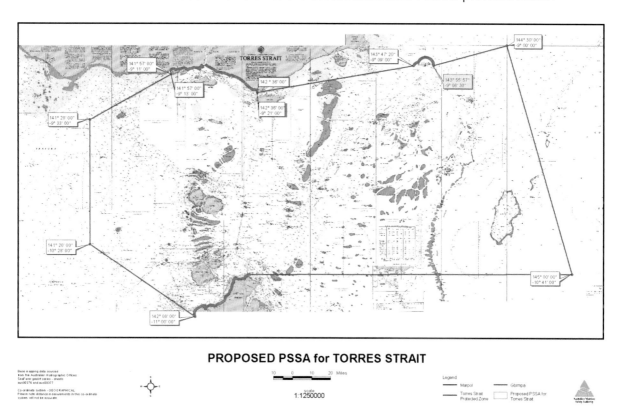

PROPOSED PSSA for TORRES STRAIT

2   Significance of the area

2.1   The tidal influences of two ocean systems result in frequent anomalous tidal regimes and have a great effect on the area's biodiversity. The massive freshwater and sediment input from nearby coastal rivers further influence this unique marine ecosystem. Benthic communities, fish assemblages, seagrass coverage and coral communities have all been well documented. The Strait provides critical habitat for many vulnerable or endangered species, including dugongs, green and flatback turtles, as well as supporting commercial fisheries for tiger and endeavour prawns, Spanish mackerel, tropical rock lobster, reef fish, pearl oysters, trochus and bêche de mer. Coral reefs and clear waters support a rich fauna of reef fish, molluscs, echinoderms and crustaceans. Due to low population pressure, only 18 islands are inhabited. The Torres Strait thus retains a high degree of natural and wilderness value.

2.2   Because of the limited water exchange in and out of the Torres Strait, there are concerns that if the Torres Strait water became polluted it would probably remain in the Strait for some time. This may pose a risk of adverse and prolonged impacts on ecological communities, indigenous and commercial fisheries and the life style of Torres Strait Islander people.

2.3   Several thousand people live in small coastal communities on Cape York, on the islands off the southern coast of Papua New Guinea and on the larger islands of the Torres Strait itself. Indigenous people of the Torres Strait traditionally hunt dugong and turtle and fish for a variety of marine species for food. The consumption of seafood by Torres Strait Islanders is amongst the highest in the world on a per capita basis. A commercial fishery, estimated at 2000 tonnes, contributed approximately A\$35 million to the Australian economy in 1999/2000. Pearl farms operate on a number of islands. The Torres Strait has a small but expanding tourism industry.

2.4   More detailed descriptions of the ecological, socio-economic and cultural, scientific and educational criteria are contained in paragraphs 3.1 to 3.3.3 of document MEPC 49/8.

3   Vulnerability of the area to damage by international shipping activities

3.1   The Torres Strait, including the Great North East Channel, is used primarily by large vessels trading between ports in southern Asia, Australia and New Zealand, South America, Papua New Guinea and Pacific Island nations, although the majority of tanker traffic bound for the Australian east coast refineries also uses it to link with the Outer Route of the Great Barrier Reef. Vessels entering or leaving the Inner Route of the Great Barrier Reef also use the Prince of Wales Channel at the western end of the Torres Strait.

3.2   Parts of the Torres Strait are isolated, remote and very demanding on the navigator. Passage through these waters also involves navigation within confined waters for long periods, with limited depths of water being a constant threat. The average depth of the Torres Strait is 30–50 metres in the east and 10–15 metres in the west. Tidal streams can be strong and variable. Most of the region has a monsoon climate and visibility is frequently adversely affected by seasonal rain squalls. The area as a whole is subject to seasonal tropical storms and cyclones.

3.3   There are narrow fairways and areas of converging traffic that, while not heavy by some standards, represent a wide range of ship types, carrying a variety of cargoes, including dangerous goods and potentially polluting materials. Ships navigating the area may encounter concentrations of fishing vessels, tourist vessels and recreational craft that, by their very numbers, increase the dangers of marine incidents.

3.4   A spill occurred in Prince of Wales Channel in 1970 (**Oceanic Grandeur**) and numerous other groundings and near misses have occurred due to the combination of shallow water, narrow channels, strong tidal streams and strong winds.

3.5   The current recommended maximum draught for ships passing through Gannet Passage is 12.2 metres, which, for a large percentage of ships, provides an underkeel clearance of one metre at the higher stages of the tide cycle. Careful calculations are required by Masters and pilots of deep-draught vessels to establish the timing of "tidal windows" for their passage through the Strait.

3.6   A detailed description of the characteristics of the maritime traffic, the transport of harmful substances, and the threats from disasters, including a description of the meteorological, oceanographical and geographical conditions, may be found in paragraphs 4.1 to 4.3 of document MEPC 49/8.

Annex 2

Associated Protective Measures

1 *Two-way route.* The forty-ninth session of the IMO Sub-Committee on the Safety of Navigation approved the implementation of a two-way shipping route through the Torres Strait. Details of this measure, including a chartlet, are provided in document NAV 49/3/3. This two-way route was amended at the ninety-fourth session of MSC in 2014. A full technical description of the amended two-way route is in part E of editions of the IMO publication "Ships' Routeing"; only chartlets of the route are included here.

Two-way route in the Great North-east Channel, Torres Strait

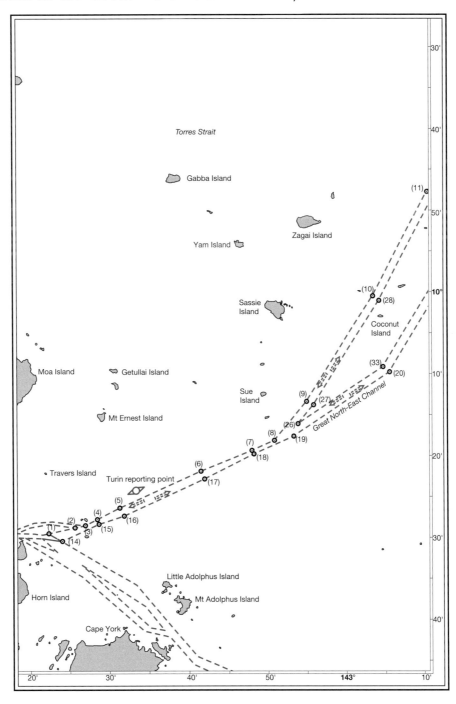

Two-way route in the Great North-east Channel, Torres Strait (west)

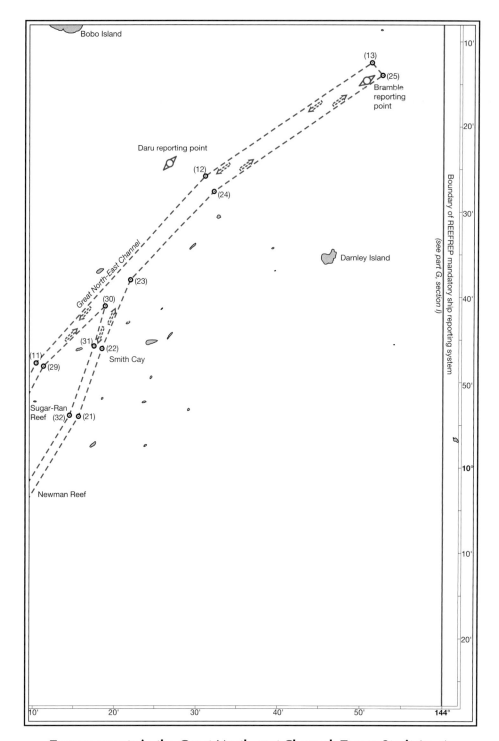

Two-way route in the Great North-east Channel, Torres Strait (east)

2 *Pilotage.* Refer to paragraph 3 of this resolution.

Resolution MEPC.268(68)

adopted on 15 May 2015

Designation of the south-west Coral Sea as an extension of the Great Barrier Reef and Torres Strait Particularly Sensitive Sea Area

THE MARINE ENVIRONMENT PROTECTION COMMITTEE,

BEING AWARE of the ecological, social, cultural, economic and scientific attributes of the south-west Coral Sea, as well as its vulnerability to damage by international shipping activities and the steps taken by the Government of Australia to address that vulnerability,

NOTING the Revised guidelines for the Identification and Designation of Particularly Sensitive Sea Areas (PSSA Guidelines), adopted by the Assembly by resolution A.982(24), and the Revised Guidance Document for submission of PSSA proposals to IMO (MEPC.1/Circ.510),

RECALLING resolution MEPC.133(53), by which the Torres Strait (TS) was designated as an extension of the Great Barrier Reef (GBR) Particularly Sensitive Sea Area (PSSA),

HAVING CONSIDERED the proposal made by the Government of Australia to extend the GBR and TS PSSA to include the south-west part of the Coral Sea,

HAVING AGREED, at its sixty-eighth session, that the criteria for the identification and designation of a PSSA provided in resolution A.982(24) are fulfilled for the extension of the GBR and TS PSSA to include the south-west part of the Coral Sea,

HAVING NOTED that the Sub-Committee on Navigation, Communications and Search and Rescue (NCSR), at its second session, approved the establishment of two 5 nautical mile wide two-way routes and a new area to be avoided in the south-west Coral Sea as associated protective measures for the application to extend the GBR and TS PSSA to include the south-west part of the Coral Sea to improve the safety of navigation and the protection of the marine environment,

1   DESIGNATES the south-west part of the Coral Sea, as defined in annex 1 to the present resolution, as an extension of the Great Barrier Reef and Torres Strait PSSA pending the final adoption of the associated protective measures for the PSSA, as set out in annex 1 of document NCSR 2/23;

2   INVITES Member Governments to recognize the ecological, social, cultural, economic and scientific attributes of the Coral Sea area, set forth in annex 2 to the present resolution, as well as its vulnerability to damage by international shipping activities, as described in annex 3 to the present resolution;

3   FURTHER INVITES Member Governments to note the associated protective measures established to address the area's vulnerability, the details of which are contained in annex 4 to the present resolution, which are expected to enter into force following final adoption by the ninety-fifth session of the Maritime Safety Committee, on a date to be circulated by the Organization to all Member Governments, and request ships flying their flag to act in accordance with such measures.

Annex 1

Description of the Great Barrier Reef, Torres Strait and Coral Sea Particularly Sensitive Sea Area

To minimize the risk of damage from ship groundings and pollution damage by international shipping activities and the destruction and degradation of these unique, diverse, and significant habitats and ecosystem, mariners should exercise extreme care when navigating in the area bounded by a line connecting the following geographical positions, which is designated as a Particularly Sensitive Sea Area:

(a) commencing at a point on the coast of Australia in latitude 11°00′ South, longitude 142°08′ East;

(b) running thence north-westerly along the geodesic to the point of latitude 10°28′ South, longitude 141°20′ East;

(c) thence north along the meridian of longitude 141°20′ East to its intersection by the parallel of latitude 09°33′ South;

(d) thence north-easterly along the geodesic to the point of latitude 09°13′ South, longitude 141°57′ East;

(e) thence north along the meridian of longitude 141°57′ Fast to its intersection by the southern coastline of the island of Papua New Guinea at low water;

(f) thence generally easterly along the southern coastline of the island of New Guinea, that is along the low-water line on that coast and across any river mouth and, in the case of the mouth of the Mai Kussa River, along the parallel of latitude 09°09′ South, thence along the southern coastline of the island of New Guinea, that is along the low-water line on that coast and across any river mouth, to its intersection by the meridian of longitude 142°36′ East;

(g) thence south along that meridian to its intersection by the parallel of latitude 09°21′ South;

(h) thence north-easterly along the geodesic between that point of intersection and the point of latitude 09°09′ South, longitude 143°47′20″ East;

(i) thence along the outer limit of the three-mile territorial sea of Black Rocks, so as to pass to the north-west of Black Rocks, to the point of intersection of that limit by the outer limit of the three-mile territorial sea of Bramble Cay;

(j) thence along that outer limit, so as to pass successively to the north and east of Bramble Cay, to the point of latitude 09°08′30″ South, longitude 143°55′57″ East;

(k) thence north-easterly to the point of latitude 09°00′ South, longitude 144°30′ East;

(l) thence generally southerly along a line joining the following geographic positions:

    a   10°41′ S, 145°00′ E

    b   13°00′ S, 145°00′ E

(m) thence easterly to a point of latitude 13°00′ South, longitude 147°00′ East;

(n) thence generally south-easterly to a point of latitude 19°00′ South, longitude 156°00′ East;

(o) thence south to a point of latitude 24°30′ South, longitude 156°00′ East;

(p) thence westerly along the parallel of latitude 24°30′ South to its intersection by the coastline of Queensland at low water; and

(q) thence generally northerly along that coastline at low water to the point of commencement.

Note: The geographic positions from sections (a) to (k) inclusive are those in resolution MEPC.133(53), adopted in 2005 to define the Great Barrier Reef and Torres Strait Particularly Sensitive Sea Area.

All coordinates are based on the WGS 84 datum and are depicted in the diagram in the chartlet below.

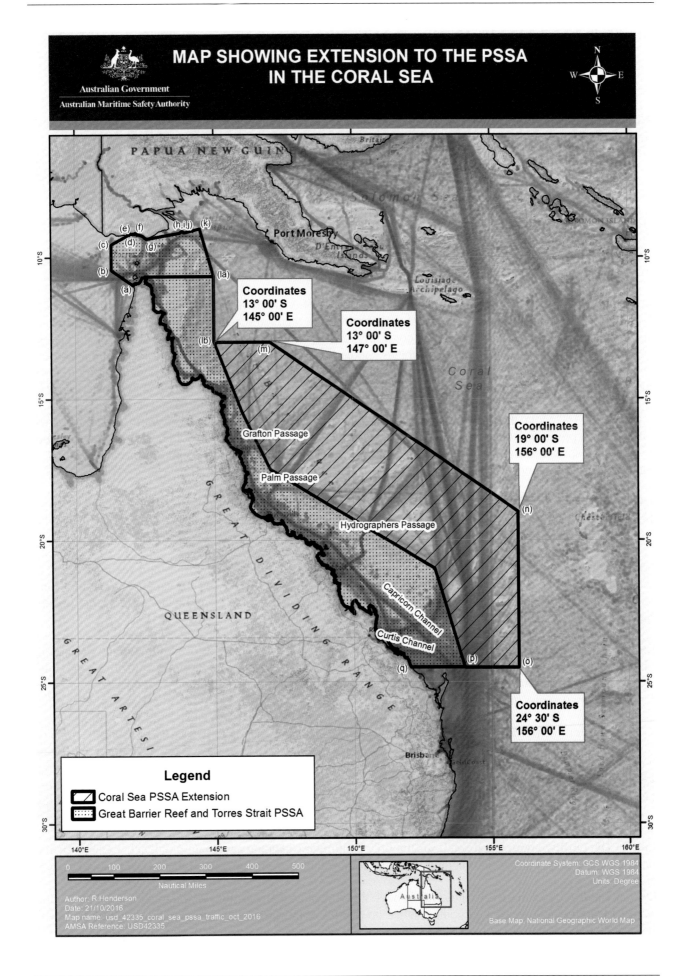

Annex 2

Ecological, socio-economic, and scientific attributes of the PSSA extension area: South-west Coral Sea

(**Note:** More detailed descriptions of the ecological, socio-economic and cultural, scientific and educational criteria are contained in paragraphs 17 to 80 of document MEPC 68/10/1.)

1   Ecological criteria

Uniqueness or rarity

1.1   The Coral Sea is considered one of the most distinctive and undisturbed natural systems in the world and is internationally recognized for its rich biodiversity, unique species and important heritage values.

1.2   In the area of the Coral Sea to be covered by the PSSA, three large-scale unique ecological features that support distinct or important ecological communities at a regional scale are present. The Queensland and Marion Plateaux together support over 20 coral reefs and cays, which provide complex habitats with diverse and abundant invertebrate and fish communities. Similarly, the northernmost parts of the Tasmantid Seamount Chain contain a diverse range of habitats, including deep-water sponge gardens and near-pristine tropical coral reef systems. Collectively these are known to be biological hot-spots, with significant species diversity.

1.3   Over millennia, the geological and oceanographic history of the region and its warm and cool current patterns have prevented the migration of species, prompting the development of flora and fauna that evolved, adapted and spread in isolation. Localized currents can act as a barrier to dispersal; as a result, the area has high levels of species endemism.

1.4   The area contains some of the world's most unique and globally significant marine species, such as the leatherback turtle *(Dermochelys coriacea)*, humphead Maori wrasse *(Cheilinus undulatus)* and nautilus *(Nautilus pompilius)*.

1.5   The Coral Sea provides migratory corridors for cetaceans, sharks, fish, turtles and seabirds, many of which are of conservation concern. Successive research efforts have highlighted the significance of the Coral Sea in patterns of dispersal, whereby the reefs provide a series of dispersal stepping-stones from the western Pacific towards the GBR.

1.6   Deep, cold water troughs and abyssal basins are habitat for an array of benthic species, many of which are a protected matter under Australia's *Environment Protection and Biodiversity Conservation Act 1999* (EPBC Act) or international agreement or are unique to the area, including 18 endemic species of deep-water sharks, rays and chimaera fish.

1.7   The remoteness and challenging environment of the area means much of its biodiversity remains undescribed and new species found nowhere else are routinely discovered. Surveys in the deeper reef habitats at Osprey Reef have revealed prehistoric six-gilled sharks, giant oil fish and many crustaceans and unidentified fish at depths of 1,400 metres. A unique, dwarf speciation of *Nautilus pompilius* was also identified on Osprey Reef. This species evolved isolated from nautilus in the nearby Coral Sea and GBR, and is a reflection of the endemic nature of ecosystems within the area.

1.8   The north-western Coral Sea hosts the only confirmed spawning aggregation of black marlin *(Makaira indica)* in the world. This species migrates throughout the Pacific Ocean, but only uses the Coral Sea to spawn.

1.9   The few detailed surveys undertaken have shown that as many as 40% of the invertebrates inhabiting seamounts in the area are new to science while up to 34% of the species may be endemic. Scientists expect that research into the lesser known, deeper areas of the region will uncover many new species.

Critical habitat

1.10 The area contains outstanding examples of reef communities and a diverse array of isolated sandy cays, islands, deep-sea plains, seamounts and canyons. Collectively, these areas provide foraging, breeding and nesting grounds for a rich array of marine species, including 341 species that are recognized for their conservation significance under the EPBC Act and under international agreements. This includes 26 species of cetaceans, 219 species of corals, 21 species of fish, 46 species of sharks and rays, five species of marine turtles and 24 species of birds. Many of these species are listed as threatened or migratory species, or both, and, whilst over half of these species show declining population trends worldwide, many are still found at healthy levels in the Coral Sea.

Dependency

1.11 The reefs of the Coral Sea provide stepping-stones for the dispersal of species between the GBR and the greater Pacific Ocean region. Maintaining the overall integrity and resilience of these reefs is therefore necessary to ensure that they can function effectively as stepping-stone habitats.

1.12 The Coral Sea also provides migratory corridors for cetaceans, sharks, fish, turtles and seabirds, many of which are of conservation concern. There are likely to be further important areas for feeding, breeding, migrating and resting that have yet to be clearly identified, and which may act as critical habitat for many species.

1.13 Thousands of species rely on the ecosystem processes within the Coral Sea region to provide opportunities for foraging, breeding and migration. These processes are largely driven by the availability of energy within the system, which in turn is dependent upon the unique interactions between the region's oceanographic and topographic features.

1.14 Localized turbulence in the lee of reefs, islands and seamounts influences biological communities by creating patches of high to intermediate productivity in the nutrient-poor open-water environment. These sites of enhanced productivity are important aggregators for a range of pelagic species, including small fish, mid-trophic predatory fish and large predators. They are also known to attract a range of species of conservation concern, including marine turtles, marine mammals and seabirds.

1.15 Cays in the area offer important habitat for seabirds to roost and nest, and for turtles to lay eggs above the high tide mark. Seabirds provide the main source of energy on these cays, through their nutrient-rich guano, eggs and carrion, which support food webs of terrestrial and intertidal invertebrates and over time facilitate the development of soil and organic matter, which in turn provides habitat for more complex plant communities.

1.16 The species assemblage and trophic structure of the region relies on the highly interlinked web of local oceanographic patterns, topography and energy inputs. An impact on any one of these can disrupt this web, destabilizing ecosystem processes and the species that rely on them.

Representativeness

1.17 The reefs, cays and herbivorous fish of the Queensland and Marion Plateaux and the northern extent of the Tasmantid Seamount Chain highlight the biological significance and ecological value of the region.

1.18 The Queensland and Marion Plateaux are considered important for aggregations of marine life and the high levels of biodiversity they support. The reefs and islands of these plateaux are approximately 200–400 kilometres from the coast and provide for diverse and abundant invertebrate (e.g. sea cucumber) and fish communities.

1.19 These reefs of the Queensland and Marion Plateaux are known for their particularly high densities of shark species, and Osprey Reef in particular is also recognized for its populations of the iconic humphead Maori wrasse and nautilus. The lagoons of these reefs are important nursery sites for sharks and predatory fish, while the island areas support critical nesting sites for the green turtle and a range of seabird species. The plateaux also abut two significant deep-water regions: the Queensland Trough, which separates the Queensland Plateau from the GBR, and the Townsville Trough, which separates the two plateaux from each other. These troughs contain canyons and gullies that are likely to support unique deep-water ecosystems.

Diversity

1.20   The reef systems in the Coral Sea are dominated by spectacular sponge gardens, and support high biodiversity. Approximately 745 species of molluscs (shellfish, squid and octopus) have been found, including several that are considered rare. Six hundred and twenty eight species of fish are known to occur in the Coral Sea. The small islets and cays of the Coral Sea are important nesting places for many species of seabirds.

1.21   Reefs in the area provide a habitat mosaic for diverse and abundant invertebrate and fish communities. A diversity of hard and soft corals, sponge gardens, crustaceans and molluscs are found in the area, as well as a distinct Coral Sea reef fish community that includes many unique species.

1.22   Significant variation in water depth and sea-floor features are contributing factors to the high levels of species diversity in the area. Sections of the continental shelf have a mosaic of rocky reefs and soft sediments, and support species from a diverse range of taxonomic groups. The extensive seamount systems of the Coral Sea contain a large variety of sponges, corals, gorgonians, sea squirts and crinoids, the latter of which can grow unusually large and are frequently very long-lived, often exceeding several hundred years.

1.23   Abyssal regions are yet to be fully explored, but there is evidence of biologically important systems likely to contain a vast reservoir of undiscovered species.

Productivity

1.24   The pelagic environment of the area is akin to a vast desert with small oases of biodiversity and productivity. These areas of primary productivity influence the spread of algae, one of the area's most abundant and diverse life forms, covering a greater region than corals and forming an important part of the food chain. Areas with a high biomass of algae increase planktonic activity and create high levels of prey abundance, attracting aggregations of higher-order herbivorous and apex predator species. These localized productivity hot-spots in an otherwise nutrient-poor environment provide habitat, migration and dispersal corridors for many iconic and endangered species.

1.25   Marine species and seabirds can journey hundreds or even thousands of kilometres to breed in the Coral Sea, or to travel through en route to breeding areas beyond the region. Areas of high productivity, such as the seamounts, are therefore critical "stepping stones" within the barren open ocean and are important aggregators for a range of species, including lantern fish, albacore tuna, billfish and sharks. These species rely on foraging opportunities supplied by productivity hot-spots in the Coral Sea to sustain them on their journey. Large marine mammals journey many kilometres to breed in the Reserve, or to travel through en route to breeding areas.

1.26   It is also thought that the organic particulates contained in nutrient-rich intrusions in the area are responsible for the settlement and sustained growth of coral reef ecosystems, which have the highest gross primary productivity of all ocean ecosystems. These waters carry organic matter into the region, where they contribute significantly to the overall productivity of the system.

Spawning and breeding grounds

1.27   The area contains critical habitat features used by numerous species to spawn and breed, and which are therefore essential for their survival.

    .1   The waters over the Queensland and Townsville Troughs appear important for attracting aggregations of large pelagic species, either to feed or spawn.

    .2   Extensive seabird rookeries within the small islets and cays of the area are of global and national importance.

    .3   The area is a major feeding and breeding location for six of the world's seven species of sea turtles, all of which are listed on the IUCN Red List of Threatened Species.

.4   Particularly sheltered regions, such as lagoons, are thought to be important nursery sites for sharks and predatory fish, while other species, such as the dwarf minke whale, the hawksbill and leatherback turtles and the endangered Herald Petrel, forage in these calmer areas.

.5   The northern extension of the Tasmantid Seamount Chain, where the seamounts extend to the surface and are capped by islands and reefs, provides feeding and breeding grounds for open-ocean species, including billfish, marine turtles and marine mammals.

.6   Each year, from September to December, black marlin aggregate in the area to spawn. This is the only known spawning location for black marlin in the world.

Naturalness

1.28   The Coral Sea is considered one of the most distinctive and undisturbed natural systems in the world.

1.29   The area is not directly threatened by land-based sources of pollution and has relatively low levels of fishing. It is one of the world's last tropical oceanic regions containing high-biodiversity coral reefs that are virtually pristine, and where large populations of pelagic predators have not been severely depleted. The topography of the area has also contributed to its pristine nature, with recent surveys identifying deep-sea ecosystems which have remained largely unchanged for millions of years.

1.30   The Coringa Cays and Lihou Islets contain important bird and turtle nesting sites that are almost totally free from anthropogenic disturbances such as lighting, beach use, pollution, feral animals, and boat traffic compared to nesting sites throughout the GBR. These areas, therefore, are reference sites to determine the impacts of such disturbances on breeding success within the populations.

Integrity

1.31   The extension area covers a large area, and encompasses parts of six provincial bioregions identified in the Integrated Marine and Coastal Regionalisation of Australia Version 4.0 (IMCRA v.4.0). These bioregions contain a wide variety of interconnected habitats, and also provide important "stepping-stone" links between the GBR and the wider Pacific Ocean.

1.32   The integrity of the area is in part due to its remote nature, with the nearest point to a mainland coast over 60 kilometres away, and the furthest point 1,100 kilometres.

1.33   The area therefore demonstrates the characteristics of an isolated, effectively self-sustaining ecological unit, as evidenced by the high proportion of endemism both within the region and between individual reef communities.

Fragility

1.34   Although the Coral Sea contains a number of critical shallow reef and terrestrial habitats, these represent less than 1% of the total area. Their small size, isolation from each other and high exposure to cyclones and storms make them more vulnerable to catastrophic impacts of natural disturbances than the contiguous reef systems of the GBR. These precarious conditions increase the area's ecological fragility and the risk of local extinctions. A high proportion of pelagic and deep-water species are particularly vulnerable to anthropogenic impacts.

1.35   While the isolation of the area's ecosystems has ensured a great deal of diversity and endemicity between communities and populations, it also means these systems can be particularly fragile and susceptible to external factors, with potentially catastrophic long-term cascade effects.

1.36   The area's deep-sea organisms are generally slow-growing, long-lived, late-reproducing species with few offspring, and as a result can take a significant amount of time to rebuild populations. The cold coral reef systems take thousands of years to develop even in areas with stable conditions. They are fragile and extremely susceptible to damage as recovery rates are immensely slow.

Bio-geographic importance

1.37   A number of biologically important areas are located within, or intersect with, the area:

    .1   Seasonal migration routes and feeding sites for cetaceans, including the humpback whale, occur throughout the region. The humpback whale is also known to breed and calve in the area.

    .2   Migration routes and foraging and feeding sites for 13 species of seabird listed under the EPBC Act as threatened, endangered and/or migratory are located in the area.

    .3   The green turtle breeds in the area, with the Coringa–Herald–Lihou area particularly important for nesting and inter-nesting activities.

    .4   In spring and summer, whale sharks aggregate to feed around Bougainville Reef and white sharks use the south-west Coral Sea, adjacent to the Swain Reefs, as they move between nursery areas and for opportunistic feeding.

    .5   The minimal impacts on the area and its relative lack of disturbance mean that its various ecosystems provide a representation of what the geographic distribution of organisms would naturally resemble in comparable but more highly impacted marine ecosystems around the world.

2   Social, cultural and economic criteria

Social or economic dependency

2.1   Commercial fisheries have a relatively small presence in the south-west Coral Sea compared to other marine regions around Australia. Commonwealth and Queensland state-managed fisheries occur in the area, including line, hand collection, trawl, purse seine, trap and net fisheries.

2.2   Almost all tourism activities that occur in the south-west Coral Sea are nature-based and reliant on an intact Coral Sea ecosystem. They include charter fishing, snorkelling, scuba diving, whale watching and cruising.

2.3   Known scuba-diving and snorkelling hotspots in the Coral Sea region include the Osprey and Shark Reefs, for their significant populations of shark. These activities also occur in the Coringa Islets, Herald Cays and at Lihou Reef, although the extreme isolation of these locations means that they are not often visited. They also take place off other islands and shallow-water seafloor features in the Coral Sea region, albeit on a limited basis.

2.4   Scuba diving and snorkelling are predominantly eco-tourism or heritage-based tourism activities, with participants preferring locations that offer near-pristine marine environments or dive wrecks of interest. Some commercial and educational organizations offer science-based tourism opportunities where divers and snorkelers participate in experiments or surveys. Cruise ships also frequent the region, some regularly visiting Willis Island.

Cultural heritage

2.5   Like the GBR and Torres Strait, the Coral Sea is also of indigenous cultural and social significance to island and coastal communities. Many Aboriginal and Torres Strait island people undertake traditional use of marine resource activities to provide traditional food, practice their living maritime culture and to educate younger generations about traditional and cultural rules and protocols.

2.6   The area contains a large number of historic shipwrecks, including the wrecks of the **Cato** and **HMS Porpoise**, which are located in protected zones established under Australia's *Historic Shipwrecks Act 1976*. The region was significant in the Battle of the Coral Sea during World War II.

3   Scientific and educational criteria

Research

3.1   Given the scale and location of the proposed extension area to the PSSA, large-scale oceanographic features are well known and documented. However, there is a lack of knowledge of finer-scale hydrodynamics linking habitats within the Coral Sea. Further, the potential impacts of climate change on the Coral Sea are yet to be understood.

3.2   In spite of the relatively few detailed studies on the area, it remains one of high scientific interest. The remote location of the area, and its reputation as one of the most distinctive and undisturbed natural systems in the world, offers researchers a rare opportunity to study a biota over an area of significant scale that has not been markedly impacted by fishing and which is likely to remain undisturbed.

3.3   Domestic and international research institutions are actively undertaking research in the area. In addition to research institutions, tourist operators and volunteer organisations maintain active monitoring programmes.

3.4   The occupied meteorological facility on Willis Island has been providing data to Bureau of Meteorology scientists and others since 1921. Automatic weather stations are located on Bougainville Reef, Cato Island, Flinders Reef (Flinders Coral Cay), Frederick Reef, Holmes Reef, Lihou Reef (Turtle Islet), Marion Reef and Moore Reef. Observations from Willis Island and the automatic weather stations are important for climate analysis and numerical weather-prediction models, for fine-tuning forecasts and warnings, and are particularly important for early warning of tropical cyclones.

Baseline for monitoring studies

3.5   The extension area to the PSSA is remote and considered a relatively undisturbed natural system. Although its location has meant that detailed studies of the area are limited, the Coral Sea is a known habitat for many protected species, and spawning aggregations and nesting locations have been identified. The area also provides migratory corridors for a variety of important species, and as such provides suitable baseline conditions for future monitoring studies.

Annex 3

Vulnerability to damage by international shipping activities

(**Note:** A detailed description of the characteristics of the maritime traffic, the transport of harmful substances, and the threats from maritime incidents, including a description of the hydrographical, meteorological and oceanographical conditions, may be found in paragraphs 81 to 109 of document MEPC 68/10/1.)

1   Vessel traffic characteristics

Operational factors

1.1   There are two major shipping routes in the region – the Inner Route and the Outer Route of the GBR. While the Inner Route lies relatively close to the Queensland coast within the GBR and Torres Strait PSSA, the Outer Route begins at the north-eastern limit of the Torres Strait (the Great North-East Channel), continues southwards through the Coral Sea and re-joins the Queensland coast near Sandy Cape (south of Gladstone) (see figure 1 of appendix 3 of document MEPC 68/10/1).

1.2   The Outer Route experiences south-east Trade Winds and heavy seas for about nine months of the year. A vessel suffering serious propulsion or power failure in the Coral Sea will be many hundreds of kilometres from towage assistance and could drift on to one of the numerous reefs or cays in the Coral Sea before any towage assistance can arrive. Anchoring is impractical due to the precipitous depths that prevail up to the edges of these reefs.

Vessel types

1.3   There is a wide variety of vessel types operating in this area. Ships entering and leaving Queensland coastal ports are primarily dry bulk carriers (most notably carrying coal) and, increasingly, liquefied natural gas (LNG) tankers. Oil and chemical carriers calling at Australian east coast ports mainly choose to use the Outer Route. Other ships transiting through the south-west Coral Sea, trading between Asia and other east coast Australian ports such as Brisbane, Newcastle, Sydney and Melbourne, transport a variety of cargoes, including containerized, dry, liquid, vehicular and general cargoes.

Traffic characteristics

1.4   In addition to ships using the Outer Route to transit between Torres Strait and east coast Australian ports, the Outer Route converges in the south-western Coral Sea with the north/south route used by ships transiting between Asian ports via Jomard Entrance (Papua New Guinea) and major Australian east coast ports such as Newcastle, Sydney and Melbourne and commodity-exporting ports in Queensland.

1.5   Ships bound to and from Queensland ports are also a major consideration in terms of the risk to the ecosystem from international shipping activities in the south-west Coral Sea. There are four main passages through the GBR that result in a corresponding concentration of traffic in the south-west Coral Sea. These are Grafton Passage (near Cairns); Palm Passage (near Townsville); Hydrographers Passage (near Mackay); and through the Capricorn and Curtis Channels in the south.

1.6   These shipping routes and passages can be identified in the Automatic Identification System (AIS) vessel traffic density information provided in appendix 2 of document MEPC 68/10/1.

1.7   Shipping activity in the Coral Sea is expected to increase in the coming years. The expansion of the Australian resources sector, which includes other east coast bulk ports such as Newcastle and Port Kembla (most ships en route to and from these ports use the north/south route through the south-west Coral Sea), is the major factor in the expected growth of 81% in the total national traffic at sea by 2020.

Harmful substances carried

1.8 A wide variety of vessels, carrying a range of potentially harmful substances, operate in this area. The Outer Route is generally used by oil and chemical tankers visiting Australian east coast ports, while there is increasing LNG tanker traffic entering and leaving Queensland ports.

2 Natural factors

Hydrographical

2.1 There are some areas immediately around Coral Sea cays, reefs and islets where the depth of water, surveyed bathymetry quality and/or final charted product scale pose some navigational risk for larger vessel types. These areas are clearly marked on nautical charts and, in general, such areas should be well avoided by commercial shipping. Shipping should always navigate with due regard for charted data, chart scale and stated reliability of data within the area of interest.

2.2 Generally, all areas within the PSSA (apart from the proposed area to be avoided (ATBA), discussed below) are too deep to offer any anchoring opportunity.

Meteorological

2.3 Parts of the area are subject to the highest frequency of tropical cyclones in eastern Australia, creating a high-disturbance regime for its ecological communities, resulting in increased diversity due to the frequent regeneration of reefs following storm events. In the last 100 years, cyclones have become less frequent but more intense, and in the last 12 years the region has experienced four extreme cyclones (category 4 or 5).

2.4 In general, during winter months, the predominant winds are from the south east with small southerly and easterly components. Summer months exhibit an increased easterly component in addition to the south-easterly winds.

2.5 Winds in these areas may produce shallow surface currents in addition to those deeper currents described below.

Oceanographic

2.6 Oceanographic processes play a significant role in the biological patterns across the Coral Sea region. There are three main currents that affect the region; the South Equatorial, Hiri, and East Australian Currents. The South Equatorial Current moves west toward Townsville and Cairns from offshore waters to the east. As it moves toward the coast it splits into the north-flowing Hiri Current and the East Australian Current. Geomorphic features interact with these ocean currents to create variable speeds and directions.

2.7 A slow and deep (>100 m) clockwise eddy, originating from the East Australian Current, circulates around the Marion Plateau. A similar gyre system of ocean currents exists atop the Queensland Plateau. The flow of these localized features is thought to create a barrier to larval dispersal that contributes to the high species endemism and localized distribution of species in the region.

2.8 The geomorphic characteristics of the coral reefs and cays reflect the constant exposure to high-energy wind and wave conditions. The East Australian Current and its associated eddy fields are large-scale, spatially predictable, ecologically important pelagic features represented in the region.

Other information

2.9 The Coral Sea's ecology is largely shaped by physical forces such as climate and weather patterns, the direction and strength of currents, the shape of the underlying seabed, and the interaction between water movement and seafloor topography. These forces affect the distribution of species, the availability of nutrients and prey, the levels of disturbance experienced by ecological communities and their ability to recover from natural and human pressures and impacts.

2.10   In addition to the shipwrecks mentioned in annex 2, there have also been a number of incidents and near misses in the region in recent years that demonstrate the potential risk of environmental harm by ships that conduct their passage through the waters of the PSSA extension. Several case studies on near misses in recent years are provided in appendix 3 of document MEPC 68/10/1.

Annex 4

Associated Protective Measures for the Great Barrier Reef, Torres Strait and Coral Sea PSSA

Recommendatory Associated Protective Measures (APMs) are:

.1 An area to be avoided (ATBA) encompassing the reefs, shoals, and islets that lie generally to the north-east of the GBR, between Palm Passage and Hydrographers Passage. Keeping transiting SOLAS ships clear of this area will mitigate the risk of groundings and allow more time for intervention, in case of developing situations (e.g. a ship suffering breakdown of its propulsion machinery) (see appendix 3 of document MEPC 68/10/1 for further information);

.2 Two 5 nautical mile wide two-way routes – one in Diamond Passage and the other to the west of Holmes Reef in the south-west Coral Sea.

.1 The two-way route in Diamond Passage extends from approximately 25 nautical miles south of Diamond Passage through to approximately 35 nautical miles north of the passage.

.2 The two-way route west of Holmes Reef extends for 32.5 nautical miles approximately north-west of Holmes Reef and 20.5 nautical miles approximately south-west of Holmes Reef; and

.3 The proposed two-way routes aim to reduce the risks of collision and grounding of ships by separating opposing streams of traffic, whilst ensuring ships avoid the shoals, reef and islands that lie close outside the two-way routes. The two-way routes also aim to allow ships to follow well-defined lanes, thereby enhancing the safety and efficiency of navigation through effective passage planning. (See appendix 4 of document MEPC 68/10/1 for further information.)

The APMs are new ships' routeing systems under SOLAS regulation V/10 and are provided in full in appendices 3 and 4 of document MEPC 68/10/1 and depicted in the chartlets below.

Description of the two-way routes and associated chartlets in the Coral Sea[*]

The ship routeing systems consist of two recommendatory two-way routes in the south-west portion of the Coral Sea, each being five nautical miles wide.

Diamond Passage

The Diamond Passage two-way route starts approximately south-east of South Diamond Islet and extends on a bearing of 019°–199°for 24.5 nautical miles. It then changes to a bearing of 008°–188°for 35 nautical miles.

From the two-way route's centreline, the closest distance to the 100 metre bathymetric contour is approximately 6.9 nautical miles in both east and west directions. This means that the passage width between those contours, at its narrowest, is approximately 13.8 nautical miles.

---

[*] These two-way routes were adopted by the MSC at its ninety-fifth session.

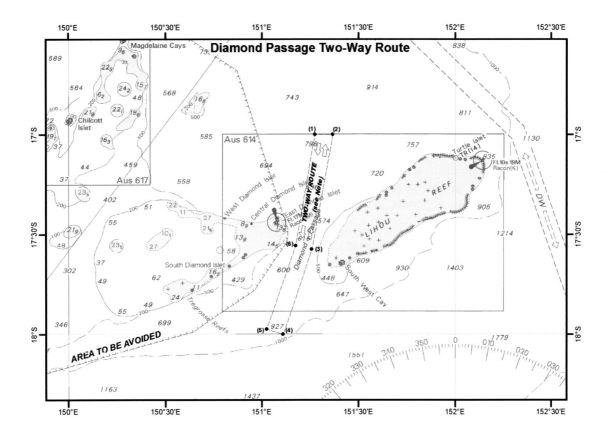

West of Holmes Reef

The Holmes Reef two-way route commences west of Flora Reef and extends along a bearing of 012°–192° for 20.5 nautical miles. The bearing changes to 040°–220° for 32.5 nautical miles. Holmes Reefs and Flora Reef are over 10 nautical miles from the eastern limit of the two-way route.

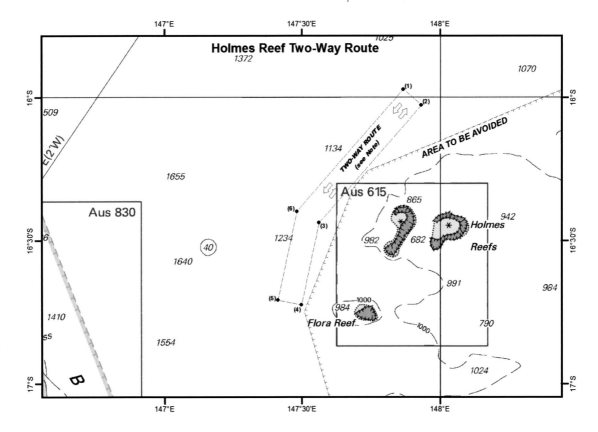

Names, numbers, editions and geodetic datums of the reference charts

Diamond Passage

Names	Number	Edition	Datum
Diamond Passage	Aus614	Ed 2	WGS 84
Willis Islets	Aus617 Pt 1	Ed 2	WGS 84
South West Islet to Magdelaine Cays	Aus617 Pt 2	Ed 2	WGS 84
Mackay to Solomon Islands	Aus4621 (INT621)	Ed 4	WGS 84

West of Holmes Reef

Names	Number	Edition	Datum
Flinders Reefs	Aus615 Pt 1	Ed 2	WGS 84
Flora Reef and Holmes Reefs	Aus615 Pt 2	Ed 2	WGS 84
Percy Isles to Booby Island	Aus4620 (INT620)	Ed 6	WGS 84

Geographical coordinates of the recommendatory two-way routes

A list of the geographical coordinates of the recommendatory two-way routes is provided below.

All geographical positions are based on WGS 84.

Individual coordinate numbering refers to those shown in figure 2 (Diamond Passage) and figure 3 (Holmes Reef).

Diamond Passage

The western limit is bounded by lines joining the following coordinates:

  (1) 16°58′.25 S, 151°15′.56 E

  (6) 17°32′.32 S, 151°10′.56 E

  (5) 17°55′.00 S, 151°02′.41 E

The eastern limit is bounded by lines joining the following coordinates:

  (2) 16°58′.95 S, 151°20′.72 E

  (3) 17°33′.50 S, 151°15′.68 E

  (4) 17°56′.64 S, 151°07′.37 E

Holmes Reef

The western limit is bounded by lines joining the following coordinates:

  (1) 15°57′.78 S, 147°51′.50 E

  (6) 16°23′.37 S, 147°28′.48 E

  (5) 16°44′.76 S, 147°23′.76 E

The eastern limit is bounded by lines joining the following coordinates:

  (2) 16°01′.08 S, 147°55′.42 E

  (3) 16°25′.69 S, 147°33′.29 E

  (4) 16°45′.81 S, 147°28′.86 E

Chartlets and a general description of area to be avoided in the Coral Sea[*]

The area lies off the north-east coast of Australia, within the PSSA in the south-west Coral Sea (figure 1). It encompasses a multitude of reefs, shoals and islets that lie generally to the north-east of the Great Barrier Reef (GBR), between Palm Passage and Hydrographers Passage (figure 2).

---

[*] This area to be avoided was adopted by MSC at its ninety-fifth session.

In order to reduce the risk of a maritime casualty and potential damage to the sensitive marine environment, transiting ships should not enter the ATBA. The ATBA will result in minor changes to the traffic pattern for ships that are required to conform to SOLAS requirements. Some of these ships (e.g. cruise ships) which demonstrate an operational need to visit a location within the ATBA and which have adequate risk-mitigation measures in place may enter the ATBA.

The ATBA is recommendatory in nature.

The ATBA extends over approximately 25,250 square nautical miles and encompasses many reefs, cays, islets, sandbars and shoal patches (figure 3). The 21 recognized, named and charted features that are within the ATBA boundary include:

- Abington Reef;
- Central Diamond Islet;
- Chilcott Islet;
- Dart Reef;
- Diane Bank;
- East Diamond Islet;
- Flinders Reefs;
- Flora Reef;
- Herald Cays;
- Herald Surprise;
- Holmes Reefs;
- Magdelaine Cays;
- Malay Reef;
- McDermott Bank.
- Moore Reefs;
- North Cay;
- South Diamond Islet;
- South West Islet;
- Tregrosse Reefs;
- West Diamond Islet; and
- Willis Islets.

Names, numbers, editions and geodetic datums of the reference charts

Name	Number	Edition	Datum
Diamond Passage	Aus614	Ed 2	WGS 84
Flinders Reefs	Aus615 Pt 1	Ed 2	WGS 84
Flora Reef and Holmes Reefs	Aus615 Pt 2	Ed 2	WGS 84
Willis Islets	Aus617 Pt 1	Ed 2	WGS 84
South West Islet to Magdelaine Cays	Aus617 Pt 2	Ed 2	WGS 84
Percy Isles to Booby Island	Aus4620 (INT620)	Ed 6	WGS 84
Mackay to Solomon Islands	Aus4621 (INT621)	Ed 4	WGS 84

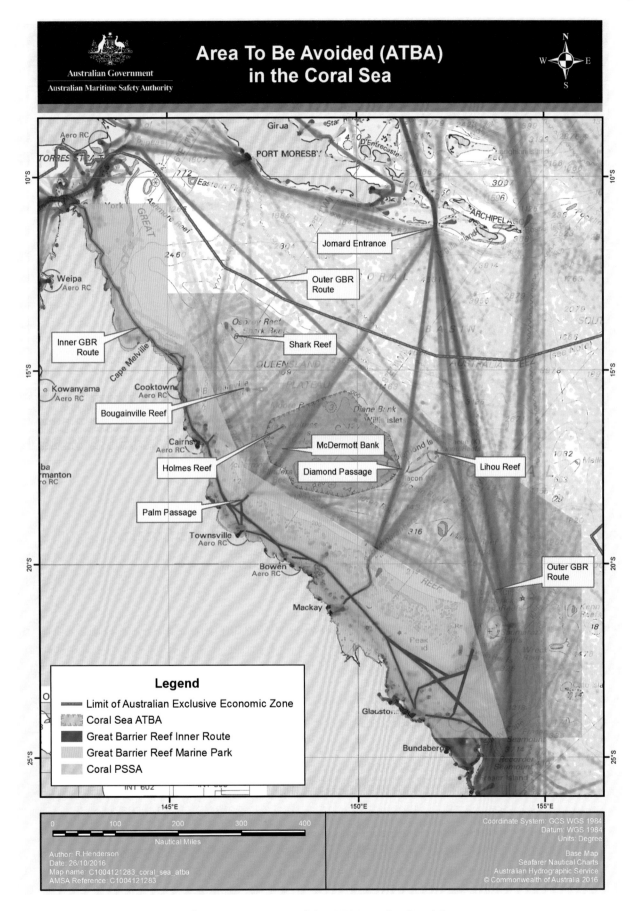

Figure 1: *Location of the ATBA in the Coral Sea*

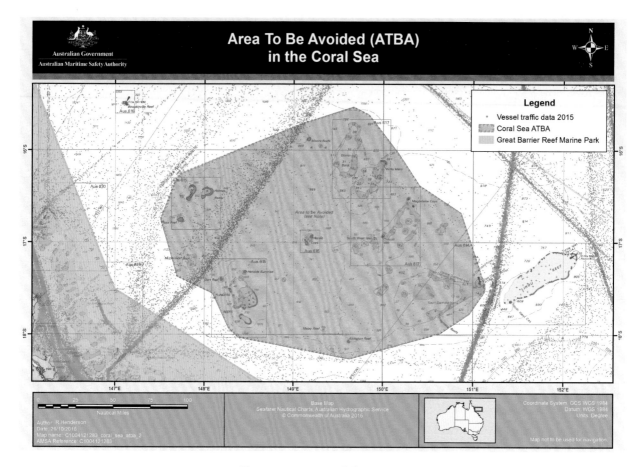

Figure 2: *Extent of the ATBA*

Geographical coordinates of the area to be avoided in the Coral Sea

The geographical coordinates of the ATBA (figure 3) are provided below.

All geographical positions are based on WGS 84.

Individual coordinate numbers in brackets refer to those shown in figure 3.

Area to be avoided

An area to be avoided is established bounded by a line connecting the following geographical positions:

(1)	15°42'.48 S,	149°06'.07 E		(11)	17°59'.43 S,	150°38'.35 E
(2)	15°31'.87 S,	149°40'.07 E		(12)	18°15'.94 S,	149°37'.97 E
(3)	15°36'.90 S,	149°50'.43 E		(13)	18°01'.91 S,	148°23'.34 E
(4)	16°01'.16 S,	150°09'.79 E		(14)	17°55'.49 S,	148°16'.26 E
(5)	16°23'.25 S,	150°24'.56 E		(15)	17°32'.90 S,	148°05'.14 E
(6)	16°40'.91 S,	150°52'.21 E		(16)	17°22'.27 S,	147°41'.63 E
(7)	17°28'.26 S,	151°08'.01 E		(17)	16°45'.01 S,	147°30'.47 E
(8)	17°30'.71 S,	151°08'.01 E		(18)	16°18'.56 S,	147°40'.61 E
(9)	17°32'.59 S,	151°07'.45 E		(19)	16°15'.00 S,	147°43'.82 E
(10)	17°46'.83 S,	150°57'.56 E				

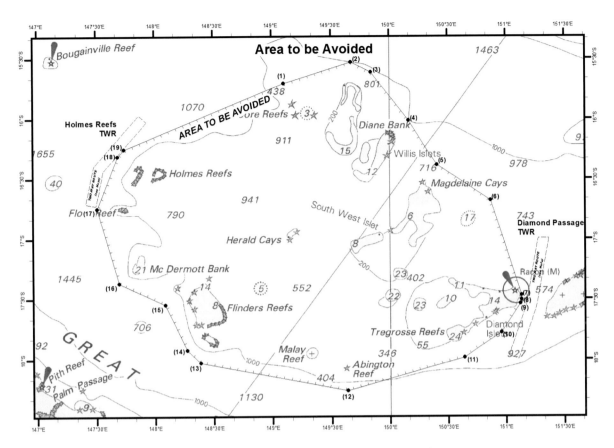

Figure 3: *ATBA and two-way routes around it*

Other routeing measures

A mandatory ship reporting system "In the Torres Strait region and the Inner Route of the Great Barrier Reef" was adopted at the 66th session of MSC and amended at its seventy-eighth and eighty-eighth sessions. The most recent amended version is shown here.

In the Torres Strait region and the Inner Route of the Great Barrier Reef (REEFREP)

1 Categories of ships required to participate in the system

Ships of the following general categories are required to participate in the reporting system:

.1 All ships of 50 metres or greater in overall length;

.2 All ships, regardless of length, carrying in bulk hazardous and/or potentially polluting cargo, in accordance with the definitions at resolution MSC.43(64), paragraph 1.4;

.3 Ships engaged in towing or pushing where either the towing or pushing vessel or the towed or pushed vessel is a vessel prescribed within the categories in subparagraphs .1 and .2.

2 Geographical coverage of the system and the number and edition of the reference chart used for the delineation of the system

2.1 The reporting system will cover the general area as shown in the chartlet at appendix 1. The area encompasses the Torres Strait between longitudes 141°45′ E and 144°00′ E, including the Endeavour Strait, and the waters of the Great Barrier Reef (GBR) between the Australian coast and the outer edge of the GBR, from the latitude of Cape York (10°40′ S) south-eastwards to 21°00′ S, 152°55′ E. From this position, the REEFREP boundary extends as follows:

> **(a)** to position 23°42′ S, 153°45′ E,
>
> **(b)** thence to position 24°30′ S, 153°35′ E,
>
> **(c)** thence westward on latitude 24°30′ S to its intersection with the Queensland coastline at the low water mark, and
>
> **(d)** thence generally north-westerly along the coastline to the latitude of Cape York (10°40′ S).

2.2 The REEFREP area is shown on charts Aus4620 (1996) and Aus4635 (2010). A series of large-scale charts is provided for coastal navigation throughout the REEFREP area.

3 Format and content of report, times and geographical positions for submitting reports, Authority to whom reports should be sent and available services

The ship report, short title "REEFREP", will be made to the REEFREP VTS Centre (REEFCENTRE) located at Hay Point in Queensland. Examples of the format and content of all required reports are shown at appendix 2. A ship may elect, for reasons of commercial confidentiality, to communicate that section of the REEFREP ENTRY report which provides information on cargo (line P) by non-verbal means prior to entering the system. This can be achieved by including cargo information in the AUSREP Sailing Plan (SP) message.

3.1 Entry and exit reports

Ships will be required to provide a full REEFREP Position Report (PR) at least two hours prior to entering the REEFREP area from seaward or when sailing from a port within the area.

Ships will also be encouraged to provide a passage plan as described below when providing an Entry Report. However, it is recognized that, at this stage in their passage, they are unlikely to have a pilot on board and are therefore unable to provide a detailed passage plan.

When finally departing the REEFREP area, or entering a port within the area, the REEFREP system will associate the required PR and the designated reporting point and automatically recognize this report as an exit message.

3.2 Passage plan reports

Ships will be required to provide a passage plan, including information such as vessel details, pilot information, route/waypoint information, within one hour of entering the REEFREP area. The provision of accurate passage plans is critical to the dissemination of accurate ship traffic information and can be provided by one of the following means:

> **.1** Nominating the route using the chartlets which will be provided by pilots
>
> **.2** Nominating the waypoints, or
>
> **.3** Using the existing Mandatory Reporting Points as listed on the charts

3.3 Intermediate position reports

Automated Position Reporting via Inmarsat-C will be the primary mechanism for ships to provide position reports while transiting the REEFREP region. REEFCENTRE will generally carry out APR remotely without any intervention by ships' crews. However, a small proportion of vessels are fitted with first-generation Inmarsat-C terminals which do not support remote programming. Masters of ships fitted with these terminals, who choose to participate, will be required to program them onboard to send position reports automatically. Instructions relating to programming of these terminals can be obtained from REEFCENTRE.

Vessels can participate in Automated Position Reporting at any time by authorizing REEFCENTRE to download a Data Network Identifier (DNID) to the ship's Inmarsat-C terminal. Once the DNID is downloaded, REEFCENTRE is able to program the ship's Inmarsat-C terminal to transmit position reports automatically at regular intervals. Vessels can communicate authorization for DNID download either by Inmarsat-C or REEFREP VHF voice communication channels as described in appendix 2.

Vessels providing intermediate position reports via APR must still comply with the other VHF reporting requirements prescribed in section 2.4 (Entering and Leaving the REEFREP SRS), section 2.5 (Pilotage Reports) and section 2.6 (Special Reports) of the *AUSREP and REEFREP* booklet.

Where a ship is unable to provide intermediate position reports via APR as required by REEFCENTRE, they will be required to provide brief position reports as advised by the operator. The VHF position reports are limited to the identity of the vessel, position, any variation to the last reported speed and course and any further information the master considers might be of value to the system.

3.4 Defect reports

The following information is to be provided when a ship within the REEFREP area suffers damage, failure or breakdown affecting the safety of the ship, makes a marked deviation from a route, course or speed previously advised or requires to report safety-related information and reports of incidents involving Dangerous Goods (DG), Harmful Substances (HS) or Marine Pollutants (MP).

- **(a)** Ship name and call sign.

- **(b)** Position (latitude and longitude) and time.

- **(c)** Name of next Mandatory Reporting Point or course, if not tracking between reporting points.

- **(d)** Estimated time of arrival (ETA) at next Mandatory Reporting Point *or* speed (ship's anticipated average speed until next report, in knots & tenths of a knot).

- **(e)** Description and details of any damage, failure or breakdown suffered:

  - **(i)** collision, grounding, fire, explosion, structural failure, flooding, cargo shifting.

  - **(ii)** failure or breakdown of steering gear, propulsion plant, electrical generating system, essential shipborne navigational aids.

- **(f)** Details of any Safety Messages (navigational safety, abnormal weather, unserviceable aids to navigation) or DG/HS/MP incident reports using the recognized IMO reporting formats.

4 Information to be provided to participating ships and procedures to be followed

REEFCENTRE will provide information to shipping on potentially conflicting traffic movements from the analysis of incoming position reports, passage plans and other data sources.

The key information to be provided to shipping includes:

- **.1** Ship traffic information

- **.2** Navigational assistance

- **.3** Maritime safety information

4.1 *Ship traffic information:* The REEFREP VTS Centre will provide information to shipping on potentially conflicting traffic movements resulting from the analysis of incoming reports.

4.2 Certain sections of the route in the Torres Strait and the far northern sector of the Inner Route of the GBR present a particular navigational hazard in situations where large ships might be passing or overtaking, especially deeper draught ships. When the REEFREP VTS Centre considers that ships are approaching such sections, any relevant traffic information held by the Centre will be passed to them. Because of the extensive size of the REEFREP area it is not be intended to routinely broadcast traffic information across the whole area but to advise individual ships as necessary.

4.3   Traffic information, including other advice received from ships or local maritime authorities, which impacts on navigational safety will be passed to ships in relevant areas. Examples include concentrations of fishing vessels, unusual weather conditions, etc.

4.4   *Navigational assistance:* In circumstances where information available to REEFCENTRE may assist on-board decision-making, REEFREP may initiate interaction with an individual ship to provide this information. This may include circumstances where information available suggests a ship may be standing into shallow water (e.g. in areas of restricted navigation where there is radar coverage) or deviating from a recommended route. The types of assistance that may be provided are described further in NAV 49/INF.4.

4.5   Maritime safety information (MSI) in the form of navigational warnings (AUSCOAST Warnings) will continue to be issued in the appropriate broadcasts from MRCC AUSTRALIA. The REEFREP VTS Centre will maintain details of MSI for the REEFREP area for the information of participating ships.

5   Communication required for the system, frequencies on which reports should be transmitted and information to be reported

5.1   The system will be based on both Inmarsat-C communications and VHF voice communications. While the use of Inmarsat-C is expected to become the main mechanism for ships to meet their position-reporting requirements and to provide other mandatory reports such as entry reports and passage plans, VHF voice communication provides an interactive mechanism for the interchange of data between ships and the REEFREP VTS Centre.

5.2   VHF channels 5, 18 and 19 in the international maritime mobile band have been allocated for the reporting points in the system.

5.3   Information of commercial confidentiality may be transmitted by non-verbal means.

5.4   The language used for reports in the system will be English, using the IMO Standard Marine Communication Phrases where necessary.

5.5   Communications associated with reporting in accordance with the requirements of this system will be free of charge

6   Rules and regulations in force in the area of the system

Compulsory pilotage rules apply in the northern section of the Inner Route (Cape York to Cairns) and in Hydrographers Passage. Other regulations apply domestic law in accordance with the terms of international conventions.

7   Shore-based facilities to support operation of the system

7.1   REEFCENTRE is located at Hay Point, on the central Queensland coast. The Centre is manned 24 hours per day, 365 days per year, and is equipped with a sophisticated traffic information management tool that integrates and assists in analysing all VHF communications, radar, AIS and APR data that is relayed to REEFCENTRE. The radar coverage is provided at the key entry and exit points to Torres Strait and the Inner Route.

7.2   The VTS Centre is equipped to provide a high standard of service to meet the system requirements and will be operated by trained and experienced personnel. Operator standards will be in accordance with "Guidelines on Recruitment, Qualification and Training of VTS Operators" (resolution A.857(20), annex 2).

7.3   The system will be operated to quality standards, with service levels being constantly monitored.

7.4   The entire area has full DGPS coverage redundancy, ensuring very high availability standards.

7.5   The REEFREP VTS Centre is also interfaced with the AUSREP system operated by RCC AUSTRALIA.

8   Alternative communication if the communication facilities of the shore-based Authority fail

In the event of failure of the system VHF communications, a report from a participating ship can be passed by any of the following methods:

.1   *Seaphone* through the commercial VHF coastal network;

.2   SATCOM; and

.3   HF radio through Townsville Radio (VIT).

9   Measures to be taken if a ship fails to comply with the requirements of the system

9.1   The primary objective of the system is to facilitate the exchange of information between the ship and the shore and so support safe navigation and the protection of the marine environment. All means will be used to encourage and promote the full participation of ships required to submit reports under SOLAS regulation V/11. If reports are not submitted and the ship can be positively identified, then information will be passed to the relevant flag State for investigation and possible prosecution in accordance with that State's legislation. A failure to report may also be investigated for breach of Australian laws relating to compulsory ship reporting.

Appendix 1

General area covered by the reporting system

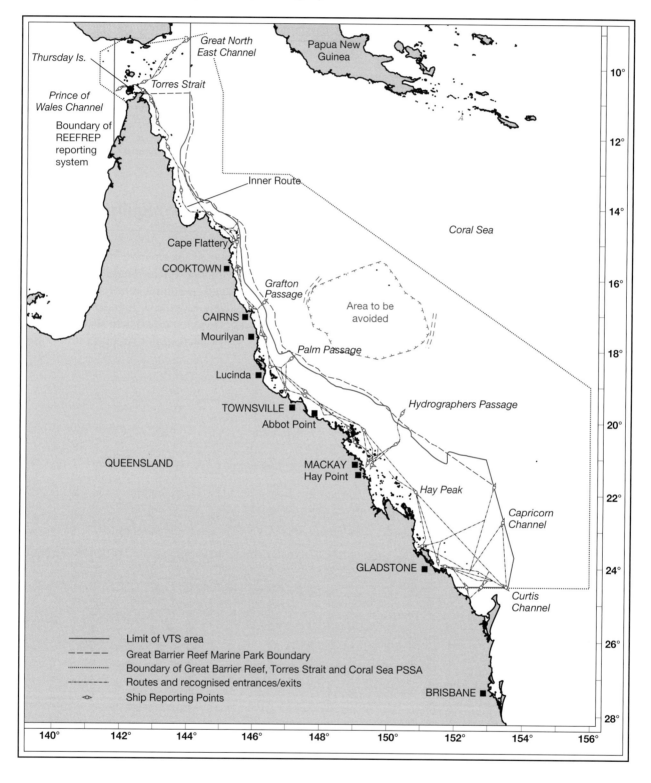

PARTICULARLY SENSITIVE SEA AREAS (PSSA) 2017 EDITION

Appendix 2

Examples of reports for the REEFREP reporting system

REEFREP ENTRY (Full report)

Example 1: Ship sailing from a port within the reporting area, routeing through the area and departing the area through Grafton Passage bound for Pusan via Jomard Entrance.

Format

A.	Ship's name and call sign
B.	Date/Time of position (UTC)
C.	Name of Reporting Point
E.	Course (normally "VARIOUS")
F.	Speed
G.	Departed (port, if outside reporting area)
H.	Date/Time of entry in system and point of entry (not required if advised at C)
J.	Pilot embarked or ordered
L.	Intended route
O.	Draught
P.	Cargo
Q.	Defects/deficiencies (only if relevant)
U.	Ship type and length (metres)
X.	Remarks

Example

REEFREP ENTRY

A.	MERIDIAN/VIPM
B.	020200Z
C.	TOWNSVILLE
E.	VARIOUS
F.	15
G.	–
J.	NO*
L.	INNER ROUTE TO GRAFTON
O.	10
P.	COAL
Q.	NIL
U.	BULK CARRIER/250
X.	JOINING INNER ROUTE AT BREWER 020400Z

Example 2: Ship entering the reporting area northbound for Port Moresby, using Inner Route and Great North East Channel.

Format

A.	Ship's name and call sign
B.	Date/Time of position (UTC)
C.	Name of Reporting Point
E.	Course (normally "VARIOUS")
F.	Speed
G.	Departed (port, if outside reporting area)
H.	Date/Time of entry in system and point of entry (not required if advised at C)
J.	Pilot embarked or ordered
L.	Intended route
O.	Draught
P.	Cargo
Q.	Defects/deficiencies (only if relevant)
U.	Ship type and length (metres)
X.	Remarks

Example

REEFREP ENTRY

A.	MERIDIAN/VIPM
B.	020200Z
C.	HIGH PEAK
E.	VARIOUS
F.	15
G.	BRISBANE
J.	PILOT EMBARKED
L.	INNER ROUTE AND GREAT NORTH EAST CHANNEL
O.	10
P.	GENERAL CARGO
U.	RESEARCH/65
X.	CONDUCTING RESEARCH ON PASSAGE

REEFREP REPORT

Example: Ship reporting at an intermediate reporting point within reporting area.

Format		**Example**
		REEFREP REPORT
A.	Ship's name and call sign	A. ENTERPRISE/VIPM
C.	Name of Reporting Point	C. CHARLOTTE
F.	Speed (if change from last report)	F. SPEED NOW 11.5
X.	Remarks	X. LARGE CONCENTRATION OF FISHING VESSELS VICINITY HANNAH ISLAND

REEFREP DEFECT

Example 1: Ship reporting defect within reporting area.

Format		**Example**
		REEFREP DEFECT
A.	Ship's name and call sign	A. ENTERPRISE/VIPM
B.	Date/Time of position	B. 030205Z
C.	Latitude/Longitude *or* Reporting Point	C. 1400S 14400E
Q.	Nature of defect/damage	Q. BOTH RADARS UNSERVICEABLE IN HEAVY RAIN SQUALLS; ALSO MINOR STEERING DEFECT
X.	Remarks	X. PROCEEDING TO ANCHOR 180 HANNAH ISLAND LT 1.0 TO EFFECT REPAIRS

Example 2: Ship defect repaired.

Format		**Example**
		REEFREP DEFECT
A.	Ship's name and call sign	A. ENTERPRISE/VIPM
B.	Date/Time of position	B. 030215Z
C.	Latitude/Longitude *or* Reporting Point	C. 1401S 14001E
F.	Speed	F. 8.5
X.	Remarks	X. DEFECT REPAIRED, REJOINING ROUTE

REEFREP EXIT

Example 1: Ship westbound reporting exit from reporting area at Torres Strait.

Format		**Example**
		REEFREP EXIT
A.	Ship's name and call sign	A. MITSUBISHI/XUGT
K.	Point of exit	K. COOK
I.	Destination (via route)	I. SINGAPORE VIA LOMBOK
X.	Remarks (must include "FINAL REPORT")	X. FINAL REPORT

Example 2: Ship reporting exit from reporting area at Palm Passage.

Format		**Example**
		REEFREP EXIT
A.	Ship's name and call sign	A. IRON MAIDEN/RXTP
K.	Point of exit	K. PALM
I.	Destination (via route)	I. PUSAN VIA ROSSEL ISLAND
X.	Remarks (must include "FINAL REPORT")	X. FINAL REPORT

Example 3: Ship reporting arrival at a port within reporting area (after transiting from another port also within the area).

Format		**Example**
		REEFREP EXIT
A.	Ship's name and call sign	A. NORTHERN STAR/CPIM
K.	Point of exit	K. CAIRNS
I.	Destination (via route) if outside REEFREP area	
X.	Remarks (must include "FINAL REPORT")	X. ARRIVED CAIRNS, FINAL REPORT

Example 4: Ship eastbound reporting exit from reporting area at Great North East Channel.

Format		**Example**
		REEFREP EXIT
A.	Ship's name and call sign	A. ENTERPRISE/VIPM
K.	Point of exit	K. DARNLEY
I.	Destination (via route)	I. PORT MORESBY DIRECT
X.	Remarks (must include "FINAL REPORT")	X. FINAL REPORT

Appendix 3

Participating in APR via Inmarsat-C

APR information will only be used by the REEFREP system whilst the ship is in the REEFREP area. The DNID will remain downloaded until the master or company advises REEFCENTRE that the ship is no longer a regular visitor. It is important that this information is passed during the final visit to Australia, as the DNID has to be deleted whilst the Inmarsat-C terminal is logged into the particular satellite region.

A ship is deemed to be a regular visitor if it is operating on the Australian coastal trade or revisiting Australia from overseas within eighteen months. Infrequent visitors will have the DNID deleted from their terminals after sending a Final Report.

Vessels can communicate authorization for DNID download either by Inmarsat-C or REEFREP VHF voice communication channels as described below:

I   Inmarsat[*]

By forwarding an APR message via Inmarsat to REEFCENTRE, the master authorizes download of a DNID into the Inmarsat-C terminal, and provides the following details for each Inmarsat-C installation:

- Vessel name, Call sign, Inmarsat-C Mobile Number (IMN), manufacturer, and model (example at Table 1).

ID	Message type	REEFREP/APR//
A	Ship name/Call sign	A/REEF CHAMPION/VJVJ//
B	Primary Inmarsat-C terminal details (Inmarsat-C Mobile Number (IMN), manufacturer, and model)	B/450309919/ THRANE & THRANE/ 3020B//
C	Secondary Inmarsat-C terminal details (Inmarsat-C Mobile Number (IMN), manufacturer, and model), where applicable.	C/450309920/ FURUNO/FELCOM12//

Table 1 – *Inmarsat-C Data Network Identifier (DNID)*

While reporting to REEFREP, masters must ensure that their INMARSAT equipment remains active in the "LOGIN" mode (Pacific Ocean Region (POR)) at all times.

II   REEFREP VHF voice communication channels

For example, at the first Reporting Point, the master (or his representative) verbally authorizes the DNID download and provides the following details for each Inmarsat-C installation:

- Inmarsat-C Mobile Number (IMN), manufacturer, and model. e.g.: 450306909, JRC, JUE75C

---

[*] APR messages sent to REEFCENTRE using Special Access Code (SAC) 861 via Perth LES using Inmarsat-C access code '222' will be reverse-charged to the SRS.

Two-way route in the Great Barrier Reef and Torres Strait

A two-way route "In the Great Barrier Reef and Torres Strait" was adopted at the ninety-third session of MSC. A full technical description of the route is in part E of editions of the IMO publication "Ships' Routeing";[*] only chartlets of the route are included here.

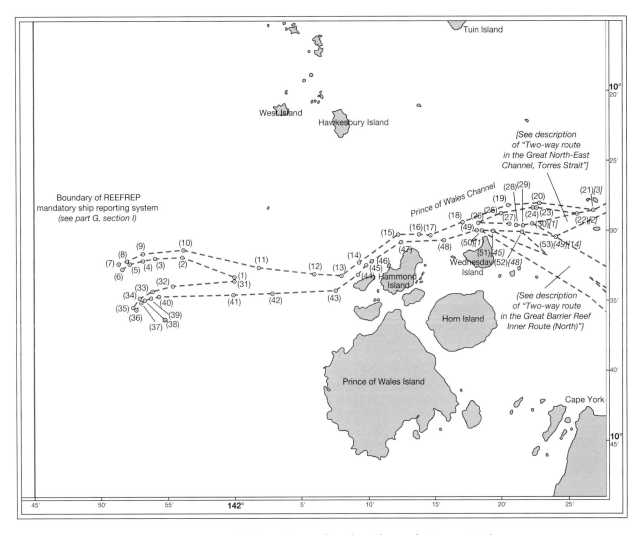

Two-way route in the Prince of Wales Channel, Torres Strait

---

[*] References to part G, section I or part D, section III on these chartlets are to parts and sections of "Ships' Routeing".

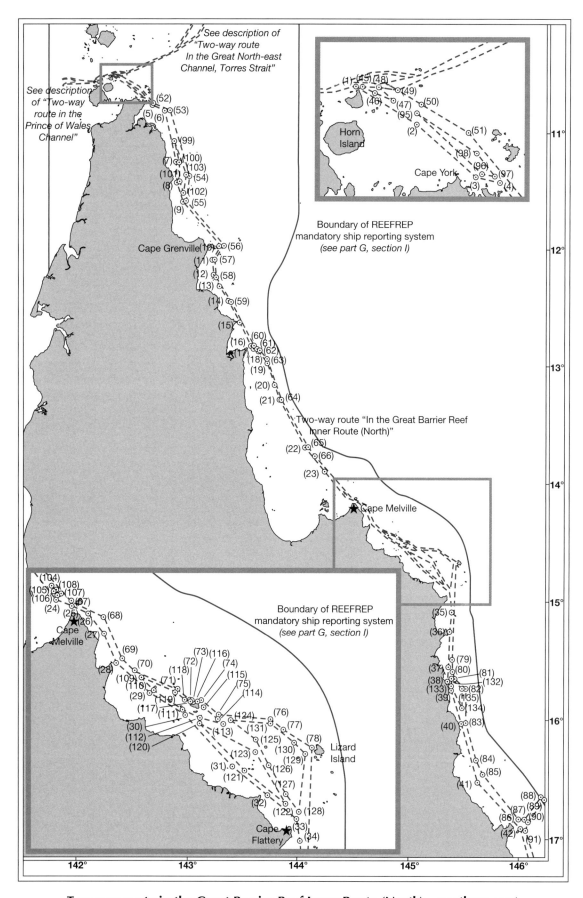

Two-way route in the Great Barrier Reef Inner Route (North) – northern part

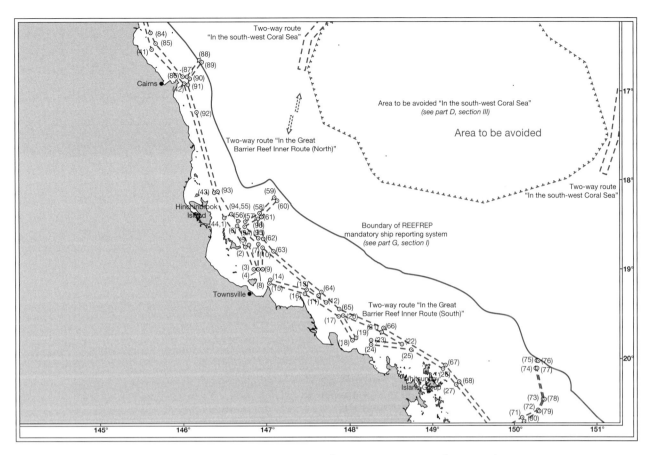

Two-way route in the Great Barrier Reef Inner Route (North) – southern part – with Inner Route (South) – northern part

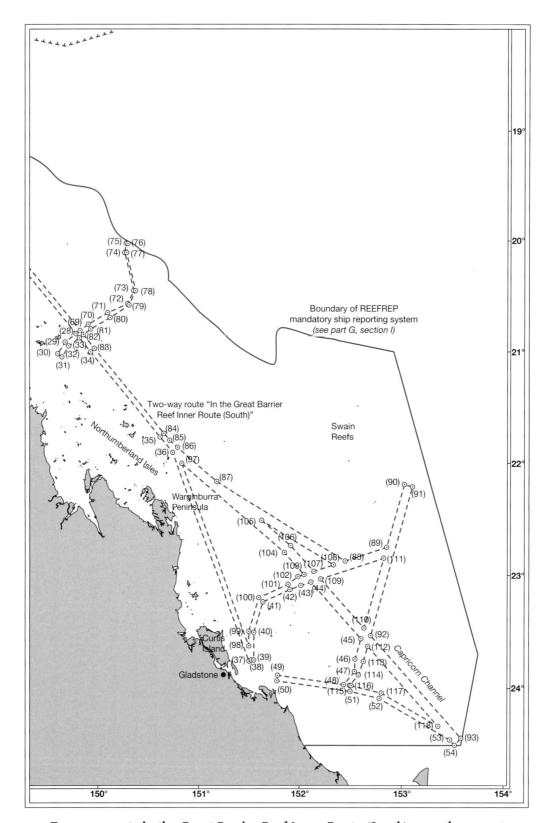

Two-way route in the Great Barrier Reef Inner Route (South) – southern part

Area to be avoided "In the region of the Great Barrier Reef"

An area to be avoided was adopted by Assembly at its thirteenth session in 1983. It was revoked at the ninety-fourth session of MSC in 2014.

Annex 7 – Archipelago of Sabana-Camagüey Particularly Sensitive Sea Area

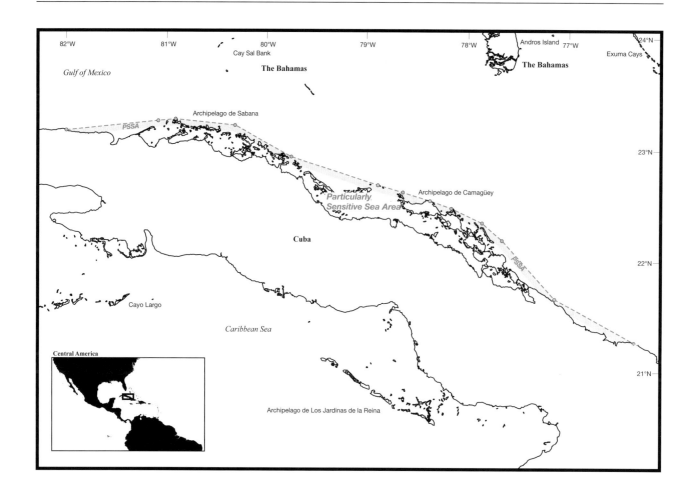

Resolution MEPC.74(40)

adopted on 25 September 1997
Identification of the Archipelago of Sabana-Camagüey as a Particularly Sensitive Sea Area

THE MARINE ENVIRONMENT PROTECTION COMMITTEE,

BEING AWARE of the ecological, social, economic, cultural, scientific and educational value of the Archipelago of Sabana-Camagüey as well as the international shipping traffic and activities in the area,

RECALLING that the Archipelago of Sabana-Camagüey is a part of the Wider Caribbean Region which has been designated as a Special Area under the provisions of regulation 5 of Annex V of the International Convention for the Prevention of Pollution from Ships, 1973, as modified by the Protocol of 1978 relating thereto (MARPOL 73/78), and that requirements in respect of this Special Area have not yet taken effect,

RECALLING ALSO that full compliance with the requirements of Annex I of MARPOL 73/78 in controlling discharge of oil is of paramount importance for the Particularly Sensitive Sea Area,

RECALLING FURTHER that the Maritime Safety Committee, at its forty-eighth session, adopted several traffic separation schemes for the waters off the northern coast of Cuba, some of which fall within the Archipelago of Sabana-Camagüey,

NOTING that article 211(6) of the 1982 United Nations Convention on the Law of the Sea is further evidence of the will of States to co-operate in defining vulnerable marine areas requiring a higher level of protection than that which generally applies,

NOTING FURTHER that the Guidelines for the Designation of Special Areas and the Identification of Particularly Sensitive Sea Areas adopted as resolution A.720(17) set out procedures for designation of Particularly Sensitive Sea Areas and for adoption of measures to be applied in such special areas,

HAVING CONSIDERED the proposal by Cuba to designate the Archipelago of Sabana-Camagüey as a Particularly Sensitive Sea Area,

RECOGNIZING that measures to be applied in the proposed area should further be considered at future sessions of the Committee and the Maritime Safety Committee before their adoption in accordance with the provisions of paragraphs 3.4 to 3.8, as applicable,

RECOGNIZING ALSO the intention of Member Governments to co-operate with the coastal State to determine measures to be applied in the proposed sea area as soon as possible,

HAVING CONSIDERED that criteria for identification of a Particularly Sensitive Sea Area provided in resolution A.720(17) are fulfilled for the Archipelago of Sabana-Camagüey,

IDENTIFIES the Archipelago of Sabana-Camagüey as defined in the annex to this resolution as a Particularly Sensitive Sea Area.

Annex

Geographical description of the Archipelago of Sabana-Camagüey

The Particularly Sensitive Sea Area is identified as waters inland of the baselines determined by the following geographical coordinates:

Latitude	Longitude	
23°11'.0 N	082°00'.0 W	Punta Tijeras
23°16'.0 N	081°05'.2 W	Cayo Mono
23°16'.9 N	080°54'.9 W	Faro Cruz del Padre
23°13'.6 N	080°19'.6 W	
22°56'.8 N	079°45'.4 W	Cayo La Vela
22°41'.4 N	078°53'.4 W	
22°37'.6 N	078°38'.8 W	Cayos Guillermitos
22°32'.9 N	078°22'.8 W	
22°28'.9 N	078°10'.0 W	Cayo Paredón Grande
22°21'.1 N	077°51'.7 W	Bajo Tributarios de Minerva
22°11'.5 N	077°39'.8 W	Cayo Confites
21°39'.8 N	077°08'.4 W	Punta Maternillos
21°16'.1 N	076°21'.4 W	

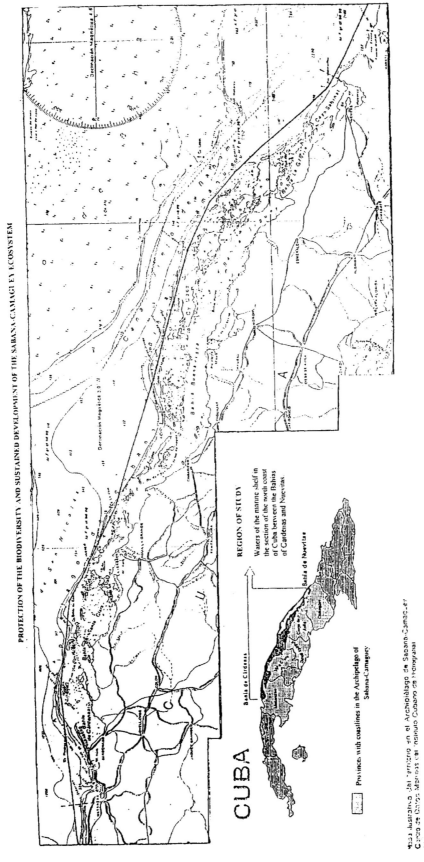

PROTECTION OF THE BIODIVERSITY AND SUSTAINED DEVELOPMENT OF THE SABANA-CAMAGÜEY ECOSYSTEM

CUBA

REGION OF STUDY

Waters of the marine shelf in the section of the north coast of Cuba between the Bahías of Cárdenas and Nuevitas.

Bahía de Cárdenas

Bahía de Nuevitas

CUBA

Province with coastlines in the Archipelago of Sabana-Camagüey

Associated Protective Measures

1   Traffic separation schemes

The traffic separation schemes in the territorial waters of the north coast, including those at the latitude of the Costa de Matanzas, the Canal Viejo de Bahamas (Old Bahama Channel) and the Punta Maternillos, within the territorial waters of the Archipelago of Sabana-Camagüey, were approved at the forty-eighth MSC session. Full technical descriptions of the traffic separation schemes and their associated inshore traffic zones are in part B of editions of the IMO publication "Ships' Routeing"; only chartlets of the schemes are included here.

Off Costa de Matanzas

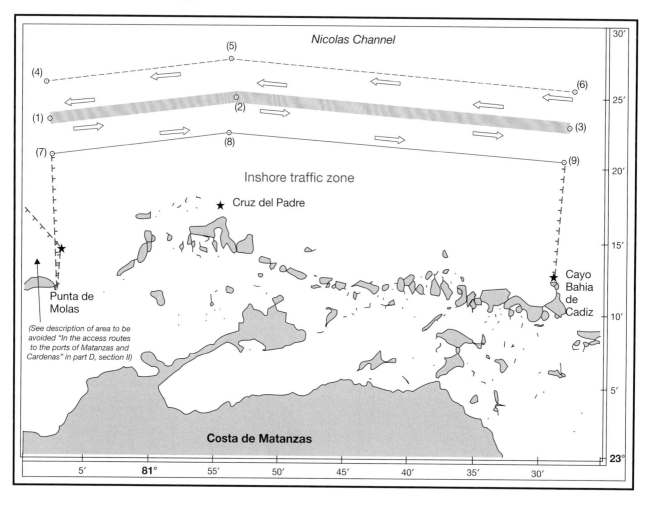

In the Old Bahama Channel

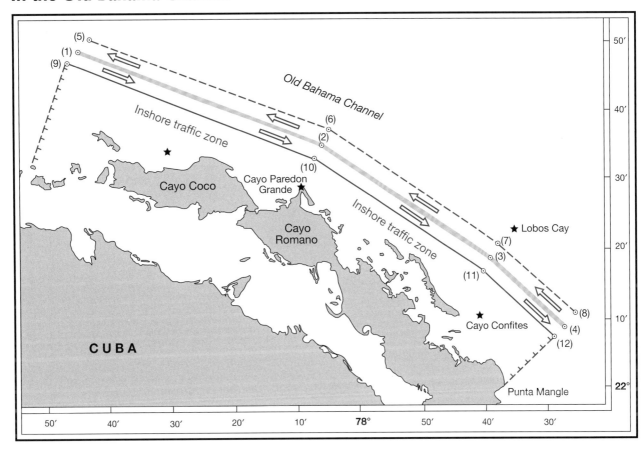

Off Punta Maternillos

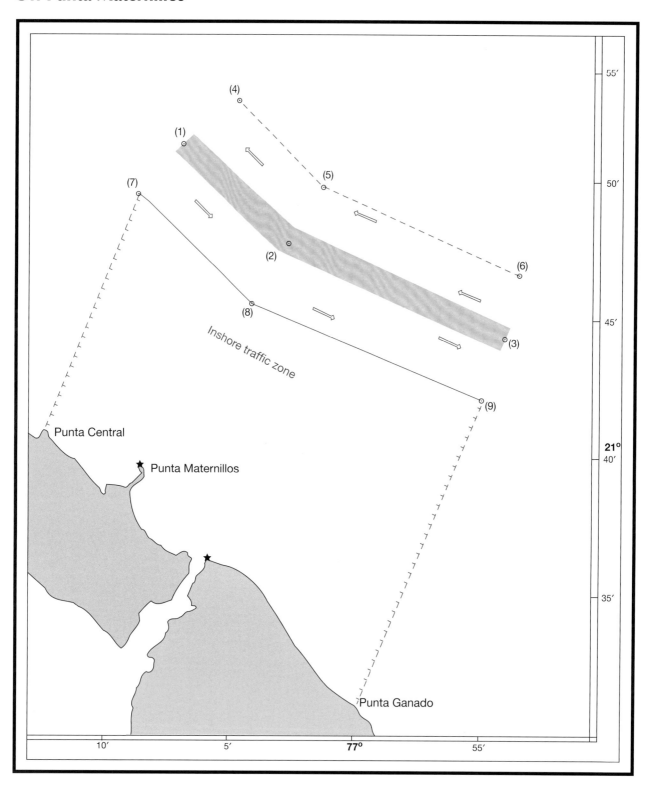

2   Regulations relating to discharges in inland and territorial waters under the jurisdiction of the Sabana-Camaguëy Archipelago

Prohibitions

Any discharges into the sea of oil, oily mixtures, noxious liquid substances, garbage or harmful substances from vessels of any type or size.

Any discharge of oil or oily mixtures from cargo tanks, including cargo pumps, from petrol tankers and from engine-room bilge areas, mixed with cargo waste.

Dumping at sea of the following types of garbage from ships of any type or size: (1) plastics, synthetic fishing lines and nets, plastics garbage bags; (2) loose stowage materials, packing materials and coverings; (3) paper, rags, glass, metal, bottles, ceramics or similar materials.

Ships should avoid discharging ballast water or discharging and reloading while transiting waters under the jurisdiction of the Sabana-Camagüey Archipelago (resolution A.774(18): Guidelines for preventing the introduction of unwanted aquatic organisms and pathogens from ships' ballast water and sediment discharges).

3   Area to be avoided

An area to be avoided in the access routes to the ports of Matanzas and Cardenas was adopted by the seventy-second session of MSC in 2000. The area should be avoided by all ships over 150 gross tonnage. A full technical description of the area is in part D of editions of the IMO publication "Ships' Routeing"; only a chartlet of the area is included here. The reference to "section IX of part B" within this chartlet relates to a section within "Ships' Routeing".

In the access routes to the ports of Matanzas and Cardenas

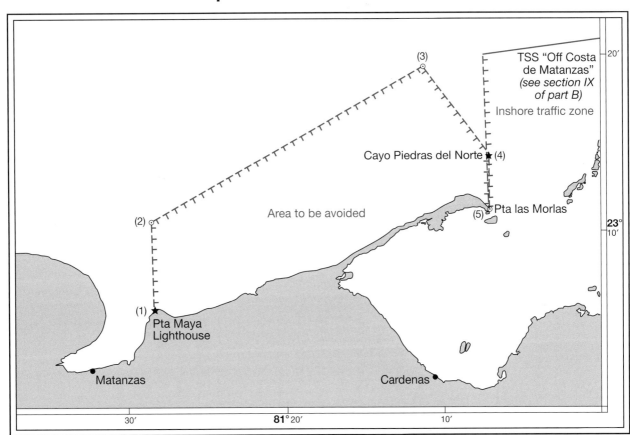

Annex 8 – Malpelo Island Particularly Sensitive Sea Area

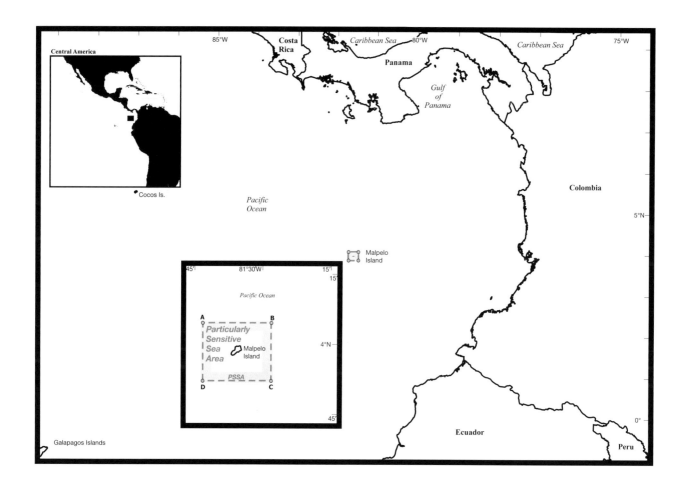

Resolution MEPC.97(47)

adopted on 8 March 2002

Identification of the sea area around Malpelo Island as a Particularly Sensitive Sea Area

THE MARINE ENVIRONMENT PROTECTION COMMITTEE,

BEING AWARE of the ecological value of the sea area around Malpelo Island, as well as the tourist and fishing activities in the area,

NOTING that article 211(6) of the 1982 United Nations Convention on the Law of the Sea is further evidence of the will of States to co-operate in defining vulnerable marine areas requiring a higher level of protection than that which generally applies,

NOTING FURTHER that the Guidelines for Identification and Designation of Particularly Sensitive Sea Areas under resolution A.927(22) set out procedures for designation of Particularly Sensitive Sea Areas and for adoption of measures to be applied in such special areas,

RECOGNIZING that the Sub-Committee on Navigation, at its forth-seventh session, agreed to a proposal to establish an area to be avoided around Malpelo Island for approval by the Maritime Safety Committee at its seventy-fifth session,

RECOGNIZING ALSO the intention of Member Governments to co-operate with the coastal State to determine measures to be applied in the proposed sea area as soon as possible,

HAVING CONSIDERED the proposal by Colombia to designate the sea area around Malpelo Island as a Particularly Sensitive Sea Area,

HAVING AGREED that criteria for identification of a Particularly Sensitive Sea Area provided in resolution A.927(22) are fulfilled for the sea area around Malpelo Island,

IDENTIFIES the sea area around Malpelo Island as defined in the annex to this resolution as a Particularly Sensitive Sea Area.

Annex

Geographical description of the Particularly Sensitive Sea Area around Malpelo Island

With a view to avoiding the risk of serious damage to important systems, to the environment, and to the economy of the area, the area bounded by a line connecting the following geographical points is designated as a Particularly Sensitive Sea Area. As a result, all fishing vessels and all other ships in excess of 500 gross tonnage should avoid this area:

(Nautical reference charts INT 6105 "Gulf of Cupica to Bay of Buenaventura" and INT 6000 "West Coast of Colombia")

A	04°04'48" N,	081°43'18" W
B	04°04'48" N,	081°28'07" W
C	03°52'09" N,	081°28'07" W
D	03°52'09" N,	081°43'18" W.

Associated Protective Measure

An area to be avoided around Malpelo Island was adopted by the seventy-fifth session of MSC in 2002. A full technical description of the area is in part D of editions of the IMO publication "Ships' Routeing"; only a chartlet of the area is included here. The "Part B, section IX" that is mentioned within this chartlet is another section of "Ships' Routeing".

Malpelo Island

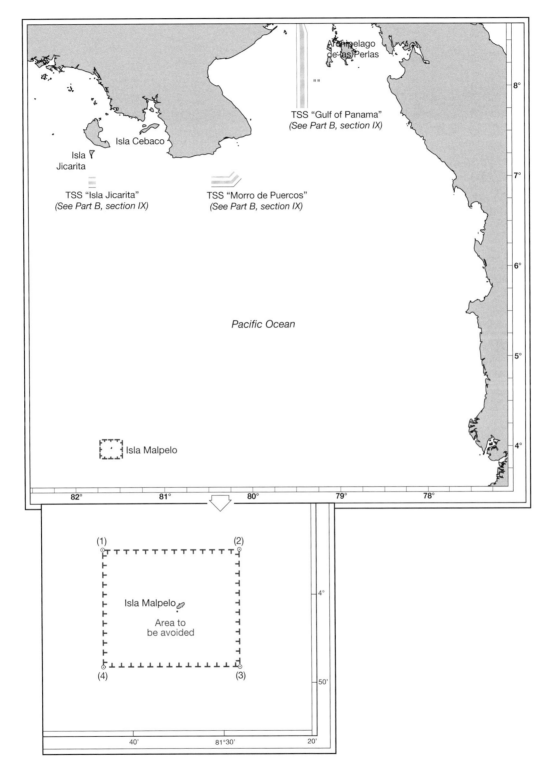

Annex 9 – Florida Keys Particularly Sensitive Sea Area

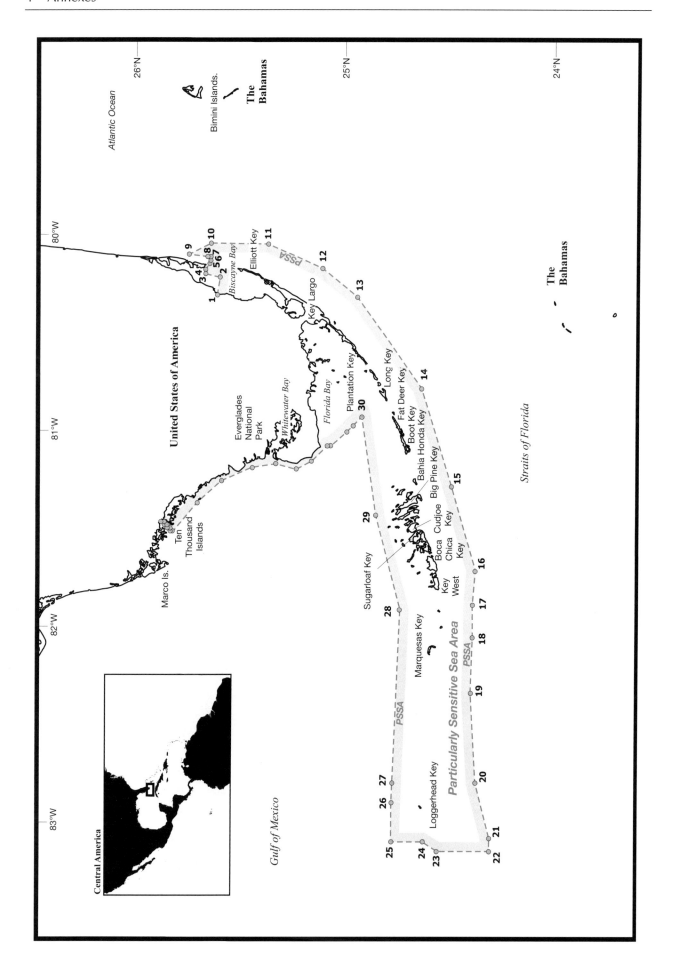

Resolution MEPC.98(47)
adopted on 8 March 2002
Identification of the sea area around the Florida Keys as a Particularly Sensitive Sea Area

THE MARINE ENVIRONMENT PROTECTION COMMITTEE,

BEING AWARE of the ecological, social, economic, cultural, scientific and educational value of the sea areas around the Florida Keys, as well as the international shipping traffic and activities in the area,

NOTING that article 211(6) of the 1982 United Nations Convention on the Law of the Sea is further evidence of the will of States to co-operate in defining vulnerable marine areas requiring a higher level of protection than that which generally applies,

NOTING FURTHER that the Guidelines for Identification and Designation of Particularly Sensitive Sea Areas adopted under resolution A.927(22) set out procedures for designation of Particularly Sensitive Sea Areas and for adoption of measures to be applied in such areas,

RECOGNIZING that the Sub-Committee on Navigation, at its forty-seventh session, agreed with several associated routeing measures for the waters around the Florida Keys for approval by the Maritime Safety Committee at its seventy-fifth session,

RECOGNIZING ALSO the intention of Member Governments to co-operate with the coastal State to determine measures to be applied in the proposed sea area as soon as possible,

HAVING CONSIDERED the proposal from the United States to designate the sea area around the Florida Keys as a Particularly Sensitive Sea Area,

HAVING AGREED that criteria for identification of a Particularly Sensitive Sea Area provided in resolution A.927(22) are fulfilled for the sea area around the Florida Keys,

IDENTIFIES the sea area around the Florida Keys as defined in the annex to this resolution as a Particularly Sensitive Sea Area.

Annex

Geographical description of the Particularly Sensitive Sea Area around the Florida Keys

In order to avoid the risk of pollution and damage to this unique, fragile, and pristine coral reef ecosystem, mariners should exercise extreme care when navigating in the area bounded by a line connecting the following geographical positions which is designated as a Particularly Sensitive Sea Area:

(Reference chart: United States 11013, 1998 edition.

Note: This chart is based on North American 1983 datum.)

(1)	25°36'.85 N,	080°18'.50 W	(16)	24°22'.30 N,	081°43'.17 W
(2)	25°36'.08 N,	080°13'.08 W	(17)	24°23'.00 N,	081°53'.50 W
(3)	25°40'.27 N,	080°12'.05 W	(18)	24°23'.00 N,	082°03'.50 W
(4)	25°40'.30 N,	080°10'.74 W	(19)	24°23'.42 N,	082°20'.52 W
(5)	25°39'.11 N,	080°08'.98 W	(20)	24°22'.00 N,	082°48'.00 W
(6)	25°38'.81 N,	080°08'.03 W	(21)	24°18'.00 N,	083°05'.00 W
(7)	25°38'.77 N,	080°06'.87 W	(22)	24°18'.00 N,	083°09'.00 W
(8)	25°39'.70 N,	080°06'.85 W	(23)	24°33'.00 N,	083°09'.00 W
(9)	25°45'.00 N,	080°06'.10 W	(24)	24°37'.00 N,	083°06'.00 W
(10)	25°38'.70 N,	080°02'.70 W	(25)	24°46'.00 N,	083°06'.00 W
(11)	25°22'.00 N,	080°03'.00 W	(26)	24°46'.00 N,	082°54'.00 W
(12)	25°06'.38 N,	080°10'.48 W	(27)	24°45'.80 N,	082°48'.00 W
(13)	24°56'.37 N,	080°19'.26 W	(28)	24°44'.00 N,	081°55'.00 W
(14)	24°37'.90 N,	080°47'.30 W	(29)	24°51'.00 N,	081°26'.00 W
(15)	24°29'.20 N,	081°17'.30 W	(30)	24°55'.00 N,	080°56'.00 W

(31) From the point of 24°55'.00 N, 080°56'.00 W, the boundary then follows the boundary of Everglades National Park in a southerly then north-easterly direction through Florida Bay and Buttonwood Sound. (The precise boundary coordinates for this area is going through a process for technical verification; however, international shipping is not likely to navigate in this area due to water depths.)

Associated Protective Measures

Areas to be avoided off the Florida coast were adopted by the seventy-fifth session of MSC in 2002. All ships carrying cargoes of oil and hazardous materials and all other ships greater than 50 metres in length should avoid the areas. A full technical description of the areas is in part D of editions of the IMO publication "Ships' Routeing"; only a summary chartlet of the areas is included here. The "part G, section II" that is mentioned within this chartlet is also within "Ships' Routeing".

Off the Florida Coast

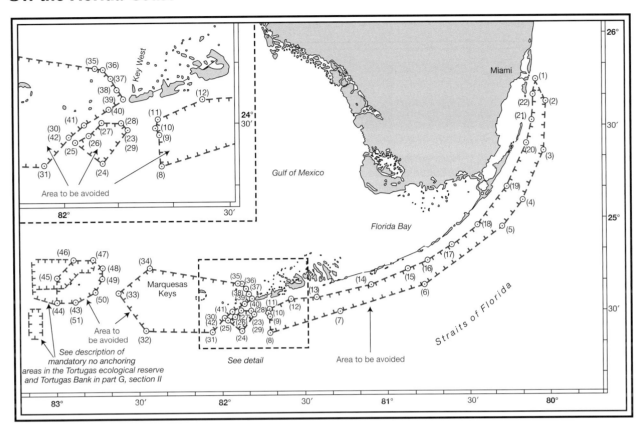

Mandatory no anchoring areas in the Tortugas Ecological Reserve and Tortugas Bank were adopted by the seventy-fifth session of MSC in 2002. All ships shall avoid anchoring in the areas. A full technical description of the no anchoring areas is in part G of editions of the IMO publication "Ships' Routeing"; only a summary chartlet of the areas is included here.

Mandatory no anchoring areas in the Tortugas Ecological Reserve and Tortugas Bank

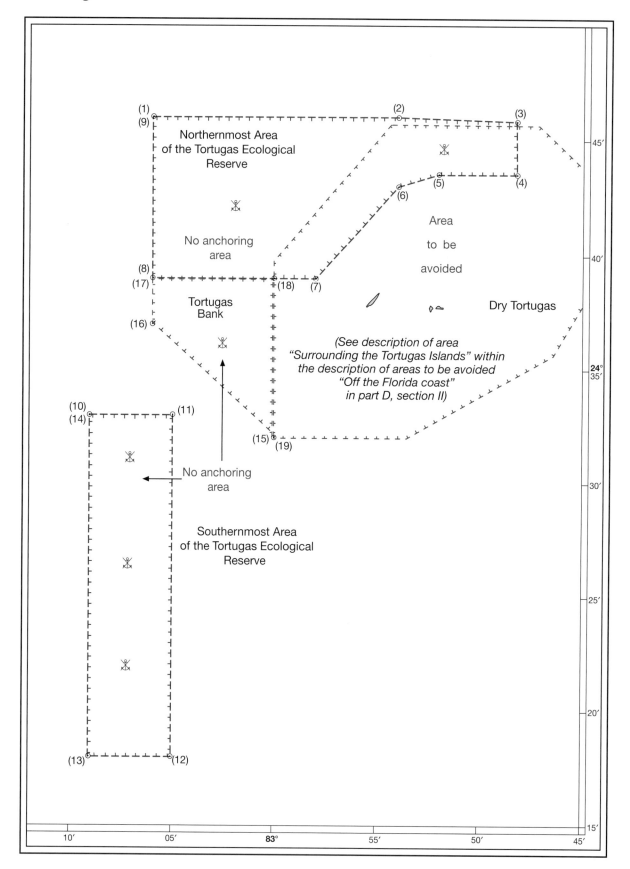

Annex 10 – Wadden Sea Particularly Sensitive Sea Area

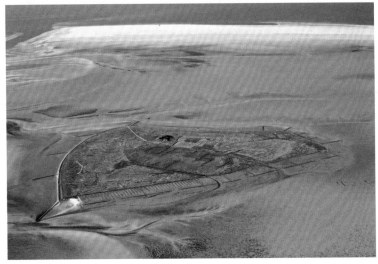

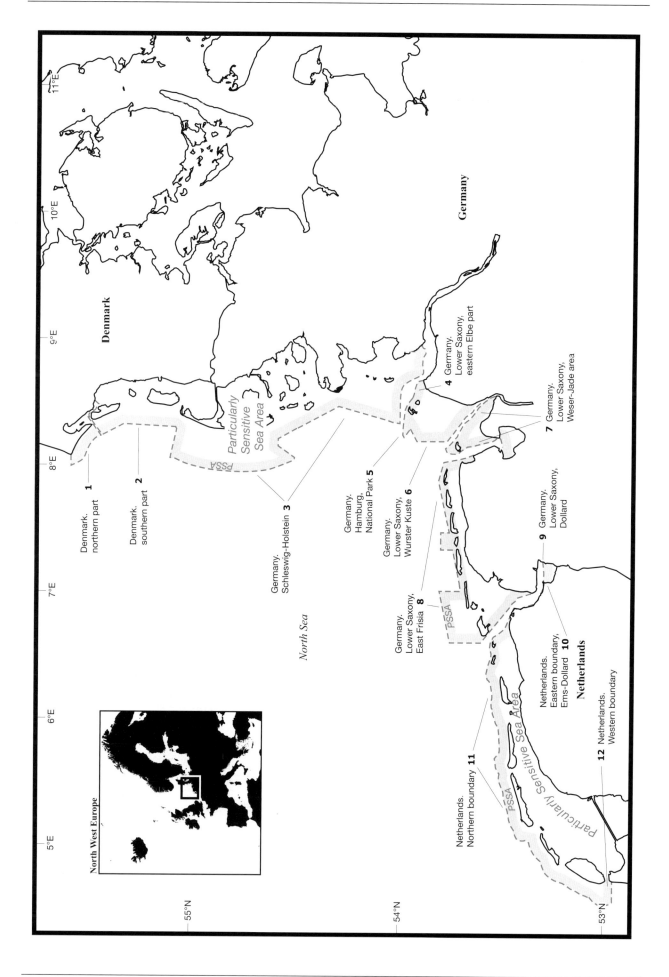

North West Europe

Denmark

Germany

Germany

1 Denmark, northern part

2 Denmark, southern part

Germany, Schleswig-Holstein 3

4 Germany, Lower Saxony, eastern Elbe part

Germany, Hamburg, National Park 5

Germany, Lower Saxony, Wurster Kuste 6

7 Germany, Lower Saxony, Weser-Jade area

Germany, Lower Saxony, East Frisia 8

9 Germany, Lower Saxony, Dollard

Netherlands, Eastern boundary, Ems-Dollard 10

Netherlands

Netherlands, Northern boundary 11

12 Netherlands, Western boundary

North Sea

Particularly Sensitive Sea Area

PSSA

Particularly Sensitive Sea Area

PSSA

Resolution MEPC.101(48)

adopted on 11 October 2002

Identification of the Wadden Sea as a Particularly Sensitive Sea Area

THE MARINE ENVIRONMENT PROTECTION COMMITTEE,

BEING AWARE of the ecological, social, economic, cultural, scientific and educational value of the Wadden Sea, as well as its vulnerability to damage by international shipping traffic and activities in the area and the steps taken by Denmark, Germany and the Netherlands to address that vulnerability,

NOTING that the Guidelines for the Identification and Designation of Particularly Sensitive Sea Areas adopted under resolution A.927(22) set out procedures for the designation of Particularly Sensitive Sea Areas,

HAVING CONSIDERED the proposal from Denmark, Germany and the Netherlands to designate the Wadden Sea as a Particularly Sensitive Sea Area,

HAVING AGREED that criteria for identification of a Particularly Sensitive Sea Area provided in resolution A.927(22) are fulfilled for the Wadden Sea,

1   DESIGNATES the Wadden Sea as defined in annexes 1, 2 and 3 to this resolution as a Particularly Sensitive Sea Area.

Annex 1

Description of the Particularly Sensitive Sea Area Wadden Sea: coordinates

A   Description

In order to avoid the risk of pollution and damage to this exceptional, highly dynamic tidal ecosystem of world importance, mariners should exercise extreme care when navigating in the area bounded by a line connecting the following geographical positions, which is designated as a Particularly Sensitive Sea Area, and in the adjacent area:

The PSSA Wadden Sea is bordered:

Seawards:	by an offshore line defined by a set of geographical coordinates (see coordinates listed under C),
Landwards:	by the main dikes, or, where the main dikes are absent, by the spring-high-tide-water line, and in the rivers, by the brackish-water limit.

The inhabited islands are excluded from the PSSA. These islands are:

in Denmark:		Rømø, Mandø, Fanø
in Germany:		
	Schleswig-Holstein:	Pellworm, Nordstrandischmoor, Hooge, Gröde, Langeneß-Oland, Föhr, Amrum, Sylt, Norderoog, Habel, Süderoog
	Hamburg:	Neuwerk
	Lower Saxony:	Borkum, Juist, Norderney, Baltrum, Langeoog, Spiekeroog, Wangerooge
in The Netherlands:		Texel, Vlieland, Terschelling, Ameland, Schiermonnikoog

B   Illustrative overview

The illustrative overview shows the different parts (1–12) of the offshore line of the proposed PSSA Wadden Sea. The numbers and names pointing to the different parts refer to the list of coordinates given in the tables under C.

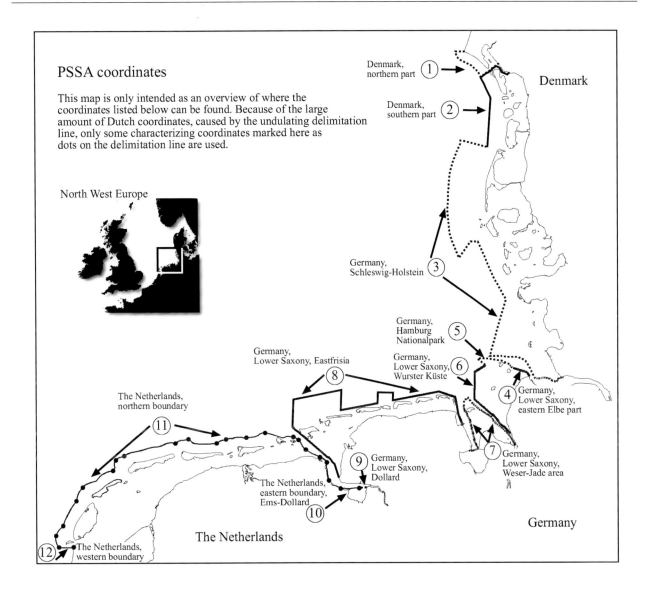

PSSA coordinates

This map is only intended as an overview of where the coordinates listed below can be found. Because of the large amount of Dutch coordinates, caused by the undulating delimitation line, only some characterizing coordinates marked here as dots on the delimitation line are used.

North West Europe

Denmark, northern part ①

Denmark, southern part ②

Denmark

Germany, Schleswig-Holstein ③

Germany, Hamburg Nationalpark ⑤

Germany, Lower Saxony, Eastfrisia

Germany, Lower Saxony, Wurster Küste ⑥

⑧

Germany, Lower Saxony, eastern Elbe part ④

The Netherlands, northern boundary

⑪

Germany, Lower Saxony, Weser-Jade area ⑦

⑨ Germany, Lower Saxony, Dollard

The Netherlands, eastern boundary, Ems-Dollard

⑩

The Netherlands

Germany

⑫ The Netherlands, western boundary

C List of geographical coordinates (projection WGS 84) for the bordering offshore line of the proposed PSSA Wadden Sea

Denmark

The proposed PSSA in the Danish Wadden Sea is divided into a northern part and a southern part by the Esbjerg Harbour shipping lane and the outer area of Esbjerg Harbour.

Northern part (1)

The PSSA delimitation consists of 28 points with the following coordinates from Blaavandshuk to the shore north of Esbjerg Harbour.

Southern part (2)

The PSSA delimitation consists of 17 points with the following coordinates, from the shore south of Esbjerg Harbour to the borderline between Denmark and Germany territorial waters.

1 Denmark, northern part		
No.	North	East
1	55°33'.463	008°04'.516
2	55°33'.48	007°59'.00
3	55°33'.21	007°59'.02
4	55°32'.99	007°59'.06
5	55°32'.74	007°59'.16
6	55°32'.50	007°59'.28
7	55°32'.28	007°59'.45
8	55°32'.04	007°59'.67
9	55°31'.83	007°59'.89
10	55°31'.62	008°00'.15
11	55°31'.43	008°00'.47
12	55°31'.26	008°00'.82
13	55°31'.10	008°01'.21
14	55°30'.95	008°01'.57
15	55°30'.82	008°01'.94
16	55°30'.71	008°02'.34
17	55°29'.23	008°08'.12
18	55°28'.14	008°10'.46
19	55°27'.38	008°11'.96
20	55°25'.593	008°13'.716
21	55°26'.916	008°16'.879
22	55°27'.228	008°18'.104
23	55°27'.873	008°19'.357
24	55°28'.608	008°20'.793
25	55°29'.056	008°21'.791
26	55°29'.109	008°21'.915
27	55°29'.467	008°22'.724
28	55°29'.866	008°23'.635

2 Denmark, southern part		
No.	North	East
29	55°27'.166	008°30'.157
30	55°26'.420	008°28'.490
31	55°27'.160	008°25'.620
32	55°27'.866	008°24'.904
33	55°28'.273	008°24'.574
34	55°28'.614	008°24'.151
35	55°28'.975	008°22'.436
36	55°28'.776	008°21'.929
37	55°28'.452	008°21'.043
38	55°27'.724	008°19'.581
39	55°27'.046	008°18'.195
40	55°26'.805	008°17'.016
41	55°25'.470	008°13'.825
42	55°25'.220	008°14'.080
43	55°19'.100	008°19'.543
44	55°12'.300	008°18'.900
45	55°03'.795	008°18'.040

Germany

Below are the coordinates for the seven parts (3–9) representing the delimitation of the proposed PSSA for Germany.

3	Germany, Schleswig-Holstein	
No.	North	East
46	55°03'.795	008°18'.040
47	55°06'.053	008°02'.716
48	55°05'.647	008°02'.618
49	55°05'.239	008°02'.547
50	55°05'.011	008°02'.395
51	55°03'.814	008°01'.635
52	55°02'.982	008°00'.960
53	55°02'.659	008°00'.708
54	55°02'.332	008°00'.471
55	55°01'.064	007°59'.598
56	55°00'.692	007°59'.354
57	55°00'.319	007°59'.133
58	54°59'.317	007°58'.572
59	54°59'.170	007°58'.493
60	54°57'.968	007°57'.853
61	54°57'.540	007°57'.640
62	54°57'.102	007°57'.451
63	54°56'.660	007°57'.292
64	54°55'.858	007°57'.032
65	54°55'.303	007°56'.876
66	54°54'.745	007°56'.765
67	54°53'.645	007°56'.591
68	54°53'.169	007°56'.531
69	54°52'.013	007°56'.429
70	54°50'.539	007°56'.279
71	54°50'.166	007°56'.253
72	54°49'.265	007°56'.209
73	54°48'.945	007°56'.203
74	54°48'.625	007°56'.209
75	54°48'.095	007°56'.234
76	54°47'.848	007°56'.218
77	54°46'.380	007°55'.986
78	54°45'.823	007°55'.921
79	54°45'.265	007°55'.899
80	54°44'.707	007°55'.925
81	54°44'.148	007°55'.995
82	54°39'.682	007°56'.732
83	54°39'.104	007°56'.800
84	54°38'.529	007°56'.918
85	54°37'.957	007°57'.083

3	Germany, Schleswig-Holstein	
No.	North	East
86	54°37'.390	007°57'.295
87	54°36'.830	007°57'.556
88	54°36'.597	007°57'.674
89	54°36'.145	007°57'.920
90	54°35'.697	007°58'.197
91	54°35'.257	007°58'.505
92	54°30'.063	008°02'.338
93	54°35'.126	008°08'.522
94	54°35'.126	008°15'.406
95	54°32'.932	008°17'.071
96	54°31'.208	008°18'.308
97	54°30'.053	008°19'.144
98	54°29'.614	008°19'.462
99	54°28'.596	008°20'.191
100	54°27'.489	008°20'.996
101	54°26'.289	008°21'.858
102	54°25'.140	008°22'.692
103	54°24'.747	008°22'.956
104	54°24'.545	008°23'.091
105	54°23'.878	008°23'.624
106	54°22'.186	008°25'.125
107	54°20'.980	008°26'.205
108	54°18'.099	008°28'.843
109	54°13'.309	008°25'.467
110	54°10'.917	008°23'.782
111	54°06'.008	008°20'.322
112	54°05'.983	008°20'.305
113	54°02'.317	008°17'.718
114	54°02'.275	008°17'.689
115	54°01'.099	008°16'.859
116	53°59'.960	008°16'.056
117	53°59'.936	008°28'.660
118	53°59'.940	008°28'.725
119	53°59'.940	008°28'.826
120	53°59'.937	008°28'.937
121	53°59'.941	008°29'.048
122	53°59'.942	008°29'.133
123	53°59'.948	008°29'.221
124	53°59'.954	008°29'.344
125	53°59'.952	008°29'.410

3	Germany, Schleswig-Holstein	
No.	North	East
126	53°59'.947	008°29'.486
127	53°59'.938	008°29'.584
128	53°59'.930	008°29'.691
129	53°59'.923	008°29'.788
130	53°59'.911	008°29'.871
131	53°59'.905	008°29'.965
132	53°59'.907	008°30'.068
133	53°59'.905	008°30'.156
134	53°59'.910	008°30'.252
135	53°59'.910	008°30'.337
136	53°59'.912	008°30'.393
137	53°59'.913	008°30'.457
138	53°59'.917	008°30'.523
139	53°59'.921	008°30'.585
140	53°59'.924	008°30'.658
141	53°59'.930	008°30'.725
142	53°59'.932	008°30'.779
143	53°59'.929	008°30'.837
144	53°59'.930	008°30'.946
145	53°59'.942	008°31'.057
146	53°59'.953	008°31'.148
147	53°59'.965	008°31'.276
148	53°59'.969	008°31'.372
149	53°59'.972	008°31'.475
150	53°59'.977	008°31'.559
151	53°59'.982	008°31'.638
152	53°59'.990	008°31'.691
153	54°00'.005	008°31'.759
154	54°00'.008	008°31'.833
155	54°00'.016	008°31'.951
156	54°00'.021	008°32'.046
157	54°00'.021	008°32'.156
158	54°00'.021	008°32'.250
159	54°00'.021	008°32'.348
160	54°00'.024	008°32'.441
161	54°00'.023	008°32'.528
162	54°00'.016	008°32'.613
163	54°00'.013	008°32'.694
164	54°00'.013	008°32'.750
165	54°00'.014	008°32'.817
166	54°00'.013	008°32'.869
167	54°00'.016	008°32'.988
168	54°00'.022	008°33'.090

3	Germany, Schleswig-Holstein	
No.	North	East
169	54°00'.022	008°33'.183
170	54°00'.021	008°33'.280
171	54°00'.022	008°33'.402
172	54°00'.019	008°33'.502
173	54°00'.013	008°33'.608
174	54°00'.005	008°33'.680
175	53°60'.000	008°33'.764
176	53°59'.994	008°33'.856
177	53°59'.990	008°33'.916
178	53°59'.985	008°34'.007
179	53°59'.977	008°34'.090
180	53°59'.968	008°34'.167
181	53°59'.965	008°34'.249
182	53°59'.948	008°34'.389
183	53°59'.937	008°34'.470
184	53°59'.913	008°34'.580
185	53°59'.903	008°34'.648
186	53°59'.885	008°34'.717
187	53°59'.827	008°34'.872
188	53°59'.793	008°34'.980
189	53°59'.764	008°35'.105
190	53°59'.746	008°35'.179
191	53°59'.729	008°35'.253
192	53°59'.709	008°35'.329
193	53°59'.690	008°35'.404
194	53°59'.677	008°35'.465
195	53°59'.667	008°35'.534
196	53°59'.630	008°35'.699
197	53°59'.611	008°35'.767
198	53°59'.580	008°35'.919
199	53°59'.535	008°36'.115
200	53°59'.504	008°36'.254
201	53°59'.480	008°36'.361
202	53°59'.460	008°36'.443
203	53°59'.431	008°36'.574
204	53°59'.391	008°36'.741
205	53°59'.354	008°36'.879
206	53°59'.324	008°37'.001
207	53°59'.306	008°37'.095
208	53°59'.289	008°37'.171
209	53°59'.250	008°37'.319
210	53°59'.226	008°37'.403
211	53°59'.189	008°37'.546

3 Germany, Schleswig-Holstein		
No.	North	East
212	53°59'.160	008°37'.657
213	53°59'.111	008°37'.780
214	53°59'.046	008°37'.947
215	53°58'.964	008°38'.173
216	53°58'.907	008°38'.333
217	53°58'.850	008°38'.496
218	53°58'.691	008°38'.868
219	53°58'.442	008°39'.105
220	53°57'.962	008°39'.598
221	53°57'.371	008°40'.199
222	53°57'.299	008°40'.267
223	53°56'.812	008°40'.749
224	53°56'.204	008°41'.362
225	53°55'.648	008°41'.924
226	53°55'.094	008°42'.487
227	53°54'.996	008°42'.595
228	53°54'.745	008°42'.861
229	53°54'.445	008°43'.118
230	53°54'.164	008°43'.361
231	53°53'.970	008°43'.529
232	53°53'.859	008°43'.634
233	53°53'.402	008°44'.022
234	53°53'.300	008°44'.096
235	53°53'.302	008°44'.185
236	53°53'.313	008°44'.265
237	53°53'.318	008°44'.347
238	53°53'.318	008°44'.443
239	53°53'.316	008°44'.514
240	53°53'.312	008°44'.591
241	53°53'.308	008°44'.681
242	53°53'.305	008°44'.744
243	53°53'.293	008°44'.818
244	53°53'.278	008°44'.898
245	53°53'.271	008°44'.962
246	53°53'.264	008°45'.039
247	53°53'.247	008°45'.121
248	53°53'.241	008°45'.196
249	53°53'.235	008°45'.272
250	53°53'.231	008°45'.356
251	53°53'.235	008°45'.475
252	53°53'.239	008°45'.570
253	53°53'.250	008°45'.699
254	53°53'.252	008°45'.789

3 Germany, Schleswig-Holstein		
No.	North	East
255	53°53'.255	008°45'.896
256	53°53'.270	008°45'.984
257	53°53'.286	008°46'.057
258	53°53'.297	008°46'.142
259	53°53'.297	008°46'.226
260	53°53'.297	008°46'.292
261	53°53'.292	008°46'.348
262	53°53'.315	008°46'.487
263	53°53'.333	008°46'.591
264	53°53'.340	008°46'.675
265	53°53'.363	008°46'.792
266	53°53'.386	008°46'.886
267	53°53'.397	008°46'.950
268	53°53'.412	008°47'.009
269	53°53'.415	008°47'.071
270	53°53'.421	008°47'.158
271	53°53'.430	008°47'.267
272	53°53'.433	008°47'.354
273	53°53'.442	008°47'.428
274	53°53'.461	008°47'.509
275	53°53'.474	008°47'.608
276	53°53'.478	008°47'.675
277	53°53'.481	008°47'.796
278	53°53'.483	008°47'.884
279	53°53'.493	008°47'.954
280	53°53'.505	008°48'.013
281	53°53'.523	008°48'.075
282	53°53'.535	008°48'.124
283	53°53'.538	008°48'.197
284	53°53'.538	008°48'.284
285	53°53'.542	008°48'.367
286	53°53'.543	008°48'.438
287	53°53'.542	008°48'.474
288	53°53'.545	008°48'.554
289	53°53'.548	008°48'.613
290	53°53'.550	008°48'.688
291	53°53'.546	008°48'.775
292	53°53'.531	008°48'.893
293	53°53'.515	008°48'.987
294	53°53'.501	008°49'.064
295	53°53'.484	008°49'.153
296	53°53'.470	008°49'.260
297	53°53'.468	008°49'.326

3	Germany, Schleswig-Holstein	
No.	North	East
298	53°53'.465	008°49'.399
299	53°53'.464	008°49'.472
300	53°53'.454	008°49'.552
301	53°53'.442	008°49'.653
302	53°53'.419	008°49'.741
303	53°53'.406	008°49'.784
304	53°53'.375	008°49'.890
305	53°53'.366	008°49'.942
306	53°53'.355	008°50'.017
307	53°53'.338	008°50'.107
308	53°53'.318	008°50'.172
309	53°53'.308	008°50'.287
310	53°53'.302	008°50'.382
311	53°53'.306	008°50'.449
312	53°53'.314	008°50'.553
313	53°53'.316	008°50'.617
314	53°53'.313	008°50'.684
315	53°53'.302	008°50'.776
316	53°53'.298	008°50'.831
317	53°53'.288	008°50'.914
318	53°53'.278	008°50'.994
319	53°53'.269	008°51'.087
320	53°53'.263	008°51'.167
321	53°53'.253	008°51'.271
322	53°53'.236	008°51'.350
323	53°53'.218	008°51'.433
324	53°53'.209	008°51'.484
325	53°53'.184	008°51'.584
326	53°53'.164	008°51'.659
327	53°53'.137	008°51'.753
328	53°53'.119	008°51'.831
329	53°53'.105	008°51'.910
330	53°53'.085	008°51'.976
331	53°53'.066	008°52'.042
332	53°53'.035	008°52'.133
333	53°52'.992	008°52'.201
334	53°52'.963	008°52'.241
335	53°52'.942	008°52'.273
336	53°52'.921	008°52'.317

3	Germany, Schleswig-Holstein	
No.	North	East
337	53°52'.884	008°52'.412
338	53°52'.852	008°52'.478
339	53°52'.821	008°52'.557
340	53°52'.792	008°52'.646
341	53°52'.767	008°52'.711
342	53°52'.737	008°52'.792
343	53°52'.716	008°52'.868
344	53°52'.670	008°52'.987
345	53°52'.645	008°53'.078
346	53°52'.623	008°53'.161
347	53°52'.591	008°53'.276
348	53°52'.564	008°53'.366
349	53°52'.524	008°53'.482
350	53°52'.498	008°53'.544
351	53°52'.459	008°53'.660
352	53°52'.440	008°53'.736
353	53°52'.410	008°53'.813
354	53°52'.377	008°53'.901
355	53°52'.364	008°53'.937
356	53°52'.327	008°54'.071
357	53°52'.311	008°54'.156
358	53°52'.283	008°54'.231
359	53°52'.256	008°54'.333
360	53°52'.233	008°54'.430
361	53°52'.207	008°54'.506
362	53°52'.182	008°54'.587
363	53°52'.162	008°54'.629
364	53°52'.142	008°54'.719
365	53°52'.144	008°54'.787
366	53°52'.111	008°54'.923
367	53°52'.091	008°55'.032
368	53°52'.067	008°55'.127
369	53°52'.034	008°55'.256
370	53°52'.008	008°55'.373
371	53°51'.989	008°55'.476
372	53°52'.011	008°55'.543
373	53°52'.035	008°55'.599
374	53°52'.062	008°55'.641

4 Germany, Lower Saxony, eastern Elbe part

No.	North	East
375	53°53'.533	008°41'.200
376	53°54'.917	008°39'.550
377	53°56'.167	008°32'.150

5 Germany, Hamburg National Park

No.	North	East
378	53°57'.42	008°30'.25
379	53°58'.36	008°26'.31
380	53°58'.76	008°21'.93
381	53°59'.02	008 °18'.90
382	53°59'.02	008 °13'.17
383	53°58'.88	008 °12'.77
384	53°56'.99	008 °17'.43

6 Germany, Lower Saxony, Wurster Küste

No.	North	East
385	53°54'.900	008°11'.533
386	53°53'.200	008°11'.533
387	53°46'.417	008°11'.533
388	53°42'.333	008°20'.150
389	53°40'.683	008°23'.583
390	53°38'.133	008°27'.683
391	53°36'.300	008°30'.683

7 Germany, Lower Saxony, Weser-Jade area

No.	North	East
392	53°32'.317	008°32'.883
393	53°32'.400	008°33'.317
394	53°36'.750	008°28'.667
395	53°41'.183	008°20'.617
396	53°43'.317	008°14'.433
397	53°45'.483	008°09'.917
398	53°46'.967	008°07'.950
399	53°45'.933	008°05'.583
400	53°43'.717	008°05'.583
401	53°40'.217	008°09'.050
402	53°33'.283	008°11'.817
403	53°31'.217	008°13'.600
404	53°30'.717	008°09'.950
405	53°30'.650	008°08'.717

8 Germany, Lower Saxony, East Frisia

No.	North	East
406	53° 38'.667	008° 05'.100
407	53° 38'.783	008° 05'.483
408	53° 39'.850	008° 04'.583
409	53° 41'.900	008° 02'.817
410	53° 45'.383	008° 01'.850
411	53° 47'.133	008° 01'.067
412	53° 48'.700	007° 52'.350
413	53° 45'.800	007° 27'.383
414	53° 48'.217	007° 27'.383
415	53° 48'.217	007° 19'.083
416	53° 44'.750	007° 19'.083
417	53° 42'.300	007° 00'.000
418	53° 45'.400	007° 00'.000
419	53° 48'.733	007° 00'.000
420	53° 45'.183	006° 34'.850
421	53° 41'.900	006° 34'.850
422	53° 38'.000	006° 34'.850
423	53° 37'.050	006° 34'.850
424	53° 36'.350	006° 35'.750
425	53° 33'.033	006° 42'.850
426	53° 28'.167	006° 52'.817
427	53° 27'.583	006° 54'.917
428	53° 26'.567	006° 56'.117
429	53° 25'.900	006° 57'.633
430	53° 22'.800	006° 59'.450

9 Germany, Lower Saxony, Dollard

No.	North	East
431	53° 19'.087	007° 14'.910
432	53° 18'.863	007° 11'.513

The Netherlands

Below are the coordinates representing the delimitation of the proposed PSSA for the Netherlands.

- Points 433 until 440 represent the eastern boundary, Ems Dollard, of the area (part 10).

- Points 441 until 453 represent the delimitation of the northern part of the area. It consists of the 3 nautical miles line from the baseline. Because this is a curved line, there are at least 1900 coordinates, but only some characterizing coordinates have been listed below. The map in annex 2 has been compiled on the basis of detailed information on the 3 nautical miles line (available from the Dienst der Hydrografie, the Hydrographical Service in the Hague, Netherlands) (part 11).

- Points 454 and 455 represent the western boundary of the area. It is the line from Den Helder towards the West, crossing the 3 nautical miles line (part 12).

10 The Netherlands, eastern boundary, Ems-Dollard		
No.	North	East
433	53°18'.882	007°11'.605
434	53°18'.655	007°00'.666
435	53°20'.860	006°54'.414
436	53°26'.439	006°53'.420
437	53°27'.797	006°50'.010
438	53°30'.069	006°41'.803
439	53°33'.289	006°37'.214
440	53°33'.688	006°35'.685

12 The Netherlands, western boundary		
No.	North	East
454	52° 56'.841	004° 43'.056
455	52° 56'.564	004° 35'.221

11 The Netherlands, northern boundary		
No.	North	East
441	53°34'.798	006°20'.487
442	53°33'.356	006°14'.347
443	53°32'.295	006°00'.295
444	53°31'.964	005°55'.497
445	53°31'.769	005°40'.285
446	53°30'.412	005°33'.542
447	53°25'.551	005°06'.734
448	53°24'.218	005°02'.336
449	53°21'.138	005°01'.358
450	53°14'.785	004°45'.087
451	53°11'.133	004°43'.325
452	53°03'.145	004°37'.086
453	52°59'.296	004°33'.291

Annex 2

PSSA chart proposed Particularly Sensitive Sea Area

Wadden Sea boundary

Reference: Nautical chart from Bundesamt für Seeschifffahrt und Hydrographie, BSH, Germany.
Nautical chart 1002, Edition 1991

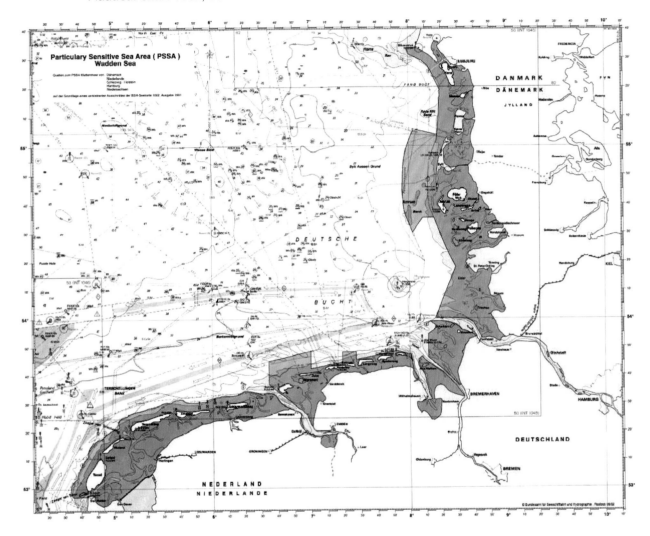

Annex 3

Existing measures

Measures adopted by IMO and at the national and EC levels

I   General measures

IMO measures

The IMO has issued numerous conventions to improve maritime safety and prevent pollution from ships, for example the International Regulations for Preventing Collisions at Sea, 1972 (as amended by resolutions A.464(XII), A.626(15), A.678(16) and A.736(18)), COLREGs and SOLAS V.

EC measures

Also, the European Union has already issued numerous Directives corresponding to IMO measures, including, e.g. directives on port State control, marine equipment, notification obligations, and on the management of ship-generated waste and cargo residues. These are continually being updated and implemented into national legislation.

According to the EC Habitat Directive (Council Directive 92/43/EEC) and the EC Bird Directive (Council Directive 79/409/EEC), Member States shall list areas of Community Interest respectively Special Protection Areas. These areas constitute the Natura 2000 network. Basically, the Wadden Sea, until 3 sea miles offshore except for the main shipping routes, has been listed as habitat areas according to the Habitat Directive and as Special Protection Areas according to the Bird Directive.

Other regional measures

Radio navigational warnings contain information that directly affects safety of life at sea and the protection of the environment. They are issued by NAVTEX, MRCC's, VTS centres or other services.

Bilateral (NL & D) Local Rules and Traffic Regulations for the Ems estuary.

National measures

Denmark	Germany	Netherlands
– Ministerial order on transfer of bunkers in the Danish territorial sea.	– **Regulations on the navigation of Federal waterways in national parks in the North Sea area.** – Navigable Waterways Ordinance. – VTS available in certain areas. – **Pilotage services and deep-sea pilotage services available for various ports and areas.** – Modern aids to navigation (AIS, GPS, buoyage, lighthouses). – SAR and MRCC services available. – Emergency towing capacity available. – Deep Sea Pilotage Services available. – Agreement with private companies on keeping helicopter capacity in reserve to permit action to be taken swiftly in the case of emergencies and accidents at sea.	– **Additional local rules and regulations (BPR, "Scheepvaartreglement Territoriale Zee" (STZ)).** – VTS available in certain areas. – Pilotage services available for various ports. – Communication facilities available. – Differential GPS available. – Buoyage available in entire area. – Lighthouses available on all major islands and along the mainland coastline. – SAR services available. – Salvage tugs available. Powerful salvage tug (M.S. "WAKER") on stand-by. – Deep-sea pilotage services available. – Numerous RACONs are available on (offshore) platforms and buoys.

II   Collision avoidance, navigation, routeing measures

IMO measures

IMO routeing schemes are in place in the North Sea to simplify traffic flows to reduce the collision hazard and to keep ships carrying certain dangerous or polluting goods away from the Wadden Sea coast. Traffic separation schemes in the concerned area adopted by the IMO are:

- At West Hinder
- Off Botney Ground
- East Friesland
- North Hinder
- Off Texel
- Jade Approach
- Terschelling–German Bight
- In the approaches to River Elbe

- Off Brown Ridge
- West Friesland
- North Friesland
- East Friesland
- Off Vlieland, Vlieland North and Vlieland Junction
- In the approaches to Hook of Holland
- German Bight Western Approach

The deep-water route and traffic separation scheme (TSS) from North Hinder to the German Bight via the Frisian Junction is mandatory for the following classes of ships:

- Tankers of 10,000 GT+ carrying oils as defined under Annex I of MARPOL 73/78;
- Ships of 5,000 GT+ carrying noxious liquid substances in bulk, categories A or B of Annex II of MARPOL 73/78;[*]
- Ships of 10,000 GT+ carrying noxious liquid substances in bulk, categories C or D of Annex II of MARPOL 73/78;[*] and
- Ships of 10,000 GT+ carrying liquefied gases in bulk.

EC measures

Reference to paragraph V.

Other regional measures

None.

National measures

None.

III   Pilotage, port entry and departure

IMO measures

Ships using the mandatory route for tankers from North Hinder to the German Bight are recommended to use adequately qualified deep-sea pilots in the North Sea.

EC measures

European Directive 93/75/EEC requires the Master and Operator of vessels carrying dangerous or polluting goods to report cargo details on entering or leaving EC ports.

---

[*] As a consequence of the revision of MARPOL Annex II that entered into force on 1 January 2007, the categorization of noxious liquid substances has been revised for the types of ships described. The consequential amendments to the existing Deep-Water Route and Traffic Separation Scheme from North Hinder to the German Bight via the Frisian Junction were adopted by MSC 83 (MSC 83/28, annex 24) and disseminated by means of COLREG.2/Circ.59.

Dangerous goods are defined in:

-   The International Maritime Dangerous Goods (IMDG) Code
-   The International Gas Carrier (IGC) Code
-   The International Bulk Carrier (IBC) Code.

Polluting goods are defined in MARPOL Annexes I, II and III.

European Directive 95/21/EEC (Port State Control)

Other regional measures

None.

National measures

Denmark	Germany	Netherlands

– Pilotage is compulsory for the following:
  – Loaded oil tankers >1500 DWT;
  – Loaded chemical tankers carrying dangerous liquid chemicals covered by the IMO Chemical Code;
  – Gas carriers;
  – Vessels carrying radioactive cargoes;
  – Towing vessels of 150 GRT+ navigating in dredged channels or marked navigation channels, into or past harbours or pilot stations (excluding harbour manoeuvres); and
  – Tankers with uncleaned tanks not secured by inert gas.
– Ships sailing to and from Danish ports shall comply with the rules laid down in the "Den danske Havnelods" (The Danish Harbor Pilot book).
– Tankers have to take a pilot when entering certain ports, terminals, etc.
	– Compulsory district pilotage for:
	  – Vessels with a length of 90 m or a breath of 13 m and more
	  – Tankers carrying gas/chemicals/petroleum/petroleum products in bulk, or unloaded tankers if not cleaned, degassed or completely inerted
	– Additional shore-based pilotage:
	  – if visibility is reduced
	  – if pilot cutter is in a sheltered position
	  – if lightbuoys are withdrawn due to ice
	  – if requested by the master
	  – if ordered by the VTS authority
	– Voluntary deep-sea pilotage available
		– Radar surveillance at Den Helder, Terschelling and Schiermonnikoog (for port entry and departure and Wadden Sea traffic only).
		– Harbour pilotage is compulsory for ships over 60 m in length and for all vessels carrying oil, gas or chemicals. Voluntary deep-sea pilotage is available for ships required to use the North Hinder–German Bight mandatory route for tankers. Communications are normally carried out via VHF radio and ships are required to maintain a listening watch on VHF. Radar assistance is available on request in some ports. Pilotage is compulsory for Harlingen and other ports in the Wadden Sea.

IV   Vessel Traffic Services (VTS)

IMO measures

None.

EC measures

None.

Other regional measures

None.

National measures

Denmark	Germany	Netherlands

– No VTS arrangement in the area.	– VTS with permanent radar surveillance in following districts:
	  – VTS German Bight
	  – VTS Ems
	  – VTS Jade
	  – VTS Weser
	  – VTS Elbe
	– Services offered:
	  – Information Service
	  – Navigational Assistance Service
	  – Traffic Organisation Service
	– Mandatory for all vessels exceeding 50 m of length (River Ems 40 m) and all vessels carrying certain dangerous goods
		– VTS Den Helder: All vessels equipped with VHF are requested to participate in this system. Vessels within the area should report when entering and leaving the VTS area. Traffic surveillance is provided;
		– VTS Terschelling: Reporting is mandatory for all vessels entering or leaving the VTS area;
		– Wadden Sea Central Reporting Station: Is responsible for coordinating the relevant maritime authorities with regard to all incidents within the Wadden Sea area;
		– VTS Schiermonnikoog: Provides radar surveillance services for the Terschelling–German Bight TSS with range up to 48 miles; and
		– VTS Delfzijl: VTS is mandatory for all vessels, which includes an information service.

V   Environmental protection measures intended to reduce or combat pollution

IMO measures

Denmark, Germany and the Netherlands are Parties to MARPOL 73/78.

The designation of the North Sea and its coastal waters west of Great Britain and Ireland (North West European Waters) as a Special Area under MARPOL Annex I. This was implemented on a national level and entered into force in all three concerned countries.

The designation of the North Sea as a Special Area under MARPOL Annex V. Annex V has entered into force in all three States concerned.

The designation of the North Sea as a SO$_x$ Emission Control Area under Annex VI of MARPOL 73/78.

The 1990 London International Convention on Pollution Preparedness, Response and Co-operation (OPRC) promotes international co-operation in the event of a major oil pollution threat between all North Sea countries. The OPRC-HNS Protocol establishes a framework for international co-operation in the event of incidents involving hazardous and noxious substances.

EC measures

Council Directive 93/75/ECC of 13 September 1993 concerning minimum requirements for vessels bound for or leaving Community ports and carrying dangerous or polluting goods (known as the HAZMAT Directive) has been in force since 1995.

The EC Directive 2000/59/EEC on port reception facilities for ship-generated waste and cargo residues, which entered into force in 2000, should be implemented by the concerned States by the end of 2002. It is the aim of the Directive to reduce the discharges of ship-generated waste and cargo residue into the sea, especially illegal discharges, from ships using ports in the Community, by improving the availability and use of port reception facilities for ship-generated waste and cargo residues.

The EC Directive 1999/32/EC relating to a reduction in the sulphur content of certain liquid fuels.

As a follow-up to the *Erika* incident, two other packages of measures are in the legislative procedure. Package *'Erika I'* is completed and contains the following elements:

  – further development of Port State Control;

  – strengthening of provisions for and the control of Classification Societies;

  – initiative for early phasing out of single-hull tankers, mentioned in paragraph 8 above and being implemented in the EU by a regulation.

The proposals concerning package *'Erika II'*, passed on to the Council on 8 December 2000, consist of the following elements:

  – setting up a common monitoring and information system for maritime traffic, which will in due course replace EC directive 93/75/EEC;

  – initiative for an additional compensation fund for damage by oil pollution;

  – establishment of the European Maritime Safety Agency (EMSA).

Other regional measures

Bonn Agreement: basic agreement for co-operation in dealing with Pollution of the North Sea by Oil and other Harmful Substances. Close co-operation between B, DK, F, D, NL, N, S and UK. Zones of responsibility are established under the Bonn Agreement, for co-operation in terms of aerial surveillance and dealing with pollution of the North Sea by oil and other harmful substances.

Joint Maritime Contingency Plans on Combating Oil and Other Harmful Substances agreed between D and DK resp. NL (DENGER- resp. NETHGER-Plans), concerning bilateral co operation especially in defined exterior and quick-response zones.

Bilateral Administrative Agreements between D and DK resp. NL on co-operation in the field of aerial surveillance (coordination of flight times and corridors, joint flights, mutual assistance by aircraft of the other party).

Bilateral arrangements also apply between the Wadden Sea states in terms of Joint Maritime Contingency Plans.

D-NL-Memorandum of Understanding on Mutual Support in the Field of North Sea Emergency Towing Capacity (March 2000): mutual assistance by emergency towing vessels in an area between the outer limitation of the VTS schemes and the coastline, including approaches to the seaports.

National measures

There are lots of different national measures regarding preventing and combating marine pollution.

Annex 11 – Paracas National Reserve Particularly Sensitive Sea Area

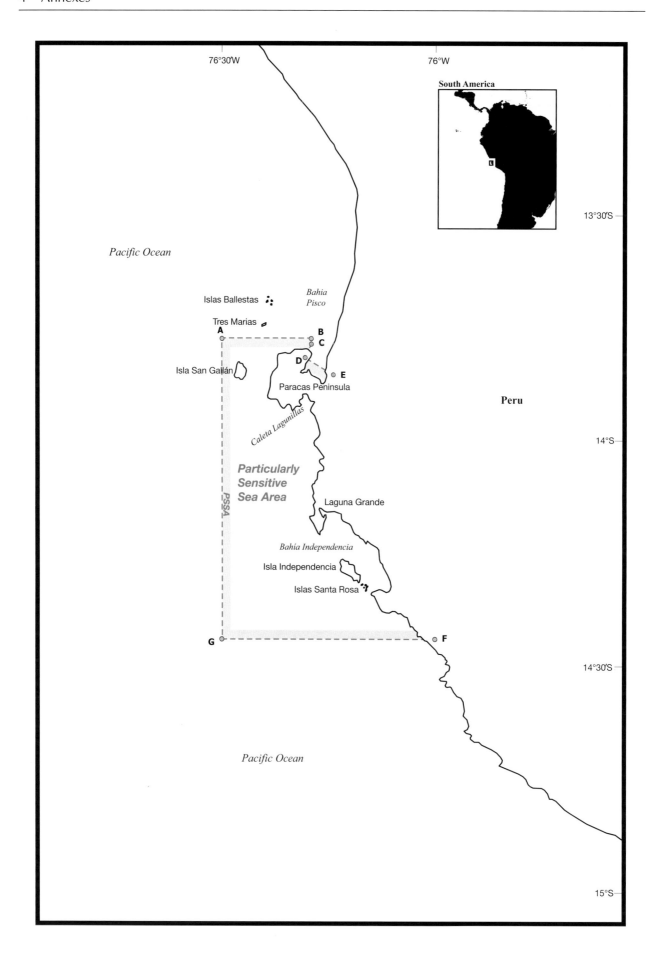

Pacific Ocean

South America

13°30'S

Bahia
Pisco

Islas Ballestas

Tres Marias

A

B
C

Isla San Gallán

D
E

Paracas Peninsula

Peru

14°S

Caleta Lagunillas

**Particularly
Sensitive
Sea Area**

PSSA

Laguna Grande

Bahia Independencia

Isla Independencia

Islas Santa Rosa

G
F

14°30'S

Pacific Ocean

15°S

Resolution MEPC.106(49)

adopted on 18 July 2003

Designation of the Paracas National Reserve
as a Particularly Sensitive Sea Area

THE MARINE ENVIRONMENT PROTECTION COMMITTEE,

BEING AWARE of the ecological, social, cultural and educational value of the Paracas National Reserve, as well as its vulnerability to damage by international shipping traffic and activities in the area and the steps taken by Peru to address that vulnerability,

NOTING that the Guidelines for the Identification and Designation of Particularly Sensitive Sea Areas adopted under resolution A.927(22) set out procedures for the designation of Particularly Sensitive Sea Areas,

HAVING CONSIDERED the proposal from Peru to designate the Paracas National Reserve as a Particularly Sensitive Sea Area,

HAVING AGREED that the criteria for the identification of a Particularly Sensitive Sea Area provided in resolution A.927(22) are fulfilled for the Paracas National Reserve,

NOTING that the forty-ninth session of the NAV Sub-Committee considered an area to be avoided (ATBA) and agreed to its establishment,

1   DESIGNATES the Paracas National Reserve as defined in the annex to this resolution as a Particularly Sensitive Sea Area.

Annex

Designation of the sea area of the Paracas National Reserve – Peru as a Particularly Sensitive Sea Area

Introduction

1   The use of ships to transport cargoes of various types and volumes, especially goods and substances which are harmful and damaging to the marine environment, and for the extraction and capture of hydrobiological resources represents a serious threat to the marine environment due to the possibility of spills or operational or accidental pollution resulting in irreversible damage to marine habitats and organisms.

2   The Peruvian Sea is one of the world's richest in hydrobiological resources thanks to the favourable oceanographic and climatic conditions off the coast of Peru. The Paracas National Reserve occupies a unique geographical area along its entire shore, since it possesses significant biodiversity, both hydrobiological species and marine mammals, birds and other species.

3   The importance of the Paracas National Reserve has been internationally recognized by the Convention on Wetlands of International Importance (RAMSAR Convention) and the Hemispheric Shorebird Reserve Network, since the Peruvian Maritime Authority established special protective measures.

4   The Government of Peru is seeking, via the International Maritime Organization, to obtain world recognition of the sea area of the Paracas National Reserve as a Particularly Sensitive Sea Area, in accordance with the established procedures, so that seafarers, irrespective of the flag under which their ship is registered, are aware of the special ecological importance of this area and provide it with due protection, thus contributing to the efforts by the entire people of Peru in this respect.

Part I – Description, importance and vulnerability of the area

1   Description of the Paracas National Reserve

1.1   The Paracas National Reserve is an area of high ecological value and environmentally sensitive, located in Pisco Province, Department of Ica, in a sea and coastal area defined by the following geographical points, as shown in chart PERU HIDRONAV-2170, "Coast of Peru: Pisco–Paracas–Bahía Independencia", annexed to this document:

    (a)   13°46′52″ South,   076°30′00″ West

    (b)   13°46′52″ South,   076°17′40″ West

    (c)   13°47′20″ South,   076°17′40″ West

    (d)   13°49′00″ South,   076°18′25″ West

    (e)   13°51′26″ South,   076°14′55″ West

    (f)   14°26′42″ South,   076°00′00″ West

    (g)   14°26′42″ South,   076°30′00″ West

1.2   The sea area of the Paracas National Reserve has a total area of 217,594 hectares, including several islands, the main ones being:

    (a)   Isla San Gallán

    (b)   Islas Ballestas

    (c)   Islas Independencia group.

1.3   The Paracas National Reserve is the only marine reserve in Peru. It was created by Supreme Decree No. 1281-75-AG of 25 September 1975, and includes within its boundaries the Paracas National Prehistoric Park, designated by Supreme Decree No. 15 of 21 June 1960.

1.4   The Reserve was created to preserve and sustainably use representative samples of the natural formations and the biological diversity in the bio-geographical areas (Udvardy, 1980) of the Pacific subtropical desert and the Pacific temperate desert, or according to another classification of zoogeographic regions: the Peru–Chilean Oceanic Zone and the Coastal Desert (Brack, 1976).

1.5   Due to the high primary productivity, it concentrates significant nuclei of terrestrial and aquatic fauna, notably the large seal populations, the high density of guano birds and the abundance of migratory birds, making it an area of particular economic and ecological interest, which combined with the Paracas culture form an area of great scientific and cultural significance and great tourist potential.

1.6   The coastline is varied, marked by geographical features such as the Bay of Paracas, the Peninsula of Paracas, Punta Carreta, Bahía de la Independencia, Morro Quemado, Punta Gallinazo and the Islas Independencia and Isla San Gallán.

1.7   These features are the result of diastrophic forces active now and in the past in Peru. The drowning of the palaeozoic range known as the "Cordillera de la Costa" is clear from observation of the Bahía de la Independencia and the group of islands bearing the same name, or the Peninsula of Paracas and Isla San Gallán. The shorelines corresponding to the high ground along the same coast are all steep, further evidence of the drowning.

1.8   The climate is conducive to the formation of subtropical desert, meaning that there is a difference of about 6 °C to 8 °C in the average temperature between the hottest and the coldest months. In February and August, it is 22 °C and 15.5 °C respectively, with an annual average of 18.7 °C. Precipitation is very low. The average annual total in the north of the Reserve is 1.83 mm with relative humidity of 82 per cent and 83 per cent in winter.

1.9   The average height of cloud is 590 metres, and it should be noted that, unlike in other parts of the coast, the sun also shines in winter, which can be explained by the fact that the beaches and plains of the Reserve, by reducing the relative humidity, disperse clouds by reflecting the heat induced on the surface by infrared rays and rising warm air.

1.10   The prevailing winds are south and south-west, reaching an average speed of 14.9 km/h. However, the strongest shore winds, known as "Paraca", reach 32 km/h.

1.11   The Bay of Paracas is shallow, ranging from 0 to 7 metres in depth, but deeper in the vicinity of Punta Pejerrey.

1.12   The principal productive activity in the area is fishing, both industrial and small-scale, including fish-farming, with barges and wharves for direct unloading of hydrobiological products. The biodiversity, beautiful scenery and archaeological sites in the Reserve make it an important tourist destination (over 120,000 visitors a year).

1.13   Also located in the Bay of Paracas is a port terminal for large ships, handling different types of cargoes for export, import and coastal trade, especially fish meal, salt and sulphuric acid, as well as a multi-buoy off-shore terminal for supplying oil from tankers to the refinery which provides fuel for the region.

1.14   There is merchant shipping and tanker traffic bound for other ports in and around the sea area of the Reserve.

2   Importance of the Paracas National Reserve

2.1   Ecological criteria

2.1.1   *Unique and representative character*

2.1.1.1 This section of the coastal and sea area includes the sea area of the Paracas National Reserve. Its characteristics make it quite unique and exceptional compared with many areas of the Peruvian coast. It is important for its upwelling currents, and its physical and environmental conditions make it one of the most productive and diverse areas of the coast.

2.1.1.2 While from latitude 5°South, off Bayovar, Piura, the coastal region offers these ecological characteristics, a series of factors combine in the area south of Pisco to produce the extraordinary wealth of environments and marine species. The Peru Current brings a constant supply of inorganic nutrients, the richest in the world, to the coast off San Juan de Marcona. These nutrients provide a high concentration of raw materials, mainly phytoplankton, which are the basis of the rich shore and aquatic fauna found there. This makes the coastal waters of Pisco-Paracas some of the most productive in the world.

2.1.1.3 The first area touched by the current is the Bahía de la Independencia, where the concentration of nutrients results in an exceptional wealth of hydrobiological life which is reflected, among other things, in the rich harvests of molluscs. The south side of the Peninsula of Paracas to some extent hinders the south to north flow and gives rise to an area where the cold water from the south mixes with the local warm waters, which then flow north-west.

2.1.1.4 The Bay of Paracas has shallow waters which are easily heated by the sun's rays. These waters receive a variable but constant inflow of fresh water from the Río Pisco, greater mainly during the summer months, which reduces their salinity.

2.1.1.5 The wealth of biological resources within the Reserve is thus supported by the dynamics of the marine ecosystem, both in the bentonic and pelagic populations. It concentrates both a wide diversity of species and considerable commercial volumes due to the physical features of the coast with its many small bays and creeks, shallow open beaches and many cliffs. The shallowness of the coastal waters encourages photosynthetic processes or primary productivity of phytoplankton and algae which start the trophic chain. The cold Peru Current and the submarine counter-currents encourage the upwelling of masses of water from the seabed to the surface, laden with nutrients on which phytoplankton and macroscopic algae feed in the extremely sunny conditions. This generates an explosion of its biomass through photosynthetic activity, starting the trophic chain which makes the sea of Paracas one of the richest in the world.

2.1.1.6 The bentonic population of the waters of the Paracas Reserve consists mainly of a great biological diversity of molluscs, algae, fish and arthropods, especially mussels, winkles, scallops, sole, cabrilla, pintadilla, chita, etc. as well as various species of marine algae. These species form the basis of the country's fish-farming, using techniques specific to the area. The pelagic population consists of wild species, especially anchovies, mackerel, sardines, silverside, machete and bonito.

2.1.1.7 The wide biological diversity of the bentonic and pelagic ecological populations of the sea of Paracas also depends on the nature and variety of the substratum (sand, mud, sandy mud, rock, stony, shells, etc.), tidal movements (with species living at the lower, middle and upper shore levels) and the physical and chemical composition of the seawater which encourages the primary growth that is the basis of the biological chain in the Peruvian Sea.

2.1.2   *Productivity*

2.1.2.1 Despite its tropical position, the most striking characteristic of the Peruvian Sea is its cold waters. This coldness is the result of the vertical stream of water from deeper layers to the surface, by the process known as the Peruvian upwelling system, which is summarized below.

2.1.2.2 The coastal area of the Peruvian Sea is considered to be one of the most productive in the world. The Trade Winds drive the coastal waters of Peru from south-east to north-west. This circulation is called the Peruvian Coastal Current. The direction and strength of the wind and the geographical shape of the west coast of the continent cause a bend in the coastal waters at right angles to the wind direction and against the coastline. This bend leaves a "void" which is filled by the upwelling of subsurface waters rich in inorganic nutrients. This extra provision of nutrients and the action of sunlight are the basis for the high phytoplanktonic and zooplanktonic productivity, which in turn sustains the famous riches of the Peruvian Sea.

2.1.3 Diversity

2.1.3.1 The diversity of coastal micro-environments, the geographical shape of its coastline, the variety of substrata and the high primary productivity of these waters support a wide variety of species which offer, in practice and potentially, a large number of alternatives for sustainable local and national development.

Group	Specific diversity (1)
Algae	317
Terrestrial plants	54
Annelids	109
Molluscs	194
Marine arthropods	286
Terrestrial arthropods	129
Other invertebrates	101
Fish	168
Reptiles	10
Birds	216
Mammals	36
Total	**1543**

Source: INRENA – January 2000

2.1.3.2 Invertebrates should be highlighted among the most important resources, of which arthropods are the most varied and molluscs offer the best prospects for farming. The most representative species include scallops (*Argopecten purpuratus*) for its great economic potential, and abalone (*Concholepas concholepas*), the wedge clam (*Donax* sp.), the Pacific clam (*Gari solida*), the mussel *Aulacomya ater*, the octopus (*Octopus* sp.). Other groups of invertebrates are also important, such as echinoderms, including the sea urchin *Loxechinus albus*, and crustaceans such as the crab *Platyxanthus orbigny*, both of which are of economic importance and constantly harvested.

2.1.3.3 Plants are another important group. Algae, for example, are a raw material in pharmaceutical research and the pharmaceutical industry as well as a traditional source of human food. Also noteworthy is the seasonal vegetation, basically herbaceous, which grows on the slopes of the hills nearest the coast which rise to over 400 metres. This "coastal hill" vegetation is encouraged by the occurrence of winter mists. In general, little is known of these formations which, in the Paracas National Reserve at least, occur in the Lechuza hills, Morro Quemado and on San Gallán Island.

2.1.3.4 The third important group consists of vertebrates. Fish are the traditional basic resource of the local economy, not only in domestic and small-scale fishing, but also industrial. The periodic appearance of sea turtles is a cause for concern since it leads to the hunting of and resulting trade in these animals, despite the fact that it is a prohibited activity. In addition, the wide diversity of migratory and resident birds, marine mammals (seals, whales and otters) are a great attraction for students, teachers, researchers and tourists.

Flora

2.1.3.5 The terrestrial flora of the Paracas Reserve is divided between local biotopes in the uplands called "coastal hill vegetation" and those growing on the shores, known as halophytic plants. The Paracas coastal desert is characterized by high temperatures and scant precipitation, with heights of 500 metres above sea level in the Peninsula of Paracas and 600 metres above sea level in the Bahía de la Independencia, which capture the humidity in the mists, encouraging the presence of hill vegetation.

2.1.3.6 In the Lechuza and Lagarto hills in the Bay of Paracas and on San Gallán Island there are sandy soils with three species of *Tillandsia*, xerophytic plants which grow in the sandy substratum and capture atmospheric humidity.

2.1.3.7 In the stony soils there are fissures and crevices which collect humus, lichens and mosses, which allow the growth of species of *Solanum*, *Oxalis* and *Spergularia*. These species dry out in summer and grow again in winter by capturing the humidity. The hill vegetation occupies very limited areas and has been altered by the local beachcombers known as guaqueros.

2.1.3.8 Halophytic species grow along the shorelines. In the Bay of Paracas, Playón and Mendieta, the species *Sesuvium portulacastrum*, *Distichlis spicata* and *Cressa truxillensis* can be found.

2.1.3.9 The marine flora consists of microscopic algae and larger seaweed (Acosta, 1977). 254 Species of marine algae are recorded in the area, 3 species of cyanophytas, 11 phaeophytas, 1 euglenophyta, 79 pyrrophytas, 104 chrysophytas and 44 rhodophytas.

2.1.3.10 Of the larger seaweeds, the most important are: *Ulva lactuca*; *Ulva fasciata*; *Ulva papenfussi* and *Ulva* sp., commonly called sea lettuce; *Grateloupia doryphora*; *Chondracanthus chamissoi*; *Chondracanthus glomerata* and *Porphyra columbina*, known as "yuyo" and used in cooking.

Fauna

2.1.3.11 The diversity of the substratum of the shores allows the presence of microhabitats and thus great biological diversity among the species making up the marine fauna, birds, fish, marine mammals and molluscs. The terrestrial fauna is very scarce, with three species of small lizard (*Tropidurus peruvianus*, *Tropidurus tigris* and a gecko) and the coastal fox.

2.1.3.12 The main species of marine fauna include: *Mugil cephalus* (striped mullet); *Engraulis ringens* (anchovy); *Dasyatis brevis* (stingray); *Urotrigon peruvianus* (ray); *Paralichthys adspersus* (sole); occasional visitors such as: *Delphinus delphis* (dolphin); small species of whales and sperm whales; *Arctocephalus australis* (South American fur seal); *Otaria byronia* (sea lion); molluscs: *Thais chocolata* (winkle); *Argopecten purpuratus* (scallop); *Octopus fontaineanus* (octopus); crustaceans: *Platyxanthus orbigny* (purple crab); and *Ocypode gaudichaudii* (crab).

2.1.3.13 The bird life consists of the following: condors; guanay cormorants; cormorants; booby; pelicans; flamingo; great egret; snowy egret; blue heron; white-cheeked pintail; turkey vulture; osprey; peregrine falcon; common oystercatcher; black oystercatcher; snowy plover; black-bellied plover; semi-palmated plover; turnstone; solitary sandpiper; sanderling; semi-palmated sandpiper; western sandpiper; lesser yellowlegs; greater yellowlegs; migrating snipe; whimbrel; skimmer; elegant tern; common tern; Peruvian tern; royal tern; band-tailed gull; kelp gull; grey gull; grey headed gull; Franklin's gull; Peruvian seaside cinclodes; and grebe.

Seals

2.1.3.14 The Paracas National Reserve, as a conservation unit, contains within its shores one of the main concentrations of seals on the entire Peruvian coast. The Reserve has three of the largest stable colonies of South American fur seals, whose population is recovering from the effects of the 97–98 El Niño phenomenon.

2.1.3.15 The creation of the Reserve put an end to their indiscriminate slaughter, primarily for profit since their skins fetched a good price on the market. In addition to the creation of the Reserve, the Peruvian Government issued Ministerial Resolution No. 00103-76-PE of 9 March 1976, pursuant to Decree-Law No. 18810, which prohibits seal hunting and it is as a result of this protection that the seal populations have been recovering, as shown by the statistics. In 1976, the total population for all colonies was 2,048 seals, in 1982 the estimated population was 15,821 seals and now these populations have increased so significantly that they are no longer considered to be endangered.

2.1.3.16 Seal colonies live on Morro Quemado, Islas Independencia and Santa Rosa, Mendieta, Isla Zárate, Punta Arquillo, Punta Lechuza, Punta Lagarto, Isla San Gallán, Islas Ballestas and Islas Chincha.

Marine invertebrates

2.1.3.17   The area of the Reserve, which includes the Bay of Paracas and Bahiá de la Independencia, is the leading place on the Peruvian coast for the production and harvesting of shellfish. In recent years, the boom in scallops, *Argopecten purpuratus*, as a result of the El Niño phenomenon requires greater attention from researchers into marine ecology, especially the bentonic subsystem.

2.1.3.18   In 10 places in the Paracas National Reserve and 14 points on the lower beach, eight biotopes can be distinguished: rocky shore; muddy sand; sandy and stony and sandy mud beds; sandy, stony and rocky.

2.1.3.19   Bentonic invertebrates of 330 types (excluding nematodes) have been found, 305 of which were identified at least to generic level. These types are grouped into 145 families, 43 orders and 15 phyla. Of the total types, 112 are mollusca (33.9%), 184 annelidae (31.5%), 75 crustacea (22.7%) and 39 belong to various other classification groups (11.8%).

2.1.3.20   More species were found in hard substrata than in soft substrata: 119 species exclusive to rocky seabeds and 39 on rocky shores; 79 species were found in the remaining six biotopes. The numerical results obtained for the main classification groups are still provisional because the samples have not been exhaustive, especially in stony and muddy sand seabeds.

2.1.3.21   The total number of molluscs, worms and crustaceans recorded in the Reserve has increased considerably from 103 to 289 species. In the case of crustaceans, species of the orders Ostracoda, Tanaidacea, Cumacea, Isopoda and Amphipoda are being recorded for the first time, the latter being significant, since the 18 species found are 12 amphipods and 6 isopods.

2.1.4   Natural character

2.1.4.1 The coast contains two-thirds of Peru's total population. Industries of various kinds have been established along the coast and the country's largest towns have grown up there. The Pisco-Paracas area is no exception. However, in its 25 years of existence, the ecosystem of the Paracas National Reserve displays relatively natural conditions compared with other parts of the coast, which reflects the resilience of its natural processes such as maintenance of productive processes, persistence of breeding zones, stability of its colonies, and resistance to drastic change, such as very strong El Niño phenomena, etc.

2.1.4.2 It is universally recognized that global populations of migratory shore birds are declining, mainly due to the accelerating destruction of the wetlands which form their habitat. Consequently, international efforts and commitments to protect migratory birds and their habitats, such as the Convention on Wetlands of International Importance (RAMSAR Convention) and the Convention on the Conservation of Migratory Species of Wild Animals (Bonn Convention); commitments to which Peru is an official party.

2.1.4.3 The situation of wetlands in Peru is no different from that found elsewhere in the world, which is why the Peruvian State is freely and absolutely committed to protecting wetlands and migratory birds.

2.1.4.4 Because of its importance and natural character, the Paracas National Reserve has been included in the List of Wetlands of International Importance of the Convention on Wetlands of International Importance (RAMSAR Convention) since 30 March 1992. Protection of the Paracas National Reserve is all the more important because in reality it is not a wetland but a series of wetlands, notably the Bay of Paracas wetland and the estuary of the Río Pisco.

2.1.4.5 Thousands of birds migrate annually to the Bay of Paracas to feed and rest. These birds mostly come from Alaska, British Columbia, Alberta and Saskatchewan in Canada. Some of them will stay there throughout the southern summer, feeding and storing energy to return to their breeding grounds. Others will continue their journey to southern Chile and Argentina. For this reason, the Paracas Reserve has also been recognized as a Regional Reserve for Migratory Birds by the Hemispheric Shorebird Reserve Network since 28 September 1991.

2.1.4.6 The habitat suitable for thousands of migratory birds arriving in the Bay of Paracas has shrunk to a small area. Migratory birds have characteristics which make them highly vulnerable to anthropogenic environmental changes. Migratory shore birds are extremely faithful to place (homeland tie), meaning that they repeat patterns of migration and stop in the same places year after year. For this reason, the degradation or loss of the wetland features of the shore of the Bay of Paracas and the Río Pisco estuary will lead to the death of these creatures or will force them to move to less suitable places. This displacement will make them spend more energy, with greater risk of falling prey to predators and greater risk to their health.

2.1.4.7 The greater expenditure of energy for the birds may mean the possibility that they do not breed or that individuals die. A migratory shore bird is generally a creature of low body weight. The loss of a few grams of fat (energy) is the difference between breeding successfully or not, and even between life and death. The main harm to migratory birds caused by the deterioration of the micro-topography of the intertidal zone of the Paracas wetlands is the loss of available food, their only source of energy.

2.1.4.8 Although a migratory specimen has a low body weight, the considerable size of the populations of these species (several thousand individuals) means that they require feeding grounds of a size directly proportional to the size of the group. In this sense, the degradation and disappearance of an optimal habitat for migratory birds has a serious impact on the global survival of the species. This characteristic adds to the singular importance of this site, since the Paracas National Reserve is the only place for thousands of kilometres where migratory birds can stop.

2.1.4.9 With the disappearance or degradation of their habitat, migratory birds are forced to go in search of alternative feeding grounds. In each place, natural predators on migratory birds follow particular hunting patterns. The prey, in this case the migratory birds, survive this pattern of hunting by natural selection. Thus, when they move, the risk of depredation rises, since they encounter a different pattern of hunting. The population movement means settling in a place with a different hunting pattern, which makes the birds more vulnerable.

2.1.4.10　Another effect of the forced population movement is the dispersion of the birds, with the consequent decline in the size of the group, which increases the probability of their capture. Groups of migratory birds which have been disturbed are inclined to break up into small groups, which further increases depredation.

2.1.4.11　Important colonies of sea birds can be found in the Reserve, mainly in the islands. Apart from guano birds, two species are of particular interest: the Humboldt penguin (*Spheniscus humboldti*) and the Peruvian diving petrel, birds in danger of extinction. In the case of the penguin, one of the three largest colonies on the Peruvian coast is found in Bahía de la Independencia. The case of the diving petrel is even more striking, since the entire population of this species in Peru is confined to the sea area of the Paracas National Reserve.

2.2　Socio-economic and cultural criteria

2.2.1　*Economic benefits*

2.2.1.1 A series of economic activities are carried on in the Paracas National Reserve, including tourism, as well as various other activities related to the exploitation of hydrobiological resources.

2.2.1.2 The flow of tourists to the Reserve is growing, as shown in the following table:

Visitors to the Paracas National Reserve 1976–1999				
1976–1980	**1981–1985**	**1986–1990**	**1991–1993**	**1994–1999**
121,323	215,044	266,808	149,253	412,211

2.2.1.3 The tourist facilities in the Reserve consist of the following resources:

   (a)　Bay of Paracas, where the liberator General San Martin landed, which is the natural home for resident and migratory birds.

   (b)　El Candelabro, a giant geoglyph 128 metres long and 67 metres wide.

   (c)　The Cathedral, a rock formation whose cliffs host a large number of guano birds and some mammals.

(d) Laguna Grande, a fishing lagoon where most of the small-scale fishing in the Reserve is concentrated.

(e) Lagunilla, a small fishing lagoon for small-scale fishermen, mainly for shellfish.

(f) Atenas Beach, which contains several archaeological *conchales* or heaps of shells with relics of early fishermen including pottery, weaving and corn in its cultural inventory, dating from 1000 to 800 BC.

(g) El Sequión Beach, which is a large natural home for birds, where flamingos, skimmers and boobies can be seen.

(h) La Mina Beach, which takes its name from the coal mines which used to be there, an area rich in fossils.

(i) Punta Arquillo, rock formations and cliffs which are home to one of the largest seal colonies in the area and caves where penguins nest.

(j) Otuma saltpans, where salt is produced.

(k) Los Frailes, a natural rock formation and refuge for guano birds.

(l) Yumaque Beach, with sports fishing and camping, and a breeding ground for oystercatchers.

(m) Mendieta Beach, for sport fishing and diving; an ideal beach for bathers and camping.

(n) Chuncho Beach, suitable for sport fishing and camping. There are some 20 dwelling mounds from the Paracas Cave era (500–200 BC). It is the largest archaeological site of the Paracas coast.

(o) Carhuaz Beach, ideal for sport fishing, swimming and camping. There are traces of human populations, *conchales* and cemeteries from the Paracas-Chavin era (600 BC) up to colonial times.

(p) Julio C Tello Site Museum and Paracas National Reserve Interpretation Centre. It has exhibitions of artefacts of the ancient peoples of the area.

(q) Chain of nine islands which are the prime habitat for the largest population of guano birds and seals in the Reserves.

(r) Leisure beaches, places for sports activities such as swimming, sailing, fishing, camping, photography, etc.

(s) Natural beauty; resident and migratory birds can be observed and seals can be seen on the cliffs.

(t) Archaeology; there are numerous remains of the civilizations that inhabited ancient Peru in this part of the country.

2.2.2 *Leisure*

2.2.2.1 Various sports and leisure activities take place throughout the year in the area of the Reserve. In the Bay of Paracas the main activities are sailing competitions, wind-surfing, water-ski and other sports.

2.2.2.2 In summer, its beautiful beaches are filled with holidaymakers from Pisco and nearby towns, concentrating in the El Chaco area in the Bay and the beaches of La Mina and Lagunillas.

2.2.3 *Human economy*

2.2.3.1 Most of the human population and the local economy in this part of the coast are basically engaged in harvesting and processing hydrobiological species and tourist related activities.

2.2.3.2 However, apart from the resident population that exploits those resources, there is a migrant population coming from any of the ports or coves along the coast of Peru. These migrants are huge during the El Niño Southern Oscillation (ENSO), mainly attracted by the scarcity of their own marine species during "normal" periods in different latitudes and the expectations created by the population explosion of scallops, a resource which supports a huge market and which involves a large number of people.

2.3   Scientific and educational criteria

2.3.1   *Research*

2.3.1.1 Scientific and technological, fisheries and marine research programmes are conducted in the Reserve by specialized public institutions such as the Peruvian Marine Institute (Instituto del Mar del Perú), the Hydrographic and Navigation Department of the Peruvian Navy, universities and natural and legal persons in the private sector.

2.3.1.2 Research activities in the Reserve include creating an inventory of its flora and fauna, comprising identification, numbers and distribution; studies of fish-farming in the environment and studies of natural stocks; periodic population censuses; biology and management of turtles and behaviour and distribution of smaller cetaceans, as well as migratory and resident birds; studies of algae, sea cucumbers, flying fish and others; constant monitoring of ecosystems and species of commercial importance, and potential threats.

2.3.2   *Basic studies and surveillance*

2.3.2.1 Studies are in progress to complete the demarcation of the Reserve for the purposes of protection, by installing boundary posts and to solve problems of private activity and services.

2.3.2.2 Various alternatives for managing the resources of the marine and coastal areas in a rational way are constantly being evaluated by planning activities so as to ensure their sustainability, while improving profitability.

2.3.2.3 After preliminary studies, areas for communal eco-development are selected within the Reserve and its area of influence to allow economic, social and ecological activities.

2.3.2.4 Periodic land and sea patrols are carried out within the Reserve for surveillance and control to safeguard its natural beauty and the natural and cultural resources of this national protected area.

2.3.3   *Educational and historical value*

2.3.3.1 Comprehensive education and information programmes are provided for students, the general public and all economic agents operating in the Paracas National Reserve, aimed at its conservation, preservation and sustainable development.

2.3.3.2 In the Paracas region, both continental and shore, there are some 104 archaeological sites, most of them within the Reserve, covering every period of prehispanic Andean societies.

2.3.3.3 This enormous potential has attracted the attention of many people from the remote past. The present area of the Reserve served for the settlement of prehispanic peoples.

2.3.3.4 The Reserve includes within its boundaries the Paracas National Prehistoric Park, designated by Supreme Decree No. 15 of 21 June 1960.

2.4   National and international importance

2.4.1   Because of its importance and natural character, the Paracas National Reserve has been included in the List of Wetlands of International Importance of the Convention on Wetlands of International Importance (RAMSAR Convention) since 30 March 1992.

2.4.2   The Paracas National Reserve has also been recognized as a Regional Reserve for Migratory Birds by the Hemispheric Shorebird Reserve Network since 28 September 1991.

2.4.3   A proposal is being prepared for submission to UNESCO to have the Paracas National Reserve declared a Biosphere Reserve.

2.4.4   At national level, it is included in the system of protected natural areas being considered as a National Reserve by the Peruvian Government in Supreme Decree No. 1281-75-AG of 25 September 1975.

2.4.5   By a resolution of the Ministry of Tourism of Peru of 5 September 1996, San Gallán Island and the Ballestas Islands were incorporated in the Reserve, in addition to two miles of the surrounding sea area measured from the coastline.

2.4.6   In addition, by Ministerial Resolution No. 1082-90-AG 1990, it was considered that the Paracas National Reserve is host to various species of fauna classified as endangered, among them:

(a)   the marine otter (*Lutra felina*)

(b)   the Humboldt penguin (*Spheniscus humboldti*)

(c)   the Chilean flamingo (*Phoenicopterus chilensis*)

3   Vulnerability of the Paracas National Reserve to damage by international maritime activities

3.1   International maritime activities in the area

3.1.1   The principal activities are the passage of merchant ships in the vicinity of the Reserve and the arrival, stay and departure of tankers at Puerto General San Martín and at the offshore multi-buoy terminal for loading and unloading of pollutants, including hydrocarbons and sulphuric acid, among others.

3.1.2   The movement of ships in the port is shown below:

Year	1990	1991	1992	1993	1994	1995	1996	1997	1998	1999
No. of ships	84	86	66	114	125	133	98	151	104	186

3.1.3   An average of 395 to 535 merchant ships a month pass in the vicinity of the Reserve or through it.

3.1.4   The meteorological conditions are basically subtropical because of the effect of the coastal upwelling and the South Pacific anticyclone which gives it an arid climate with high temperatures. The average air temperature ranges from 16.2 °C to 22.7 °C, with the highest temperatures recorded in February. The maximum ranges from 20.2 °C to 27.7 °C.

3.1.5   The relative humidity ranges from 82 to 84 per cent. The average total annual precipitation is 0.09 mm/m^2 in summer and 0.60 mm/m^2 in winter.

3.1.6   One of the dominant characteristics of the desert climate of the Peruvian coast is the constant presence of wind. The winds are persistent, highly constant in direction and with a marked daily cycle caused by the heating of the coastal desert. The hourly pattern of variations is calm during the morning, strengthening from midday. Then comes a period of calm in the evening, followed by greater strengthening in the early hours of the night, with gusts up to 15 to 17 m/s.

3.1.7   Due to the thermal balance between the ocean and the continent which occurs in the early hours of the morning, the winds are light, between 1 and 6 knots, inclined to calm, increasing gradually in the evening to reach speeds of 16 to 20 knots (roughly between 1800 and 2100 local time) and absolute maximum speeds of up to 30 knots.

3.1.8   There are no wave measurements available for the area of the Reserve, but visual observations have been made at various times of year. Shown below is a table of average directions and heights of waves for the region between 10°and 15°South (information from "Sailing for South America"). The table is very general but it does allow an appreciation of the range of wave heights and the approximate predominant direction. This information was obtained from 6907 observations and refers to swell waves, which are waves which originate in the open sea and travel large distances. This type of wave is the main source of the height of waves whose impact determines the dynamics of the coast of the Reserve.

Distribution of swell waves
(10°–15°South)

Height (metres)	W	SW	S	SE	E
	%	%	%	%	%
0.3–1.8	0.7	9.7	35.4	8.2	–
1.8–3.6	0.3	6.7	25.2	6.3	0.4
>3.6	–	1.0	2.3	0.5	0.3
Total	1.0	17.4	62.9	15.0	0.7

According to this information, the predominant directions of waves are south and south-west, while the other directions are less frequent.

3.1.9 The system of currents off the coast of Peru runs in a northerly direction.

3.1.10 There have not been any accidents to date involving shipping, such as grounding, collisions or spills. However, it can be assumed that an operational or accidental spill could occur at any time, in addition to discharge into the sea of garbage and foul water from unidentified ships.

3.2 Potential harm

3.2.1 The Paracas National Reserve is a highly sensitive ecosystem with limited capacity to absorb adverse environmental effects.

3.2.2 The Reserve is highly vulnerable due to the risk presented by the transport and transhipment of oil, sulphuric acid and other noxious substances harmful to the environment, resulting from the operation of tankers. The quantities used and handled make this a major source of environmental risk, above all because of the possibility of spills, toxicity and flammability.

3.2.3 With the privatization of state enterprises, including the ports, it is estimated that movements of these products will increase, as the economy of the country and the region grows.

3.2.4 The pumping of bilge water, discharge of sewage and waste from ships are also activities which put at risk the ecological health of the Reserve.

3.2.5 The increase in shipping in the vicinity of the Reserve adds to the chance of accidents such as collisions, grounding or other accidents which could seriously endanger the present biodiversity in the Reserve and affect its natural wealth, such as beaches and tourist areas, with an economic impact on the people of the area engaged in harvesting hydrobiological products, tourism and leisure.

Part II – Appropriate protection measures and IMO's power to adopt such measures

4 The International Maritime Organization is requested to consider the sea area of the Paracas National Reserve as a "Particularly Sensitive Sea Area", so that all ships engaged in international navigation adopt appropriate measures to avoid actions which might harm the ecological health of the Reserve.

5 The first measure required is prohibition of navigation of tankers within the sea area of the Paracas National Reserve, as duly defined in shipping charts – PERU HIDRONAV-2710, "Coast of Peru: Pisco–Paracas–Bahía Independencia".

6 Another measure is to prohibit any kind of discharge from ships within the sea area of the Reserve, including discharge of sewage and waste.

7 The above-mentioned measures will contribute to ensuring adequate protection for the largest area of marine biodiversity in Peru, encouraging migratory species from places as far away as Alaska, Canada and Antarctica.

8   The prohibition of tanker navigation within the sea area of the Reserve, apart from those entering and leaving the port, will not cause harm or financial loss to their owners since they do not need to pass through the Reserve en route to other ports, thus they will not waste any time in avoiding the area.

9   Finally, to summarize, the Peruvian Government has so far taken the following steps to protect the Paracas National Reserve:

9.1   It has been included in the List of Wetlands of International Importance of the Convention on Wetlands of International Importance (RAMSAR Convention) since 30 March 1992.

9.2   It has also achieved recognition as a Regional Reserve for Migratory Birds by the Hemispheric Shorebird Reserve Network since 28 September 1991.

9.3   A proposal is being prepared for submission to UNESCO to have the Paracas National Reserve declared a Biosphere Reserve.

9.4   At national level, it is included in the system of protected natural areas, being declared a National Reserve by the Peruvian Government in Supreme Decree No. 1281-75-AG of 25 September 1975.

9.5   By a resolution of the Ministry of Tourism of Peru of 5 September 1996, San Gallán Island and the Ballestas Islands were incorporated in the Reserve, in addition to two miles of the surrounding sea area measured from the coastline.

9.6   In order to protect the Paracas National Reserve, the Peruvian Maritime Authority issued a national regulation in Departmental Resolution No. 0103-96-DCG of 17 April 1996, which prohibited the passage of ships carrying cargoes of hydrocarbons and other polluting substances in the Paracas National Reserve sea area.

9.7   At the request of the Peruvian Maritime Authority, at its seventy-second session in May 2000, the Maritime Safety Committee approved Peru's proposal, as a special protection measure, to establish four maritime traffic separation schemes for four ports, including Puerto de Pisco, which is located in an area adjacent to the Paracas National Reserve.

Paracas National Reserve

Restricted area

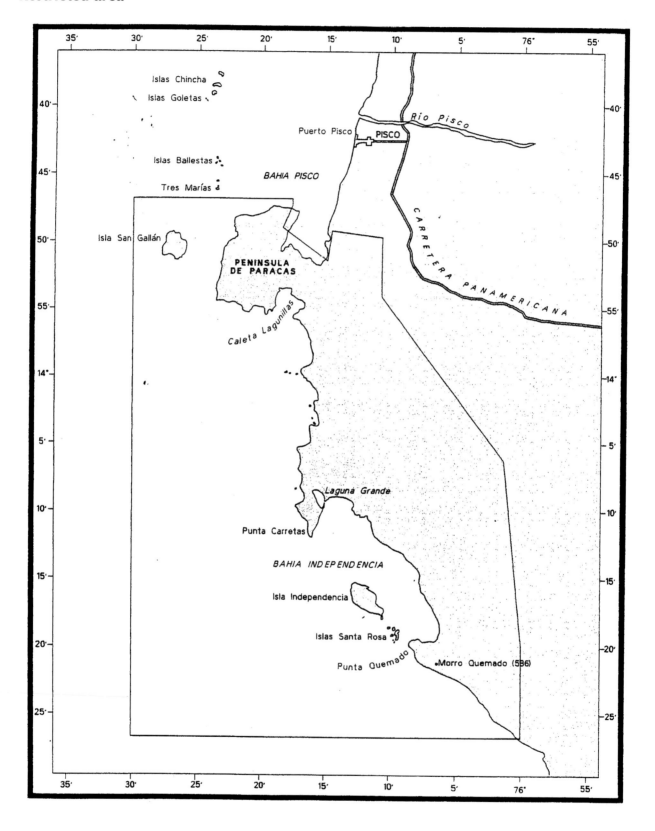

Location sketch map of the Peruvian coast

Paracas National Reserve

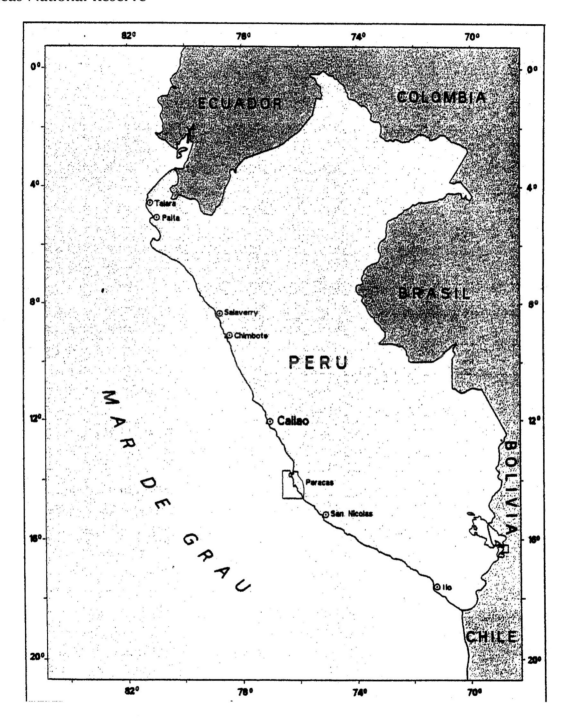

Associated Protective Measures

Area to be avoided in the Paracas National Reserve

The area to be avoided in the Paracas National Reserve was approved at the seventy-second session of MSC. Ships of more than 200 gross tonnage carrying hydrocarbons and hazardous liquids in bulk should avoid the area. A full technical description of the area is in part D of editions of the IMO publication "Ships' Routeing"; only a summary chartlet of the area is included here. The "part B, section VIII" that is shown on this chartlet is within "Ships' Routeing".

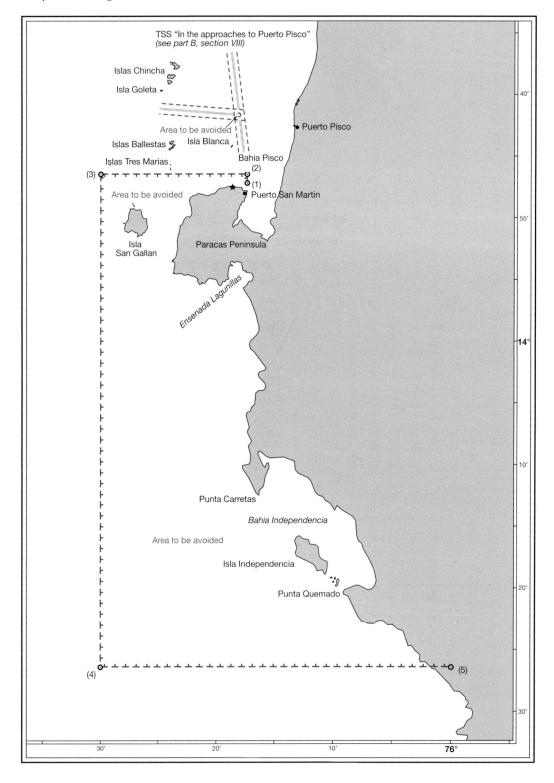

Traffic separation scheme "in the approaches to Puerto Pisco"

The traffic separation scheme "In the approaches to Porto Pisco" was adopted at the seventy-second session of MSC in 2000. A full technical description of the area is in part B of editions of the IMO publication "Ships' Routeing"; only a summary chartlet of the area is included here.

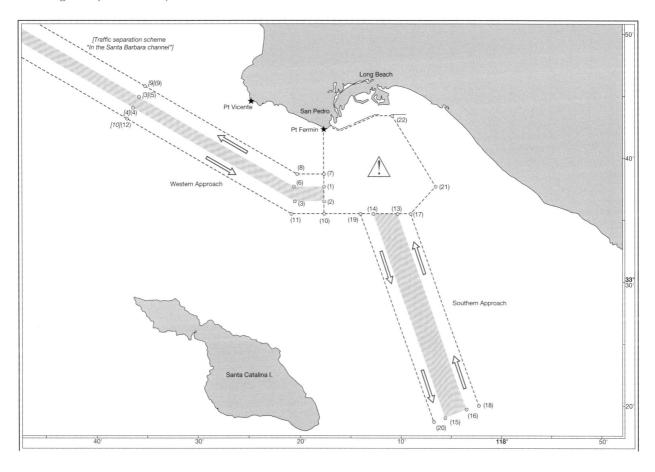

Annex 12 – Western European Waters Particularly Sensitive Sea Area

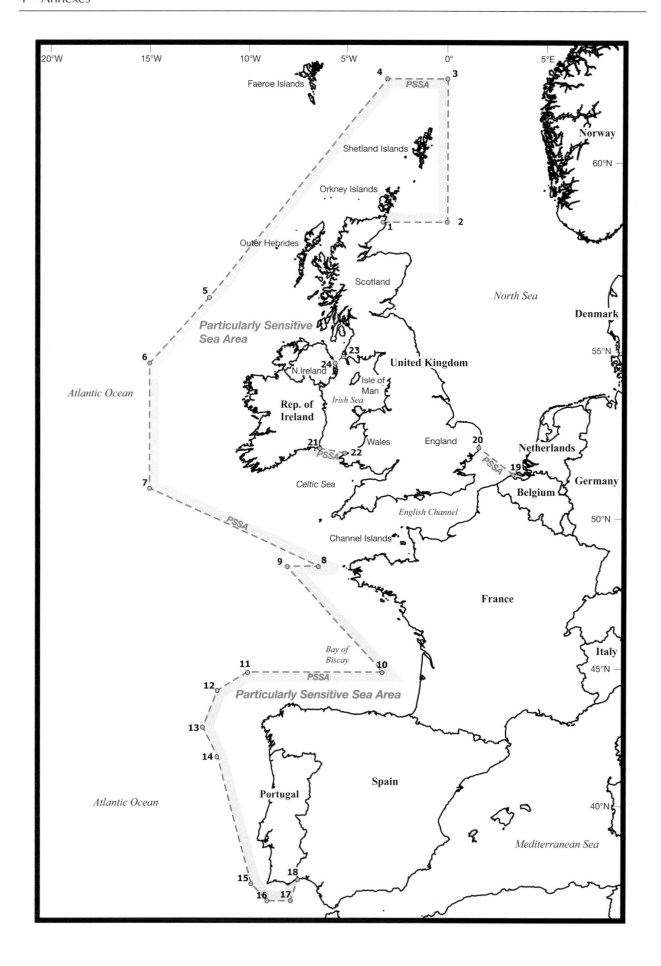

Resolution MEPC.121(52)

adopted on 15 October 2004
Designation of the Western European Waters as a Particularly Sensitive Sea Area

THE MARINE ENVIRONMENT PROTECTION COMMITTEE,

BEING AWARE of the ecological, social, economic, cultural, scientific and educational value of the Western European Waters, as well as its vulnerability to damage by international shipping traffic and activities in the area and the steps taken by Belgium, France, Ireland, Portugal, Spain and the United Kingdom to address that vulnerability,

NOTING that the Guidelines for the Identification and Designation of Particularly Sensitive Sea Areas adopted under resolution A.927(22) set out procedures for the designation of Particularly Sensitive Sea Areas,

HAVING CONSIDERED the proposal from Belgium, France, Ireland, Portugal, Spain and the United Kingdom to designate the Western European Waters as a Particularly Sensitive Sea Area,

HAVING AGREED that criteria for identification of a Particularly Sensitive Sea Area provided in resolution A.927(22) are fulfilled for the Western European Waters,

1   DESIGNATES the Western European Waters as defined in annexes 1, 2 and 3 to this resolution as a Particularly Sensitive Sea Area.

2   INVITES Committee Members to note the establishment of the new mandatory ship reporting system as an Associated Protective Measure for ships entering the Western European Waters Particularly Sensitive Sea Area in accordance with the provisions of SOLAS regulation V/11. The mandatory ship reporting system will enter into force at 0000 hours UTC six months after the adoption by the Maritime Safety Committee in December 2004.

Annex 1

Description of the Particularly Sensitive Sea Area Western European Waters:
coordinates

1 Description of the area

1.1 The area covers the western coasts of the United Kingdom, Ireland, Belgium, France, Spain and Portugal, from the Shetland Islands in the North to Cape S. Vicente in the South, and the English Channel and its approaches, as shown in the map below.

1.2 The PSSA is the area bounded by a line connecting the following geographical coordinates (all the coordinates are in WGS 84 reference system):

Number		Latitude	Longitude
1	(UK)	58°30′ N	UK coast
2	(UK)	58°30′ N	000°
3	(UK)	62°N	000°
4	(UK)	62°N	003°W
5	(UK + Irl)	56°30′ N	012°W
6	(Irl)	54°40′ 40.9″ N	015°W
7	(Irl)	50°56′ 45.3″ N	015°W
8	(Irl + UK + F)	48°27′ N	006°25′ W
9	(F)	48°27′ N	008°W
10	(F + S)	44°52′ N	003°10′ W
11	(S)	44°52′ N	010°W
12	(S)	44°14′ N	011°34′ W
13	(S)	42°55′ N	012°18′ W
14	(S + P)	41°50′ N	011°34′ W
15	(P)	37°00′ N	009°49′ W
16	(P)	36°20′ N	009°00′ W
17	(P)	36°20′ N	007°47′ W
18	(P)	37°10′ N	007°25′ W
19	(B)	51°22′ 25″ N	003°21′ 52.5″ E
20	(UK)	52°12′ N	UK east coast
21	(Irl)	52°10′.3 N	006°21′.8 W
22	(UK)	52°01′.52 N	005°04′.18 W
23	(UK)	54°51′.43 N	005°08′.47 W
24	(UK)	54°40′.39 N	005°34′.34 W

1.3 The geographical coordinates for the identification of a PSSA are solely for that purpose and must not be interpreted as having any bearing upon issues related with maritime limits and boundaries.

PSSA chart

Western European Waters Particularly Sensitive Sea Area

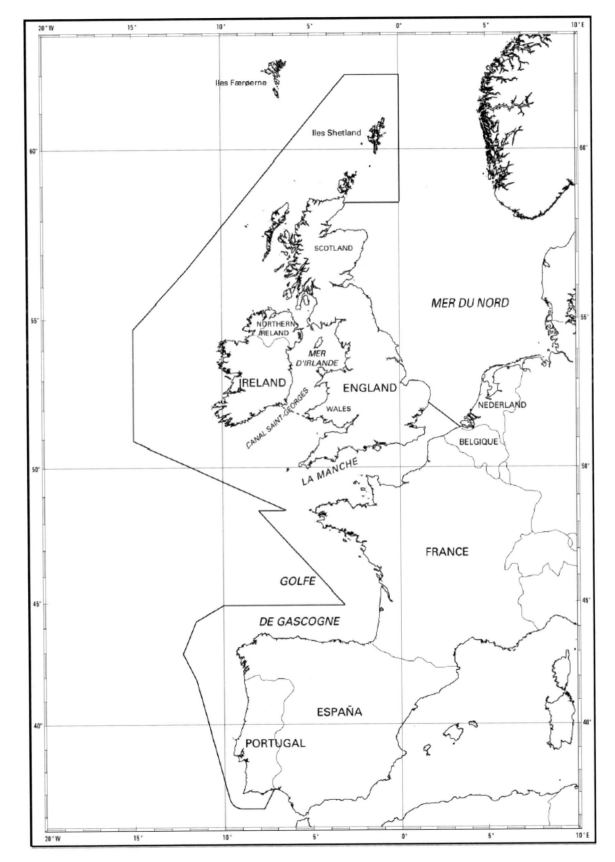

2 Significance of the area

2.1 General

2.1.1 From the North to the South of the PSSA, and within the transition between the bio-geographical moderate heat and boreal areas, there is a rich variety of ecosystems.

2.1.2 The coasts of North-west Scotland, the Shetland Islands, the Orkney Islands and the Hebrides are environmentally significant, including areas with high concentrations of vulnerable seabirds and with a medium to low level of offshore fishing activity.

2.1.3 The coastline of western and southern Ireland is a heavily indented one, screened in parts by outlying islands, rocks and skerries. These coasts (from Donegal in the North-west to Waterford in South-west) measure 5,140 km in length. The west coast in particular has a very high species diversity of both macro-fauna and flora. Offshore waters contain some of the richest fishing grounds in Europe. Prevailing currents (oceanographic and meteorological) are south-westerly.

2.1.4 The water column to the West and South of Ireland lies above continental shelf in the main, and is consequently relatively shallow. The body of water is a biologically diverse and highly productive marine environment. There are 10 million pairs of seabirds of 28 species regularly breeding on the Irish coasts of the PSSA. The open-water areas support important populations of marine birds, both offshore species such as petrels, gulls, auks and gannets and inshore species of ducks, divers, cormorants and terns.

2.1.5 Many of these species spend most of their time feeding at sea and are vulnerable to surface pollutants such as oil.

2.1.6 Off the south and west coasts of Ireland there is a very large grey seal population. The west coast of Ireland also supports a wide variety of cetaceans. In particular, the Shannon estuary supports a resident population of Bottlenose Dolphins (*Tursiops truncatus*). These waters also support 200 species of fish.

2.1.7 The importance of these areas on the coasts of Ireland has been recognized internationally through the creation of marine nature reserves, RAMSAR sites and Special Protection Areas (SPAs). Also particularly noteworthy is the continental shelf break, where upwellings and a front system create high productivity with rich plankton communities and a diverse benthos.

2.1.8 A number of the RAMSAR sites designated in Ireland are along the bays and inlets of the south and west coast and contain a unique and important diversity of marine flora and fauna.

2.1.9 In Belgium, the area is recognized as particularly important for flatfish and brown shrimp fisheries. The coastal zone is an essential spawning and nursery area for these species. It is characterised by the presence of sandbanks which are slightly covered by seawater all the time, a natural habitat type of Community interest under the European Habitat Directive. In 1984, part of these sandbanks were designated as Wetlands of International Importance under the RAMSAR Convention, and in 1996 Belgium designated a Special Area of Conservation in that environment under the Habitat Directive. The Belgian government is now in the process of establishing three Special Protection Areas for seabirds in the area to provide the large seabird populations that concentrate in the winter with better protection. The entire coastline has a high amenity value and is one of the major European tourist resorts.

2.1.10 In France, the area enjoys great biodiversity and biological wealth, due to the contrast between the moderate tidal range of the Bay of Biscay and the very high tidal range in the English Channel, together with the influence of three large rivers (the Seine, the Loire and the Gironde), which are separated by vast areas of their fluvial deposits. These three large estuaries, where the land, fresh water and salt water meet, are areas of particular significance for biodiversity.

2.1.11 Another characteristic of this shore is the presence of about fifteen islands between the Côtes d'Armor and the Charente-Maritime. Although their surface area is low compared to the total surface of the shoreline, they are nevertheless of very great interest from the ecological point of view.

2.1.12 This great ecological interest can be highlighted by the presence of emblematic species such as the marine mammals (seals, dolphins, whales), seabirds (puffins, skuas, terns, gulls, etc.), and fish.

2.1.13 The north-east Atlantic and the Bay of Biscay coasts, because of their rich fauna and flora, beautiful landscapes and interesting geological aspects, have a remarkable cultural, scientific and touristic value to Spain.

2.1.14 It is important to emphasize that, in this area, the Atlantic Islands National Park is located, which area includes:

a) *Cies Islands*

Area limited by a point North of Monteagudo, South of Bajos de Carrumeiros, South of Castros de Agoeiros and Islote de Biduidos, comprising Monte Faro, Monteagudo and San Martiño islands and adjoining islets.

This group of islands is placed near the Ría de Vigo (Vigo), and includes about 2658 sea-hectares and 433 land-hectares.

b) *Ons and Onza Islands*

Area limited by Punta Centolo, Bajos de los Camoucos, Bajos Laxiña de Galera, Bajo Menguella, Bajo Cabeza del Rico and Bajos de Bastián de Val.

Comprising Ons and Onza Islands and adjoining islets, this group of islands is placed near the Ría de Pontevedra (Bueu) and includes about 2171 sea-hectares and 470 land-hectares.

c) *Sálvora and adjoining islands*

Area limited by Islas Sagres, East of Seijo de Vionta and South of Punta Besugueiros.

Comprising Sálvora and adjoining islets, this group of islands is placed in the west part of Ría de Arousa (Ribeira), and includes about 2309 sea-hectares and 248 land-hectares.

d) *Cortegada, Malveiras and adjoining islands*

Area limited by high tide maximum equinoctial line and Cortegada, Malveira Grande, Malveira Chica, Briñas and Islote de Con.

This group of islands is placed in the Ría de Arousa (Villagarcia de Arousa) and includes 43.8 land-hectares. In this area, regional authorities have established additional forms of environmental protection: natural reserves, natural parks, protected landscapes, natural monuments, etc.

2.1.15 Other international protected areas created in the Atlantic Spanish coast are as follows:

– RAMSAR areas;

– Special areas for the protection of birds and areas of common European interest, included within Red Natura 2000, under European Directives on birds (79/409/EEC) and habitats (92/43/EEC);

– Biosphere reserve (Urdaibai) under the UNESCO programme on man and biosphere.

2.1.16 Portugal has a mainland coastline of circa 1000 km and an Exclusive Economic Zone of 17,000 km², the largest in the European Union. More than 50% of the Portuguese population lives near the coastline.

2.1.17 In Portugal, around 50% of mainland coast is classified into one of the following categories: Protected Areas, Special Areas of Conservation, or Natura 2000 sites. They include ecosystems as diverse as marine areas, estuaries, coastal lagoons, sand dunes and rocky cliffs, involving nature's treasures of great importance, where one can find species of fauna and flora with a high degree of endemicity, as well as particularly sensitive habitats in need of protection.

2.1.18 The uniqueness, significance and diversity of several areas along the Portuguese coastline are highly vulnerable to pollution damage. Extended biological productivity of coastal waters allows traditional fishing activities with great economical significance from the north to south-east end of the area.

2.2   Detailed description of significance

2.2.1   Detailed descriptions of the ecological, socio-economic and cultural, scientific and educational criteria are contained in document MEPC 49/8/1.

3   Vulnerability of the area to damage by international shipping activities

3.1   The marine and shore environment of the Belgian, French, Irish, Portuguese, Spanish and United Kingdom coasts, the English Channel and its approaches are particularly vulnerable to the risks induced by the carriage of goods by sea.

3.2   This area constitutes one of the most significant sea routes on an international scale, because of the number of ships and of the quantities of dangerous or polluting goods transported: 25% of the world commercial traffic converges towards the English Channel. It constitutes the main area of maritime transit of commercial flows, with destination to the great industrial areas and harbours of Northern Europe.

3.3   There is also significant cross-channel commercial traffic between Ireland and the United Kingdom, between Ireland, the United Kingdom and the mainland of Europe, and North European traffic bound for western Atlantic ports.

3.4   A detailed description of the characteristics of the maritime traffic, the transport of harmful substances, and the threats from disasters, including a description of the meteorological, oceanographical and geographical conditions, may be found in documents MEPC 49/8/1 together with MEPC 49/8/1 Add.1 and MEPC 49/8/1 Corr.1.

Annex 2
Relevant rules and regulations in force in the Western European Waters Particularly Sensitive Sea Area

Measures adopted by IMO

1   Conventions

- Convention on the International Regulations for Preventing Collisions at Sea, 1972 (COLREGs), as amended
- International Convention for the Prevention of Pollution from Ships, 1973, as modified by the Protocol of 1978 relating thereto (MARPOL 73/78)[*]
- International Convention for the Safety of Life at Sea (SOLAS), 1974, as amended.

2   Traffic separation schemes

- West of the Scilly Isles
- South of the Scilly Isles
- Off Lands End, between Seven Stones and Longships
- Off Ushant
- Off Casquets
- In the Strait of Dover and adjacent waters
- In the SUNK area and in the northern approaches to the Thames estuary
- Off Fastnet Rock
- Off Smalls
- Off Tuskar Rock
- Off Skerries
- In the North Channel
- Off Neist Point in The Minches
- Off Finisterre
- Off Cape Roca
- Off Cape S. Vicente

3   Deep-water routes

- Deep-water route leading to the Port of Antifer
- Deep-water route forming part of the north-eastbound traffic lane of the traffic separation scheme "In the Strait of Dover and adjacent waters"
- Deep-water route in the approaches to the River Scheldt
- Deep-water route west of the Hebrides

---

[*] The English Channel and its approaches are part of the North-West European Waters Special Area.

4 Areas to be avoided

- Around the CS4 buoy in the Dover Strait (to be avoided by all ships)

- Around the F3 station within the traffic separation scheme "In the Strait of Dover and adjacent waters" (to be avoided by all ships)

- At West Hinder

- In the outer precautionary area of the traffic separation scheme "In the SUNK area and in the northern approaches to the Thames estuary" (to be avoided by all ships)

- In the region of the Orkney Islands (to be avoided by ships of more than 5000 gross tonnage carrying oil or other hazardous cargoes in bulk)

- In the region of the Fair Isle (to be avoided by ships of more than 5000 gross tonnage carrying oil or other hazardous cargoes in bulk)

- In the region of the Shetland Islands (to be avoided by all vessels over 5000 gross tonnage carrying, or capable of carrying, oil or other liquid hazardous cargoes in bulk)

- In the region of the Rochebonne Shelf (to be avoided by all tankers carrying oil)

- Between The Smalls Lighthouse and Grassholme Island (to be avoided by all tankers, gas carriers, chemical tankers carrying noxious liquid substances, and all other ships of 500 gross tons or over)

- In the region of the Berlengas Islands (to be avoided by all vessels above 300 gross tonnage, except duly authorized ships navigating between Portuguese ports and not carrying dangerous cargoes or other harmful substances)

5 Routeing measures

- Recommended directions of traffic flow within the precautionary area around the Foxtrot 3 station in the Dover Strait

- Two-way route and recommended route in the SUNK area and in the northern approaches to the Thames estuary

- Precautionary area in the vicinity of Thornton and Bligh Banks

- Recommended routes in the Fair Isle Channel

- Recommendations on navigation around the United Kingdom coast

- Recommended routes in The Minches

6 Mandatory ship reporting systems

- The West European Tanker Reporting System

- Off "Les Casquets" and the adjacent coastal area

- In the Dover Strait/Pas de Calais

- Off Ushant

- Off Finisterre

- Off the coast of Portugal

7 Coastal Vessel Traffic Services (VTS)

- Gris-Nez VTS

- Dover, Channel Navigation Information Service (CNIS)

- Jobourg VTS

- Finisterre VTS

- Coast of Portugal VTS

Annex 3

*Mandatory ship reporting system for the Western European
Particularly Sensitive Sea Area*

Summary

1   Ships required to report

In the reporting system WETREP, every kind of oil tanker of more than 600 tonnes deadweight, carrying a cargo of:

–   heavy crude oil, meaning crude oils with a density at 15°C of higher than 900 kg/m^3;

–   heavy fuel oils, meaning fuel oils with a density at 15°C of higher than 900 kg/m^3, or a kinematic viscosity at 50°C of higher than 180 mm^2/s;

–   bitumen and tar and their emulsions.

2   Position for submitting reports

Ships on voyage to and from the Western European Reporting Area shall send reports:

.1   on entry into the Reporting Area; or

.2   immediately on departing from a port, terminal or anchorage within the Reporting Area; or

.3   when they deviate from routeing to their original declared destination port/terminal/anchorage or position "for orders" given at time of entry into the Reporting Area; or

.4   when deviation from planned route is necessary due to weather or equipment malfunction or a change in the navigational status; and

.5   when finally exiting from the Reporting Area.

Ships need not report if, while on normal passage routeing during transit of the Reporting Area, the boundary of the Reporting Area is crossed on other occasions apart from the initial entry and final exit.

3   Reference chart

United Kingdom Hydrographic chart No. 4011 (datum WGS 84).

4   Reporting format

System identifier: WETREP

Data to be transmitted in WETREP:

A: Ship identification (ship name, call sign, IMO identification number and MMSI Number)

B: date time group

C: Position

E: True course

F: Speed

G: Name of last port of call

I: Name of next port of call, with ETA

P: Oil cargo type(s), quantity, grade(s) and density (If those tankers carry other hazardous cargo simultaneously: the type, quantity and IMO class of that cargo, as appropriate)

Q: To be used in cases of defects or deficiency affecting normal navigation

T: Address for the communication of cargo information

W: Number of persons on board

X: Various information applicable for those tankers:

- characteristics and estimated quantity of bunker fuel, for tankers carrying more than 5000 tonnes of bunker fuel

- navigational status (for example, under way with engines, restricted in ability to manoeuvre, etc.)

5   Authority receiving the report

5.1   Upon entering the WETREP reporting area, ships will notify the coordination centre of the responsible authority of the Coastal State participating in the system. The vessel traffic services, RCC, coastal radio station or other facilities to whom the reports must be sent are listed in the appendix to this annex.

5.2   Should the ship be unable to send the report to the nearest coastal radio station or other facility, the report shall be sent to the next-nearest coastal radio station or other facility as listed in the appendix.

6   Communication

Reports may be sent by any modern communication form, including Inmarsat-C, telefax and e-mail, as appropriate.

Appendix

Vessel Traffic Services, RCC, coast radio station or other facilities to whom the reports must be submitted (Geographical positions refer to WGS 84)

Position coordinates

Belgium

MRCC – SAR Oostende: 51°14′ N, 002°55′ E

Tel: +32 59 70 10 00

Tel.:   +32 59 70 11 00

Fax: +32 59 70 36 05

Telex: 82125

VHF :   9, 16, 67, 70

MF: 2182

MMSI: 002059981

France

MRCC Gris-Nez: 50°52′ N, 001°35′ E

Tel.:   +33 3 21 87 21 87

Fax: +33 3 21 87 78 55

Telex: 130680

Inmarsat-C: 422799256

VHF: 16, 70

MMSI: 002275100

MRCC Corsen: 48°25′ N, 004°47′ W

Tel.:   +33 2 98 89 31 31

Fax: +33 2 98 89 65 75

Telex: 940086

Inmarsat-C: Nil

VHF: 16, 70

MMSI: 002275300

Ireland

MRCC Dublin

Tel: +353 1 6620922/23

Fax: +353 1 6620795

e-mail: mrccdublin@irishcoastguard.ie

Communications may be sent to MRCC Dublin via:

MRSC Valentia (EJK):   51°56′ N, 010°21′ W

MRSC Malin Head (EJM):   55°22′ N, 007°21′ W

Portugal

Roca Control: 38°41′.508 N, 009°17′.915 W

Tel: +351 214464838

Fax: +351 214464839

e-mail: oper.vs@imapor.pt

VHF: 22 & 79

MMSI: 002633030

Position coordinates

Spain

MRCC Madrid:		40°24' N, 003°43' W
Tel:	+34 91 7559133	
Fax:	+34 91 5261440	
Telex:	+5241210, +5241224	
e-mail:	cncs@sasemar.es	

MRCC Finisterre:		42°42' N, 008°59' W
Tel:	+34 981 767500	
Fax:	+34 981 767740	
Telex:	+5282268, +5286207	
e-mail:	finister@sasemar.es	
VHF:	16 & 11	
MF:	2182	
MMSI:	002240993	

MRCC Bilbao:		43°20'.8 N, 003°01' W
Tel:	+34 944 839286	
Fax:	+34 944 839161	
e-mail:	bilbao@sasemar.es	
VHF:	16 & 10	
MMSI:	002241021	

United Kingdom

MRCC Falmouth

Tel:	+(0)1326 317575
Fax:	+(0)1326 318342
Telex:	+51 42981
Inmarsat-A and Inmarsat-C	
e-mail:	falmouthcoastguard@mcga.gov.uk

Sea Area A2 – MF DSC Coast Stations

		MMSI
MRCC Aberdeen	57°25' N, 001°51' W	002320004
MRCC Clyde	55°58' N, 004°48' W	002320022
MRCC Falmouth	50°08' N, 005°07' W	002320014
MRSC Holyhead	53°19' N, 004°38' W	002320018
MRSC Humber	54°05' N, 001°10' W	002320007
Cullercoats	55°04' N, 001°28' W	(sub-station)
MRSC Milford Haven	51°41' N, 005°03' W	002320017
MRCC Shetland	60°09' N, 001°08' W	002320001
MRSC Stornoway	58°13' N, 006°20' W	002320024

Annex 13 – Canary Islands Particularly Sensitive Sea Area

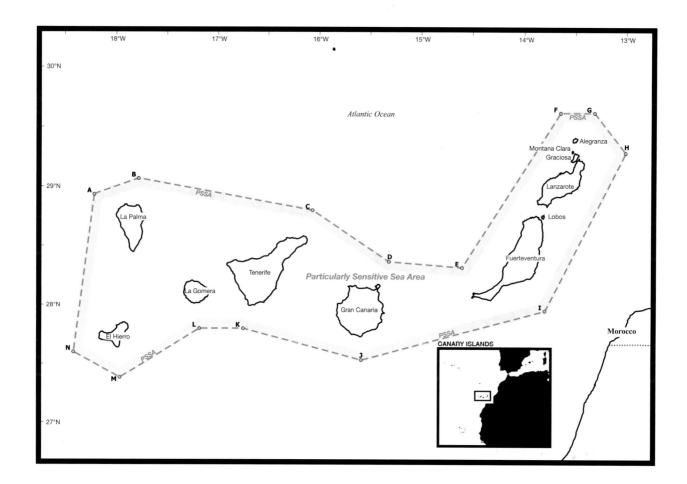

Resolution MEPC.134(53)

adopted on 22 July 2005

Designation of the Canary Islands
as a Particularly Sensitive Sea Area

THE MARINE ENVIRONMENT PROTECTION COMMITTEE,

BEING AWARE of the ecological, social, economic, cultural, scientific and educational value of the Canary Islands, as well as its vulnerability to damage by international shipping traffic and activities in the area and the steps taken by Spain to address that vulnerability,

NOTING that the Guidelines for the Identification and Designation of Particularly Sensitive Sea Areas adopted under resolution A.927(22) set out procedures for the designation of Particularly Sensitive Sea Areas,

HAVING CONSIDERED the proposal from Spain to designate the Canary Islands as a Particularly Sensitive Sea Area,

HAVING AGREED that criteria for identification of a Particularly Sensitive Sea Area provided in resolution A.927(22) are fulfilled for the Canary Islands,

1   DESIGNATES the Canary Islands as defined in annex 1 to this resolution as a Particularly Sensitive Sea Area; and

2   INVITES Member Governments to note the establishment of associated protective measures defined in annex 2. The associated protective measures and the date of their entry into force are expected to be adopted by the Maritime Safety Committee at its eighty-first session in May 2006.

Annex 1

Description of the Canary Islands Particularly Sensitive Sea Area

1   Description of the area

1.1   The Canary Isles, comprising seven larger islands and six islets lying at latitude 28°–29°N, form an archipelago of volcanic origin in the Atlantic Ocean, some 100 km off the western coast of Africa. Their total area is 7273 km². For administrative purposes, they are divided into two provinces: Santa Cruz de Tenerife, comprising the islands of Tenerife, La Palma, La Gomera and El Hierro; and Las Palmas, comprising Gran Canaria, Lanzarote and Fuerteventura. The islets, called Alegranza, La Graciosa, Montaña Clara, Roque del Este, Roque del Oeste and Lobos, are all grouped around the two last-named islands.

1.2   The Canarian island margin is made up of the seven islands and the islets forming the archipelago, as well as a number of submerged mountains, all of them volcanic and rising directly from deep in the Earth's mantle. Owing to their volcanic origin, the characteristics of the island margins are unique. In general terms, the depth profile and underwater morphology of the Canary Isles are sharply defined, with very narrow island shelves and steeply sloping shores scored by landslide channels that descend rapidly to the abyssal plain, transporting collapsed materials for tens of kilometres.

1.3   As to the shelf profile of the various islands, there are two different groupings. The first, comprising Gran Canaria, Fuerteventura, Lanzarote and La Gomera, has shelves that, although limited in size, are still large in relation to those of the second group made up of Tenerife, La Palma and El Hierro.

1.4   The physiography of the sea-beds around the archipelago is testament to the continuous volcanic activity and their location on a prograding margin; the morphological units caused by landslides and intrusions are frequent, and the sea-beds in the proposed area are largely unstable.

1.5   The morphology of the coasts reflects the qualities of their constituent materials, which range from steep cliffs containing basalt formations to low coastlines made of pyroclastic materials and porous rocks that are difficult to restore once accidentally polluted.

1.6   The beaches generally lie on the south side of the islands, their morphology highly influenced by the effects of the prevailing Trade Winds.

1.7   These winds magnify the scale of any accidental spillage, helping to solve problems in some areas and making the disaster still worse in others.

1.8   The area is defined by a line:

A	28°56′ N, 018°13′ W
B	29°04′ N, 017°47′ W
C	28°48′ N, 016°04′ W
D	28°22′ N, 015°19′ W
E	28°19′ N, 014°36′ W
F	29°37′ N, 013°39′ W
G	29°37′ N, 013°19′ W
H	29°17′ N, 013°06′ W
I	27°57′ N, 013°48′ W
J	27°32′ N, 015°35′ W
K	27°48′ N, 016°45′ W
L	27°48′ N, 017°11′ W
M	27°23′ N, 017°58′ W
N	27°36′ N, 018°25′ W.

1.9   A chartlet of the Canary Islands PSSA and its associated protective measures is provided below.

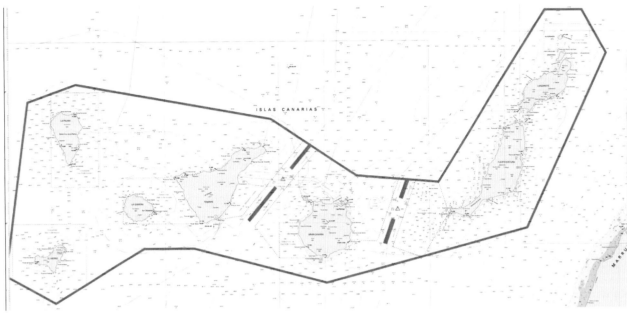

2   Significance of the area

2.1   Ecological criteria

2.1.1   By its Decision of 28 December 2001, the European Commission adopted a list of sites of Community importance with respect to the Macaronesian biogeographical region, in implementing Directive 92/43/CEE on the conservation of natural habitats and of wild fauna and flora.

2.1.2   The Canary Isles have unique volcanic tubes and lava bubbles, and unique and representative geomorphological formations with a high level of endemisms. Another unique ecosystem is formed by the 'sebadales', biologically rich meadows of spermatophytes that play an important role in the breeding and nutrition of bentonic organisms.

2.1.3   In 1983, UNESCO declared part of the island of La Palma a biosphere reserve. Called El Canal y Los Tiles, the area's 500 hectares made it the smallest of its kind in Spain.

2.1.4   The islands' geographical position and morphological characteristics, including cliffs, rocks and tunnels of volcanic origin, determine the kind of organisms that occupy each habitat, and together give rise to a unique, highly diverse and species-rich biocoenosis.

2.1.5   Out of 168 habitats listed in the European Habitats Directive, 24 are in the Canary Isles. The Spanish waters around the islands contain 20 cetaceous species, from dolphins to large whales, over 500 species of fish and thousands of invertebrates. Extending over a surface area of 7554 km² and a coastline of 1540 km, the islands contain more than 300 protected spaces, including four national parks, 7 rural parks, 11 integrated marine reserves, 15 special natural reserves, 2 marine reserves, 27 special bird protection areas, 3 islands declared Biosphere Reserves, 174 sites of Community interest, 11 natural parks, 19 sites of scientific interest, 51 natural monuments and 27 protected landscapes.

2.1.6   The islets to the north of Lanzarote offer a highly important nesting area and refuge for birds, recognized as such by the European Union. They contain a high concentration of marine and terrestrial species, both indigenous and migratory. Birds constitute one of the main biological resources of these islets, which are home to a broad sample of threatened species, some having found their last refuge in the Canaries. Particularly important in this context are Bulwer's petrel (*Bulweria bulwerii*), the little shearwater (*Puffinus assimilis*), the common petrel (*Hydrobates pelagicus*), the white-faced storm petrel (*Pelagodroma marina*) and the Madeira petrel (*Oceanodroma castro*), the osprey (*Pandion haliaetus*), the Egyptian vulture (*neophron percnopterus*) the peregrine falcon (*Falco peregrinus*) and Eleonora's falcon (*Falco eleonorae*). Only very few pairs remain of most of these species, and their conservational importance is thus extremely high. This area was also the site of extinction of one of the most important birds to have lived only in the archipelago: the black oystercatcher (*Haematopus meadewaldoi*).

2.1.7   On the leeward side of Jandía, in the south of Fuerteventura, lies an extensive area of sand containing large lakes formed by the sea, with halophyte vegetation at its margin. This has become a breeding site for lute turtles, and is the only place in the European Union where they lay their eggs.

2.1.8   In the seas off Teno-Rasca, in the south of Tenerife, Mogán, in the south of Gran Canaria, and Santiago Valle Gran Rey (Gomera), the existence of warm and calm waters for most of the year and the presence of deep water near the coast have created unrivalled living conditions for a number of cetaceous species. This is the distribution area of the bottleneck dolphin, while of the other cetaceous species present (*Globicephala macrorhynchus, Steno bredanensis, Stenella frontalis, Delphinus delphis, Stenella coeruleoalba, Grampus griseus, Physeter macrocephalus* and *Balaenoptera edeni*), some maintain resident populations and others visit for feeding or reproductive purposes. This is also an area vitally important to the Atlantic loggerhead sea turtle, which comes to the Canaries to rest and adjust its body temperature. Its population is estimated to be several hundred, and large numbers can be seen on their migratory journey through the area.

2.1.9   The 'sebadales', or marine spermatophytes, found at Guasimeta, off Lanzarote, or at Corralero, off Fuerteventura, are important breeding areas for species of fishing and/or ecological importance, and play an important part in ensuring the presence of long-range pelagic fish.

2.1.10   The intensive use made of the inshore waters, the frequent shipping movements, water pollution, illegal fishing methods and floating refuse all combine to make the coastline of the Canaries especially vulnerable.

2.1.11   The marine environment of the Canaries has a limited biological production capacity in general terms, owing to the restricted surface area of the coastal depths or coastal shelves and the low nutrient concentration of its oligotrophic waters. This is offset by the existing temperature range and the variety of biotopes or sea-beds, which generate high biodiversity but low production or biomass. In other words, these are fragile and delicate systems in which the ecological balance can easily be altered.

2.2   Social, cultural and economic criteria

2.2.1   International recognition of the waters of the Canary Isles as a Particularly Sensitive Sea Area entails the likely regulation and control of the intensive shipping in the region, in order to prevent polluting spillages and, when necessary, minimize the effects of accidental pollution.

2.2.2   The Canaries are a leading tourist destination in the European context. There is no need to emphasize the impact that damage to the marine environment would exert on the tourist industry, or on the service sector, which accounts for 80 per cent of the islands' overall economy.

2.2.3   In recent years, the marine environment of the Canaries archipelago has been the subject of international, regional and national research projects, and the focus of many expeditions by scientific and commercial vessels, in the fields of oceanography, biological investigation into fishing and biodiversity of the Canaries.

2.2.4   The faculties of La Laguna University, the Faculty of Marine Sciences at the University of Las Palmas de Gran Canaria, the Canarian Institute for Marine Sciences (Ministry for Education and Science, Canaries Government) and the Canaries Oceanographic Centre (Spanish Institute of Oceanography, Ministry of Science and Technology) constitute an important teaching and study resource. There also exist many institutions or centres focusing on specific activities: they include the Museum of Natural Sciences in Tenerife, the Island Marine Agency in La Palma and Tenerife, and the Gran Canaria animal recovery centre (which every year cares for dozens of turtles damaged by oil and around fifteen beached cetaceans).

2.3   Vulnerability of the area to damage by international shipping activities

2.3.1   There is extensive maritime activity in the waters of the Canaries archipelago owing to their geostrategic location; its ports provide an ideal operational base for many types of vessel that rely on them for their fishing activities, fuel, crews, spare parts, provisions and other materials. To these operational activities must be added the shipping which supplies the island population, the vessels carrying goods for export, and the considerable tourist traffic.

2.3.2   There are a large number of vessels that sail the waters of the archipelago, but the major problem lies with the intensive traffic of large oil tankers bound for the Persian Gulf. These vessels sail in ballast along the north/south route, and loaded along the south/north route. In both cases, there is uncontrolled spillage of oil residues. The number of such vessels is estimated to be 1500 per year. The oil refinery, with a sea terminal on the island of Tenerife, receives an average of 4 million tonnes of oil per year; it distributes its products for local, national and international consumption. Chemical tankers are also a notable presence, either sailing the above-mentioned routes or heading for Canarian ports to serve local industry.

Annex 2
Associated Protective Measures

A   Traffic separation schemes for the Canary Islands

The traffic separation scheme between Grand Canary and Fuerteventura, and its associated precautionary area and inshore traffic zone, and the traffic separation scheme between Grand Canary and Tenerife, and its associated precautionary area and inshore traffic zone, were approved at the eighty-first session of MSC in 2006. Full technical descriptions of the traffic separation schemes and their associated precautionary areas and inshore traffic zones are in part B of editions of the IMO publication "Ships' Routeing"; only chartlets of the schemes are included here. The "sections and parts" that are shown on these chartlets refer to "Ships' Routeing".

Between Grand Canary and Fuerteventura

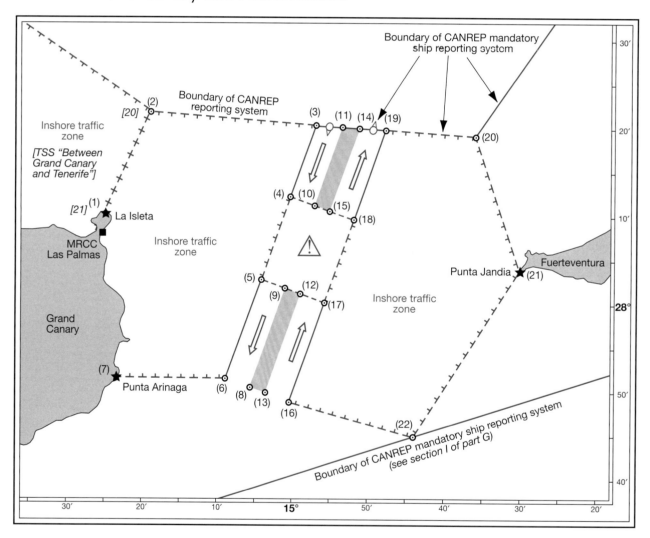

Between Grand Canary and Tenerife

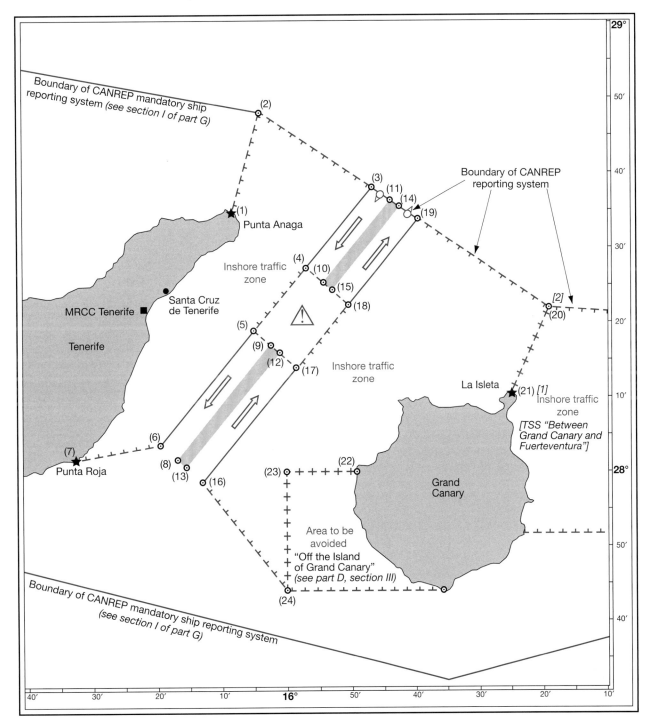

B   Areas to be avoided by ships transiting the Canary Islands

Five areas to be avoided near the Canary Islands were adopted at the eighty-first session of MSC in 2006. All five areas are to be avoided by all tankers and ships over 500 gross tonnage carrying oil or dangerous bulk cargo as cargo. Full technical descriptions of the areas are in part D of editions of the IMO publication "Ships' Routeing"; only chartlets of the areas are included here.

Off Lanzarote Island (biosphere reserve)

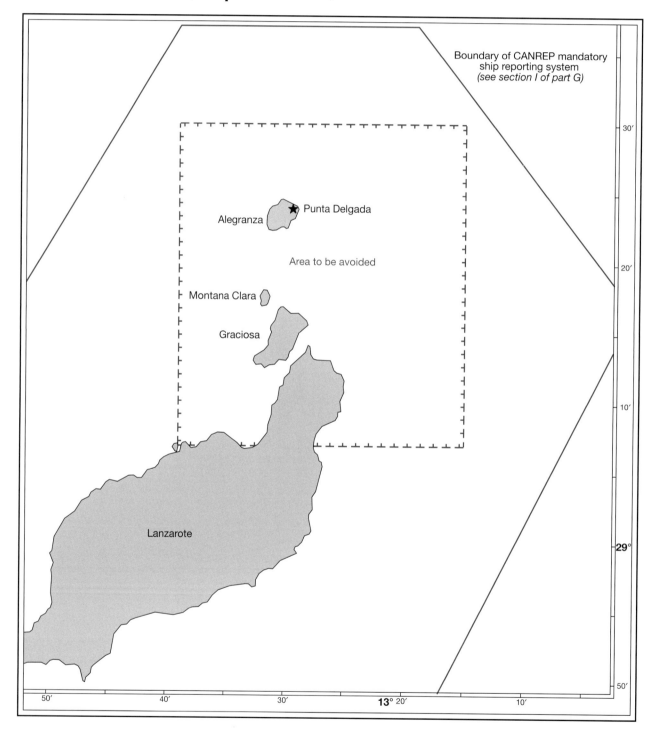

Off the island of Tenerife (cetacean breeding ground)

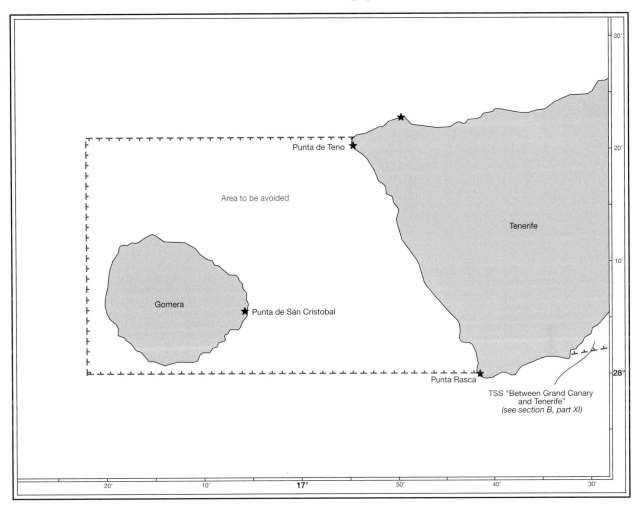

Off the island of Grand Canary (cetacean breeding ground)

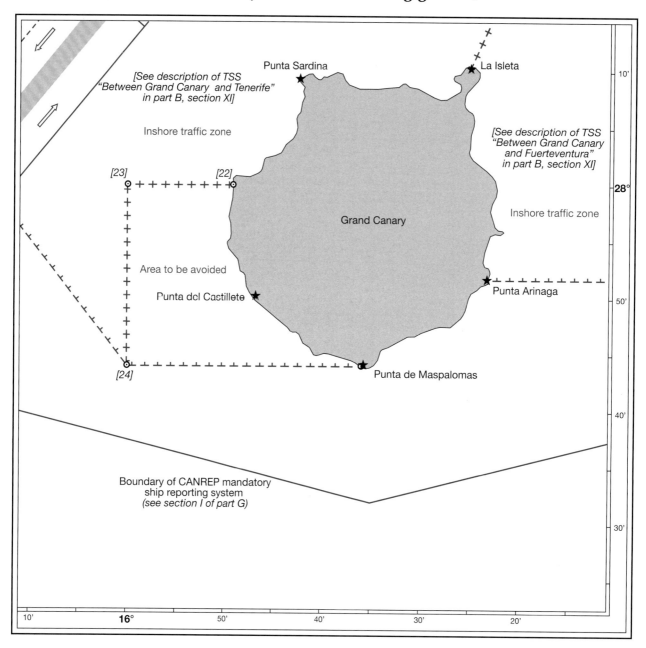

Off La Palma Island (biosphere reserve)

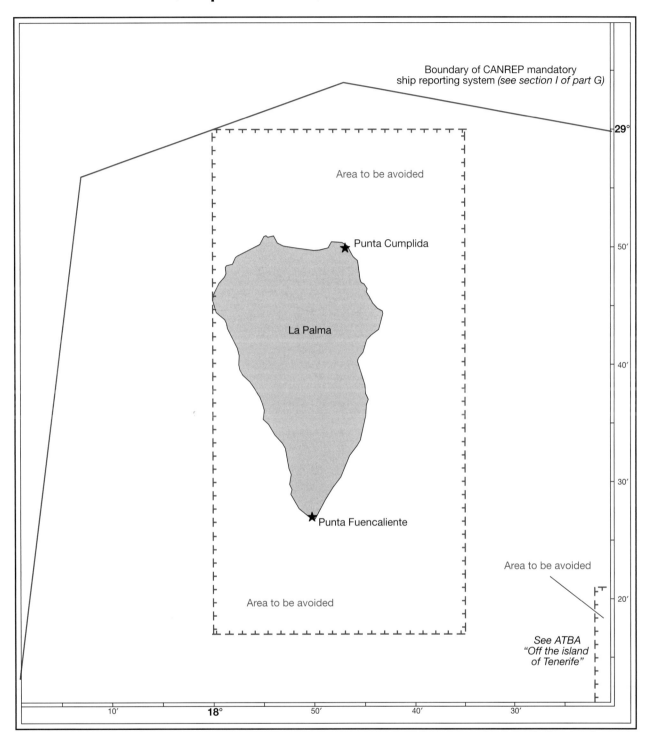

Off the island of El Hierro (biosphere reserve)

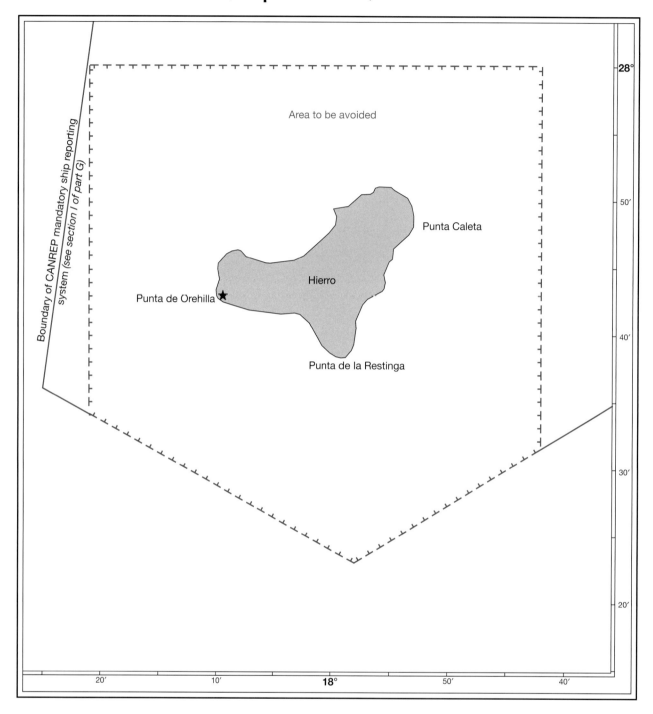

C Mandatory ship reporting system for the Canary Islands

A mandatory reporting system for ships in the Canary Islands (CANREP) is established in the Canary Islands.

1 Types of ship required to take part in the system

1.1 Ships required to take part in the CANREP system:

Tankers of 600 deadweight tonnage and upwards, either transiting the Canary Islands or sailing to or from Canarian ports or involved in inter-island navigation, carrying the following:

.1 heavy-grade crude oils with a density greater than 900 kg/m³ at 15°C;

.2 heavy fuel oils with a density greater than 900 kg/m³ at 15°C or kinematic viscosity greater than 180 mm²/s at 50°C; or

.3 bitumen, coal tar and their emulsions.

2 Geographical limits of the Canary Islands reporting area

2.1 The maritime area is bounded by a polygonal line connecting points along the outer limit of the territorial sea (12 nautical miles) that surrounds the archipelago, and having the following inflection points (see chartlet in appendix 3):

Point	Latitude	Longitude
A	28°56′ N	018°13′ W
B	29°04′ N	017°47′ W
C	28°48′ N	016°04′ W
D	28°22′ N	015°19′ W
E	28°19′ N	014°36′ W
F	29°37′ N	013°39′ W
G	29°37′ N	013°19′ W
H	29°17′ N	013°06′ W
I	27°57′ N	013°48′ W
J	27°32′ N	015°35′ W
K	27°48′ N	016°45′ W
L	27°48′ N	017°11′ W
M	27°23′ N	017°58′ W
N	27°36′ N	018°25′ W

2.2 The reference chart is No. 209 of the Spanish Navy Hydrographical Institute (WGS 84 datum).

3 Format and content of reports; time and geographical position for submitting reports; authority to which they must be sent; available services

3.1 Format

3.1.1 CANREP reports must be sent to one of the Maritime Rescue Coordination Centres listed in appendix 1 and drafted in accordance with the format described in appendix 2.

3.1.2 The reporting format conforms with paragraph 2 of the appendix to resolution A.851(20).

3.2   Content

3.2.1   The reports to be submitted by participating ships must contain the information needed to achieve the system's aims:

.1   the ship's name, call sign, IMO or MMSI number and position are necessary in order to establish its identity and initial position (A, B and C);

.2   the ship's course, speed and destination are important for monitoring its track and launching search and rescue measures should information about it fail to appear on the screen, for ensuring safe navigation, and for preventing pollution in areas where weather conditions are extreme (E, F, G and I);

.3   the number of people on board, and other relevant information, are important factors when it comes to assigning the resources for a search and rescue operation (P, T and W);

.4   in accordance with the relevant provisions of the SOLAS and MARPOL Conventions, ships are required to supply information on defects, damage, deficiencies and other limitations (under Q), as well as other information (under X).

3.3   Time and geographical position for submitting reports

3.3.1   Ships must submit a report:

.1   on entering the reporting area as defined in paragraph 2; or

.2   immediately after leaving a port, terminal or anchorage situated in the reporting area; or

.3   when deviating from the route leading to the originally declared destination, port, terminal, anchorage or position "for orders" given on entry into the reporting area; or

.4   when it is necessary to deviate from the planned route owing to weather conditions, damaged equipment or a change in navigational status; and

.5   on finally leaving the reporting area.

3.3.2   Ships are not required to send a report if, during normal sailing through the reporting area, they cross the area's boundary on other occasions apart from initial entry or final departure.

3.4   Land-based authorities to which reports must be sent

3.4.1   On entering the CANREP reporting area, ships must report the fact to one of the MRCCs listed in appendix 1, according to the following criteria:

(i)   Ships that enter the CANREP reporting area at a position east of the meridian of longitude 015°30′ W should notify the Las Palmas MRCC.

(ii)   Ships that enter the reporting area at a position west of the meridian of longitude 015°30′ W should notify the Tenerife MRCC.

3.4.2   On leaving the CANREP reporting area, ships must report the fact to the same MRCC to which they reported on entry.

3.4.3   Reports must be completed in accordance with the format shown in appendix 2.

3.4.4   Reports may be sent by any means capable of being received by the media indicated in appendix 1.

4   Information to be provided to participating ships and procedures to be observed

4.1   When requested, the MRCCs listed in appendix 1 should provide ships with information vital to navigational safety in the ship's reporting area, using their broadcasting equipment.

4.2   If necessary, any ship may ask for information on its own behalf about specific local conditions.

5   Requirements regarding radiocommunications for the system, reporting frequencies and information to be reported

5.1   The Maritime Rescue Coordination Centres to which reports must be sent are listed in appendix 1.

5.2   The reports completed by a ship on entering and passing through the reporting area must begin with the word CANREP and include a two-letter abbreviation to indicate their type (sailing plan, final report or deviation report). Reports with these prefixes may be sent free of cost.

5.3   Depending on the type of report, the following information must be included, as described in paragraph 6 of appendix 2:

A: Ship's identity (name, call sign, IMO No. and MMSI No.);

B: Date and time;

C: Position;

E: True course;

F: Speed;

G: Name of last port of call;

I: Name of next port of call and estimated time of arrival;

P: Type(s) of cargo, quantity and IMO classification if carrying potentially dangerous goods;

Q: Used in the event of defects or deficiencies that impair normal navigation;

T: Address for communication of cargo information;

W: Number of people on board;

X: Miscellaneous information relating to tankers:

–   estimated quantity and characteristics of bunker fuel for tankers carrying an amount of it greater than 5000 tonnes;

–   navigational status (e.g. moving under own propulsion, limited manoeuvrability, etc.).

5.4   The reporting format must be consistent with resolution A.851(20).

6   Regulations in force in the area covered by the system

6.1   Regulations on collision prevention

The International Regulations for Preventing Collisions at Sea (COLREG), 1972, as amended, applies throughout the area covered by the system.

7   Shore-based establishments responsible for operation of the system

7.1   The MRCCs to which these reports must be sent are listed in appendix 1.

7.2   The MRCCs or any other establishment forming part of the service are to be manned constantly.

7.3   The training given to MRCC staff must comply with the national and international recommendations and include a general study of navigational safety measures and the relevant national and international (IMO) provisions.

7.4   All means of communication that can be received by the media indicated in appendix 1 are acceptable.

8 Action to take in the event of a ship's non-compliance with system requirements

8.1 The system's objectives are to initiate maritime search and rescue and anti-pollution measures as quickly and effectively as possible if an emergency is reported or if a ship that is supposed to report does not and no contact can be established with it. All possible means will be deployed to obtain the participation of the ships required to send in reports. Should these fail to materialize and the offending ship can be identified beyond doubt, the competent authorities in the relevant flag State will be informed with a view to their investigating the situation and possibly starting legal proceedings under their national legislation. The CANREP mandatory ship reporting system exists only for the exchange of information, and does not confer additional powers to impose change in a ship's operations. The reporting system will be implemented in accordance with the provisions of UNCLOS, the SOLAS Convention and other relevant international instruments, and the reporting system will not constitute a basis for preventing the passage of a ship in transit through the reporting area.

Appendix 1

Installations to which reports must be sent (positions refer to WGS 84 datum)

MRCC Tenerife 28°28′ N, 016°14′ W

Tel.: +34 900 202 111.
E-mail: canrep.tenerife@sasemar.es
VHF channels: 16 and 70
MF channel: 2182
Automatic identification system (AIS)

MRCC Las Palmas 28°09′ N, 015°25′ W

Tel.: +34 900 202 112.
E-mail: canrep.laspalmas@sasemar.es
VHF channels: 16 and 70
MF channel: 2182
Automatic identification system (AIS)

Appendix 2

Mandatory reporting system for the Canary Islands (CANREP)

Instructions for reports

1   Ships heading for the reporting area of the Canary Islands must send a report:

.1   on entering the reporting area; or

.2   immediately after leaving a port, terminal or anchorage situated in the reporting area; or

.3   when deviating from the route leading to the originally declared destination, port, terminal, anchorage or position "for orders" given on entry into the reporting area; or

.4   when it is necessary to deviate from the planned route owing to weather conditions, damaged equipment or when information under Q is required; and

.5   on finally leaving the reporting area.

2   Ships are not required to send a report if, during normal sailing through the reporting area, they cross the area's boundary on other occasions apart from initial entry or final departure.

3   On entering the CANREP reporting area, ships must report the fact to one of the MRCCs listed in appendix 1, according to the following criteria:

(i)   Ships that enter the CANREP reporting area at a position east of the meridian of longitude 015°30′ W should notify the Las Palmas MRCC.

(ii)   Ships that enter the reporting area at a position west of the meridian of longitude 015°30′ W should notify the Tenerife MRCC.

4   On leaving the CANREP reporting area, ships must report the fact to the same MRCC to which they reported on entry.

5   Every report must begin with the word CANREP and a two-letter abbreviation enabling the type of report to be identified. Messages with this prefix will be sent free of charge and treated as URGENT.

6   Reports must be in accordance with the following table. Sections A, B, C, E, F, G, I, P, T, W and X are compulsory for sailing plans, A, B, C, E and F for final reports, and A, B, C, E, F and I for deviation reports. The Q designation is included whenever a problem arises in the reporting area, be it defects, damage, deficiencies or circumstances, that affects normal navigation.

Designator	Function	Text
Name of system	Code word	CANREP
	Type of report: Sailing plan Final report Deviation report	One of the following 2-letter identifiers: SP FR (on finally leaving reporting area) to include only A, B, C, E and F DR to include only A, B, C, E, F and I
A	Ship	Name and call sign (Name of ship, call sign, IMO No. and MMSI No.), (e.g. **NONESUCH/KTOI**)
B	Date and time corresponding to position at C, expressed as UTC	A six-digit group followed by a Z. The first two digits indicate day of the month, the second two the hours and the last two the minutes. The Z indicates that the time is given in UTC (e.g. **081340Z**)
C	Position (latitude and longitude)	A four-digit group giving latitude in degrees and minutes, with the suffix N, and a five-digit group giving longitude in degrees and minutes, with the suffix W (e.g. **2836N** or **01545W**)
E	Course	True course. A three-digit group (e.g. **210**)
F	Speed	Speed in knots. A two-digit group (e.g. **14**)
G	Name of last port of call	Name of the last port of call (e.g. **Strait of Gibraltar**)
I	Destination and ETA (UTC)	Name of destination and date and time group as expressed in B (e.g. **Cape Town 181400Z**)
P	Cargo	Type(s) of cargo, and quantity and IMO classification if carrying potentially dangerous goods
Q	Defects, damage, deficiencies, limitations	Brief details of defects, including damage, deficiencies and other circumstances that impair normal navigation
T	Address for the communication of cargo information	Name, telephone No. and fax, e-mail or URL
W	Total number of people on board	State the number
X	Miscellaneous	Miscellaneous information concerning those tankers: Characteristics and approximate quantity of bunker fuel for tankers carrying an amount of it greater than 5,000 tonnes Navigational status (e.g. **moving under own propulsion, at anchor, no steering, limited manoeuvrability, depth restriction, moored, aground, etc.**)

7   The *sailing plan* (SP) is sent as an initial report:

(a)   When entering the reporting area, as defined in paragraph 2.1.

(b)   On leaving the last port of call located in the reporting area.

Example:

Name of station to which report must be sent: CANREP – SP
A.   GOLAR STIRLING/9001007
B.   261520Z
C.   2836N01545W
E.   210
F.   15
G.   STRAIT OF GIBRALTAR
I.   CAPE TOWN 230230Z
P.   56,000 TONNES HEAVY FUEL OILS
T.   J Smith, 00 47 22 31 56 10, Fax 00 47 22 31 56 11
W.   23
X.   NONE, NONE

8   The *final report* (FR) is sent:

(a)   When leaving the reporting area.

(b)   On arrival at a port of destination located in the reporting area.

Example:

Name of station to which report must be sent: CANREP – FR

A.   GOLAR STIRLING/9001007

B.   261805Z

C.   2802N01614W

E.   175

F.   16

9   The deviation report (DR) is sent:

(a)   When deviating from the route leading to the originally declared destination, port, terminal, anchorage or position "for orders" given on entry into reporting area.

(b)   When it is necessary to deviate from the planned route owing to weather conditions, damage to equipment or a change in navigational status.

Example:

Name of station to which report must be sent: CANREP – DR

A.   GOLAR STIRLING/9001007

B.   261605Z

C.   2821N01557W

E.   280

F.   14

I.   SANTA CRUZ DE TENERIFE 261645Z

X.   NONE, SATISFACTORY.

Appendix 3

Chartlet

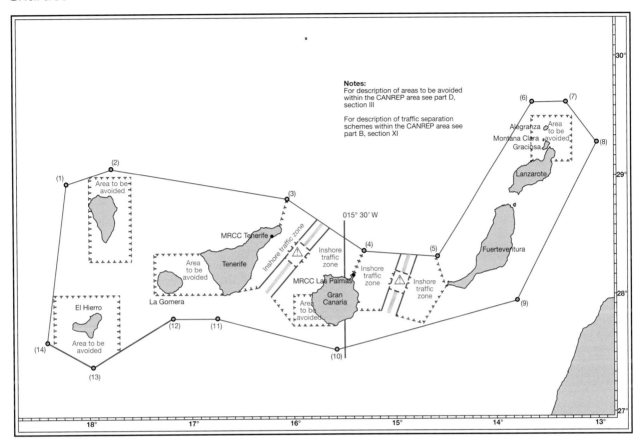

Note: the parts and sections that are mentioned in this chart are in "Ships' Routeing".

Summary of the mandatory ship reporting system for the Canary Islands

1   Types of ship required to participate in the system

1.1   Ships required to take part in the CANREP mandatory reporting system:

Tankers of 600 deadweight tonnage and upwards, either transiting the Canary Islands or sailing to or from Canarian ports or involved in inter-island navigation, carrying the following:

– heavy-grade crude oils with a density greater than 900 kg/m^3 at 15°C;

– heavy fuel oils with a density greater than 900 kg/m^3 at 15°C or kinematic viscosity greater than 180 mm^2/s at 50°C;

– bitumen, coal tar and their emulsions.

2   Geographical position for submitting reports

Ships travelling towards the Canary Island reporting area or leaving it must report:

.1   on entering the reporting area; or

.2   immediately after leaving a port, terminal or anchorage located in the reporting area; or

.3   when deviating from the route leading to the originally declared destination, port, terminal, anchorage or position "for orders" given on entry into the reporting area; or

.4   when it is necessary to deviate from the planned route owing to weather conditions, damaged equipment or a change in navigational status; and

.5   on finally leaving the reporting area.

3   Reference charts

The reference chart is No. 209 of the Spanish Navy Hydrographic Institute (WGS 84 datum).

4   Reporting format

A: Ship's identity (name, call sign, IMO No. and MMSI No.);

B: Date and time;

C: Position;

E: True course;

F: Speed;

G: Name of last port of call;

I: Name of next port of call and estimated time of arrival;

P: Type(s) of cargo, quantity and IMO classification if carrying potentially dangerous goods;

Q: Used in the event of defects or deficiencies that affect normal navigation;

T: Address for communication of information on cargo;

W: Number of people on board;

X: Various particulars relating to tankers:

–   estimated quantity and characteristics of bunker fuel for tankers carrying an amount of it greater than 5,000 tonnes;

–   navigational status (e.g. moving under own propulsion, limited manoeuvrability, etc.).

5   Shore-based authorities to which reports must be sent

5.1   On entering the CANREP reporting area, ships must report the fact to one of the MRCCs listed in appendix 1, according to the following criteria:

(i)   Ships entering the CANREP reporting area at a position east of the meridian of longitude 015°30′ W should notify the Las Palmas MRCC.

(ii)   Ships entering the reporting area at a position west of the meridian of longitude 015°30′ W should notify the Tenerife MRCC.

5.2   On leaving the CANREP reporting area, ships must report the fact to the same MRCC to which they reported on entry.

6   Telecommunications

Reports may be sent cost-free by any means capable of being received by the media indicated in appendix 1.

Annex 14 – Galapagos Archipelago Particularly Sensitive Sea Area

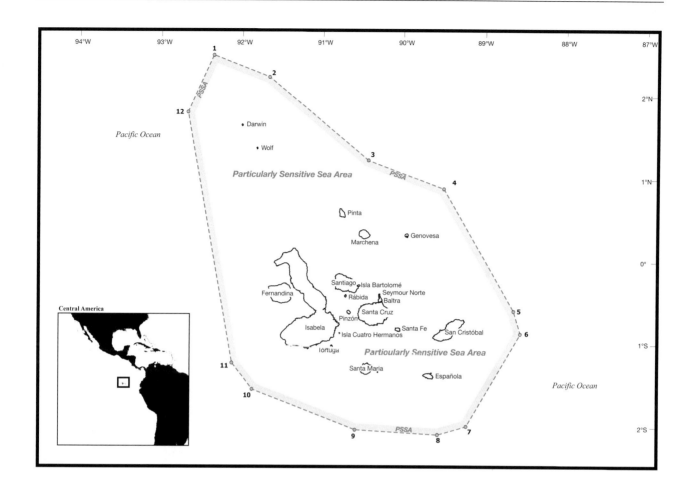

Resolution MEPC.135(53)

adopted on 22 July 2005
Designation of the Galapagos Archipelago as a Particularly Sensitive Sea Area

THE MARINE ENVIRONMENT PROTECTION COMMITTEE,

BEING AWARE of the ecological, social, economic, cultural, scientific and educational value of the Galapagos Archipelago, as well as its vulnerability to damage by international shipping traffic and activities in the area and the steps taken by Ecuador to address that vulnerability,

NOTING that the Guidelines for the Identification and Designation of Particularly Sensitive Sea Areas adopted under resolution A.927(22) set out procedures for the designation of Particularly Sensitive Sea Areas,

HAVING CONSIDERED the proposal from Ecuador to designate the Galapagos Archipelago as a Particularly Sensitive Sea Area,

HAVING AGREED that criteria for identification of a Particularly Sensitive Sea Area provided in resolution A.927(22) are fulfilled for the Galapagos Archipelago,

1   DESIGNATES the Galapagos Archipelago as defined in annexes 1 and 2 to this resolution as a Particularly Sensitive Sea Area; and

2   INVITES Member Governments to note the establishment of the associated protective measure defined in annex 3. The associated protective measure and the date of its entry into force are expected to be adopted by the Assembly at its twenty-fourth session in November/December 2005.

Annex 1

Description of the Galapagos Archipelago Particularly Sensitive Sea Area

1   Description of the area

1.1   The Galapagos Archipelago is a group of islands of volcanic origin, located 502 nautical miles west of the Ecuadorean coast between latitude 02°00′ N, longitude 087°30′ W, and latitude 02°24′ S, longitude 093°30′ W. They are crossed by the Equator line at the Wolf and Ecuador volcanoes on Isabela Island. The total surface area of the Galapagos Islands is 8006 km². The distance from Darwin Island in the North to Española Island in the South is 414 km, and from Pitt Point (San Cristóbal) to Cape Douglas (Fernandina) 268 km. The Archipelago comprises five islands greater than 500 km² (Isabela, Santa Cruz, Fernandina, San Salvador and San Cristóbal); 8 islands between 14 and 173 km² (Santa Maria, Marchena, Genovesa, Española, Pinta, Baltra, Santa Fe and Pinzón); 6 islands between 1 and 5 km² (Rábida, Baltra, Wolf, Tortuga, Bartolomé and Darwin); 42 islets smaller than 1 km², and 26 rocks. The largest island, Isabela, with an area of 4,588 km², is divided in two by the Perry Isthmus, the northern part covering 2,112 km² and the southern 2,476 km². Isabela has the islands' highest point, namely the summit of Wolf Volcano, at 1,707 m.

1.2   The area of the PSSA is defined by a line connecting the following geographical positions:

(1)	02°30′.02 N,	092°21′.27 W
(2)	02°14′.20 N,	091°40′.02 W
(3)	01°14′.15 N,	090°25′.75 W
(4)	00°53′.24 N,	089°30′.03 W
(5)	00°35′.38 S,	088°38′.59 W
(6)	00°52′.00 S,	088°33′.59 W
(7)	01°59′.01 S,	089°12′.87 W
(8)	02°05′.01 S,	089°33′.70 W
(9)	02°01′.43 S,	090°34′.53 W
(10)	01°32′.28 S,	091°51′.89 W
(11)	01°13′.08 S,	092°07′.08 W
(12)	01°48′.88 N,	092°40′.36 W

1.3   A nautical chart showing the PSSA and the area to be avoided is provided in annex 2.

2   Significance of the area

Uniqueness

2.1   The marine and coastal environment of the Galapagos Islands, as well as their terrestrial environment, have very special natural features which are conditioned by the islands' equatorial setting and by their position at the confluence of a complex system of marine currents, whose effects vary in terms of space and time. The geographical isolation and widespread nature of the islands have influenced the distribution and evolution of the species that exist there, creating biogeographic zones.

Dependency

2.2   The marine environment is crucially important to the survival of a large number of land or coastal organisms. Reptiles (sea turtles and the native marine iguanas), mammals (two endemic seal species and a wide variety of cetaceans) and seabirds (Galapagos penguins, albatross, petrels, flightless cormorant, boobies, seagulls, pelicans and frigates, including a surprisingly high number of endemic species) depend not only on the inshore waters but the whole area of the Galapagos marine reserve and beyond, so important are the "bajos", the Equatorial Front, the upwelling zones of the Cromwell Current and the equatorial currents as feeding grounds.

Representativeness

2.3   Around Galapagos there are cold ocean currents, upwelling zones, and water masses of diverse origin, all of them forming a complex system containing bio-elements from tropical and subtropical regions of South America and from the Indo-Pacific biotic region; the islands are thus cordoned off genetically, creating an area of biogeographical diversification. Galapagos is acknowledged as showing biogeographical affinities not only with the tropical and subtropical South American mainland, but also with representative elements of the Peru–Chile and western Pacific biogeographical regions.

Diversity

2.4   The Galapagos marine reserve has high biodiversity. Galapagos is unique, and is one of the few ocean archipelagos in the world that still maintains its ecosystems and biodiversity without interference from human activities. Its mangroves offer a gathering-place for fish, crustacean and mollusc species. There are also nesting grounds for sea and land birds, some of which, such as the mangrove finch, are found nowhere else in the world.

Productivity

2.5   Primary productivity. These values are generally high and comparable with those recorded in the Gulf of Guayaquil, which are associated with the availability of nutrients produced by upwellings in the photic zone. The highest values for chlorophyll concentration were recorded in the West of the Archipelago. The areas of high productivity inside the Archipelago are associated with local upwellings.

Natural character

2.6   The Galapagos Islands are characterized by unspoilt surroundings, leading to conditions of exceptional environmental purity as compared to most of the world's marine areas. The Archipelago has been recognized as a unique group of oceanic islands which still retains most of its terrestrial and marine biodiversity, thanks to a relatively low-key human presence. The tendency observed in the rest of the world is for biological richness to decrease rapidly as human activities increase.

Scientific and educational criteria

2.7   Since island ecosystems, both terrestrial and marine, are less complex than continental ones, they provide researchers with more tangible clues about the adaptation and dispersion of species, especially if they are unspoilt or relatively unchanged. Galapagos has turned itself into one of the most important places to study evolution, biogeography and animal behaviour. The islands and their surroundings are excellent sites for learning about natural processes, and this is combined with a management strategy to show the island inhabitants how to make good use of the limited existing resources and ensure that those natural processes survive in the long term.

3   Vulnerability of the area to damage by international shipping activities

3.1   In the past ten years, the waters of the Galapagos Islands have been polluted by the groundings of three ships: the **Galapagos Explorer**, the **Don Felipe** and the **Jessica**. On 16 January 2001, the tanker **Jessica** was carrying fuel when it ran aground on the shores of San Cristóbal Island, releasing a mixture of diesel fuel and IFO which spread across a considerable part of the marine reserve. Fortunately, the weather conditions were favourable and rapid intervention by the navy, the SPNG and local people, backed by advice from several international organizations, ensured that the impact was less than expected.

3.2   During normal operations and when accidents such as the one just described occur, ships discharge a variety of marine pollutants which directly affect marine biodiversity and the large number of protected species that live on land but rely on the sea for food. These substances are usually oils, harmful liquids, sewage water, garbage of all kinds, paints, foreign organisms and harmful solids.

3.3   On average, two or three international ships per year pass outside the Galapagos marine reserve (at 40 nautical miles) carrying pollutants and radioactive waste. Likewise, general international cargo traffic passes to the north, at approximately 20 nautical miles from Isabela Island, always keeping its distance from the marine reserve, before heading for Panama. If one of these international vessels containing pollutants or radioactive waste were involved in an accident at a geographical location that allowed its cargo to be carried by the marine currents towards the coasts of the Archipelago, particularly to a critical habitat containing sensitive species, the result would be irreparable and major damage.

3.4   The Galapagos Archipelago and its surrounding waters have been declared a national and World Heritage site, recognized worldwide for its scientific and cultural importance.

3.5   The designation of the Galapagos Archipelago as a PSSA will enhance maritime safety, safety of navigation and protection of the marine environment in the area concerned.

Annex 2

Particularly Sensitive Sea Area and area to be avoided chart

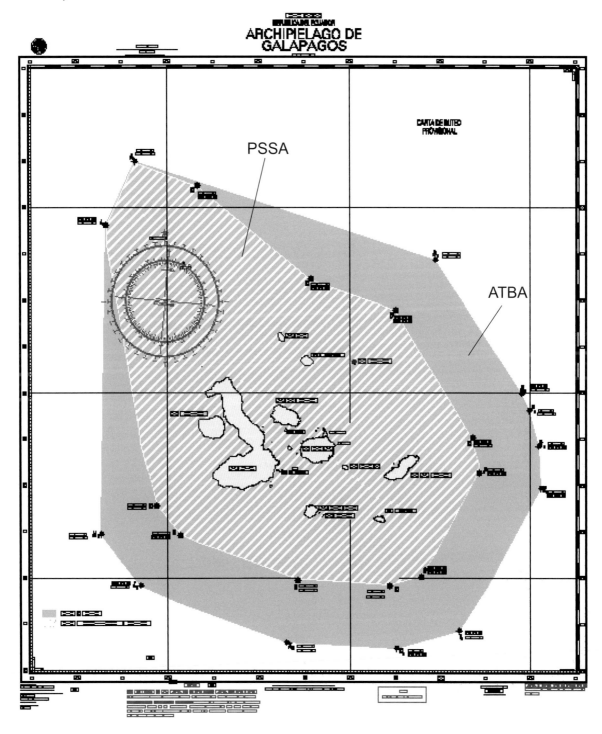

Reference chart I.O.A. 2 (1st Edition, 2003)

Datum: Provisional América del Sur 1956 (La Canoa, Venezuela)

Annex 3

Establishment of Associated Protective Measures in the Galapagos Archipelago Particularly Sensitive Sea Area

An area to be avoided that should be avoided by all ships and barges carrying cargoes of oil or hazardous material and all ships of 500 gross tonnage and above solely in transit was adopted by the twenty-fourth session of Assembly in 2005. A full technical description of the area is in part D of editions of the IMO publication "Ships' Routeing"; only a chartlet of the area is included here.

Area to be avoided in the Galapagos Archipelago

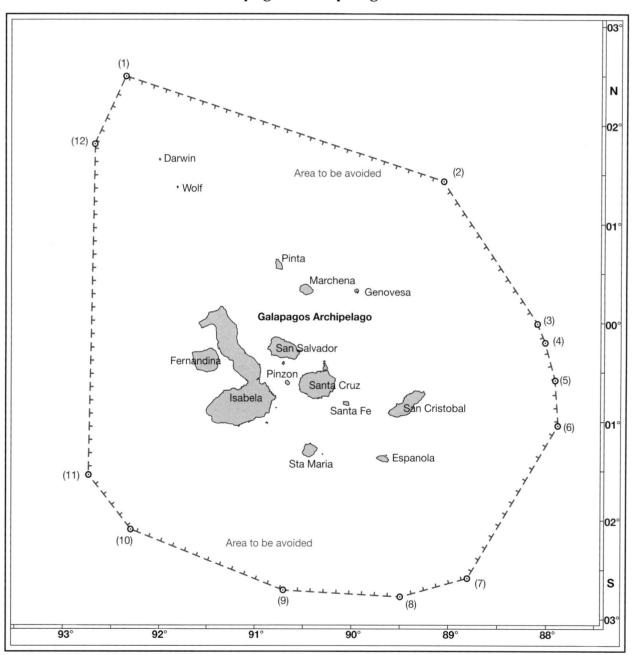

Recommended tracks, which are mandatory as a condition of port entry, through the Galapagos area to be avoided to enter the Particularly Sensitive Sea Area (PSSA) were adopted at the eighty-third session of MSC in 2007. A full technical description of these recommended tracks is in part E of editions of the IMO publication "Ships' Routeing"; only a chartlet of the tracks is included here.

Recommended tracks, which are mandatory as a condition of port entry, through the Galapagos area to be avoided to enter the Particularly Sensitive Sea Area (PSSA)

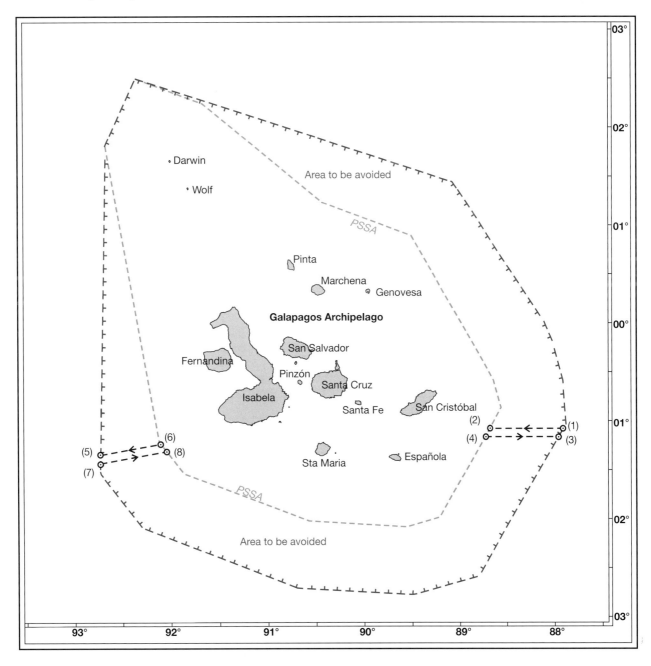

A mandatory ships routeing system in the Galapagos Particularly Sensitive Sea Area was adopted at the eighty-second session of MSC in 2006.

In the Galapagos Particularly Sensitive Sea Area (PSSA) (GALREP)

1   Categories of ships required to participate in the system

All ships are required to participate in the mandatory ship reporting system.

2   Geographical coverage of the system and the number and edition of the reference chart used for delineation of the system

2.1   The operational area of GALREP covers the Galapagos area to be avoided and the Particularly Sensitive Sea Area as shown on the chartlet given in appendix 1.

2.1.1   The co-ordinates of the mandatory ship reporting system are as follows:

Point	Latitude	Longitude
A	02°30′ N	092°21′ W
D1	01°26′ N	089°03′ W
E1	00°01′ S	088°06′ W
F1	00°12′ S	088°01′ W
G1	00°35′ S	087°54′ W
H1	01°02′ S	087°53′ W
I1	02°34′ S	088°48′ W
J1	02°46′ S	089°30′ W
K1	02°42′ S	090°42′ W
L1	02°05′ S	092°18′ W
M1	01°32′ S	092°44′ W
L	01°49′ N	092°40′ W

2.2   The reference chart is I.O.A. 20 (2nd edition 1992, updated and reprinted in 2006), issued by the Ecuadorean Navy Oceanography Institute (INOCAR), based on WGS 84 datum.

3   Format and content of report, times and geographical positions for submitting reports, Authority to whom reports should be sent and available services

3.1   Reports may be sent by any modern means of communication, including Inmarsat-C, telephone, fax and e-mail, and other available means as described in appendix 2.

3.2   Format

3.2.1   The ship report shall be drafted in accordance with the format shown in appendix 3. The information requested from ships is derived from the Standard Reporting Format shown in paragraph 2 of the appendix to IMO resolution A.851(20).

3.3   Content

3.3.1   A full report from a ship should contain the following information:

A: Ship identification (name, call sign, IMO Number, MMSI number or registration number)

B: Date/time group

C: Position

E: True course

F: Speed

G: Name of last port of call

I: Destination and expected time of arrival

P: Type(s) of oil cargo, and quantity, quality and density. If these tankers are also carrying other hazardous material, the type, quantity and IMO classification should be stated, as appropriate.

Q: Used in the event of defects or deficiencies which affect normal navigation

T: Address for communication of information concerning cargo

W: Number of persons on board

X: Miscellaneous information concerning ships:

–   estimated quantity and characteristics of liquid fuel

–   navigational status (e.g. moving under own propulsion, limited manoeuvrability, etc.)

3.3.2   Every reporting message must begin with the word GALREP and include a two-letter prefix to enable identification, i.e. sailing plan "SP", final report "FR" or deviation report "DR". Messages using these prefixes will be cost-free to ships.

3.3.3   The reports must be written in accordance with the following table:

.1   Designators A, B, C, E, F, G, I, P, T, W and X are compulsory for sailing plans;

.2   Designators A, B, C, E and F must be used for final reports;

.3   Designators A, B, C, E, F and I must be used for deviation reports; and

.4   Designator Q is included whenever a problem arises in the reporting area, whether defects, damage, deficiencies or circumstances that affect normal navigation in the reporting area.

3.4   Geographical positions for submitting reports

3.4.1   A ship must give a full report at the following positions:

.1   on entering the reporting area;

.2   immediately after leaving a port or anchorage located in the Galapagos PSSA (the co-ordinates of which are at appendix 4);

.3   when deviating from the route leading to the port of destination or anchorage reported originally;

.4   when it is necessary to deviate from the planned route owing to weather conditions, damaged equipment or a change in navigational status; and

.5   on finally leaving the reporting area.

3.5 Authority

3.5.1   On entering the GALREP mandatory reporting area, ships must send a message to notify the Santa Cruz Maritime Rescue Sub-Centre via Puerto Ayora Radio or Baquerizo Moreno Radio. The Maritime Rescue Sub-Centres and coastal radio stations to which reports must be sent are shown in appendix 2.

3.5.2   If a ship is not able to send a message to Puerto Ayora Radio, it must send one to Baquerizo Moreno Radio, in accordance with the information given in appendix 2.

4   Information to be provided to ships and procedures to be followed

4.1   Ships are required to keep a continuous listening watch in the area.

4.2   The Puerto Ayora Maritime Rescue Sub-Centre will provide ships with the information necessary for safe navigation in the reporting area as required, using the radio transmission resources available in the area.

4.3   If necessary, a specific ship may be informed individually about particular local weather conditions.

5   Communication required for the system, frequencies on which reports should be transmitted and information reported

5.1   Radiocommunications required for the system is as follows:

The reports can be made by any modern means of communication, including Inmarsat-C, telephone, fax, and e-mail, and other available means as described in appendix 2.

5.2   Information of commercial confidential nature may be transmitted by non-verbal means.

5.3   The languages of communication used in this system are Spanish or English, using IMO Standard Marine Communication Phrases, where necessary.

6   Rules and regulations in force in the area of the system

6.1   Vessel Traffic Services (VTS)

Vessel traffic services are available at Puerto Ayora through Puerto Ayora Radio, which provides information for shipping in the Galapagos Particularly Sensitive Sea Area.

6.2   SAR Plan

6.2.1   The national maritime SAR plan establishes the Coast Guard Command as the Maritime Rescue Co-ordination Centre and DIGMER as the SAR co-ordination centre, with its headquarters under the supervision of the Director General for the Merchant Marine. The Galapagos PSSA comes under the jurisdiction of the Galapagos Archipelago administrative area, at the SAR co-ordination sub-centre for the island region, which is responsible for deploying Coast Guard units operating in that area.

6.2.2   The National Maritime Authority is responsible for prevention and control of pollution produced by oil and other harmful substances in Ecuador's waters and along its coasts. Given the extent of the damage that can be caused by oil spills, there is a national contingency plan to deal with them, whether at sea or along the coasts or rivers. The plan covers the mainland waters, the Galapagos island waters and the rivers of the western region. With regards to planning, implementation and control, geographical areas have been established corresponding to the maritime section of the island region, which includes the Galapagos PSSA, under the responsibility of the island naval operations command in co-ordination with the harbour masters' offices at Puerto Ayora, Puerto Baquerizo Moreno, Puerto Villamil and Seymour, and supported by the fleet air arm, the coast guard and the Galapagos National Park.

7 Shore-based facilities to support the operation of the system

7.1 System capability

7.1.1 The VTS, Maritime Rescue Sub-Centres, and coastal radio stations are shown in appendix 2; all have skilled personnel constantly on duty.

7.1.2 The accepted means of radiocommunication that are available are listed in appendix 2.

8 Information concerning the applicable procedures if the communication facilities of shore-based Authority fail

If a ship is not able to send a message to Puerto Ayora Radio, it must send one to Baquerizo Moreno Radio, in accordance with the information given in appendix 2.

9 Measures to be taken if a ship fails to comply with the requirements of the system

If a ship in breach of the mandatory ship reporting system can be identified, any enforcement actions taken shall not be incompatible with international law.

Appendix 1

Chart of area covered by the mandatory ship reporting system

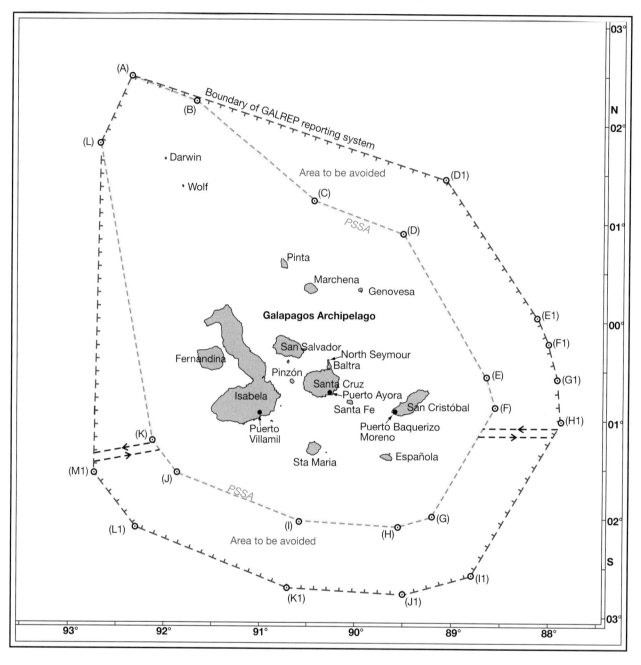

Appendix 2

Vessel traffic services, maritime rescue sub-centres, coastal radio stations and other establishments to which reports must be sent

Ecuador – Galapagos Islands

Santa Cruz: Puerto Ayora Radio

Name: HCY
Geographical co-ordinates: 00°44'.59 S, 090°28'.29 W
MRSC – SAR Puerto Ayora: 00°44'.59 S, 090°28'.29 W

Tel.:   +593 5 2527473
Fax: +593 5 2527473
E-mail: ayoraradio@islasantacruz.com

Inmarsat-C: 473575713

Inmarsat Mini-M:
Voice: 761609548
Fax: 761609549
Data: 761609550

VHF channels:

156.800 MHz	H-24	SIMPLEX	C-16
156.525 MHz	H-24	SIMPLEX	C-70

MF channels:

4125.0 kHz	H-24	SIMPLEX	C-421
2182.0 kHz	H-24	SIMPLEX	
2187.5 kHz	H-24	DSC SIMPLEX	

MMSI: 007354757.

Puerto Baquerizo Moreno: Baquerizo Moreno Radio

Name: HCW
Geographical co-ordinates: 00°54' S, 089°37' W
MRSC – SAR Puerto Baquerizo Moreno: 00°54' S, 089°37' W

Tel.:   +593 5 2520346
Fax: +593 5 2520346
E-mail: capbaq@digmer.org

VHF channels:

156.800 MHz	H-24	SIMPLEX	C-16
156.525 MHz	H-24	SIMPLEX	C-70

MF channels:

4125.0 kHz	H-24	SIMPLEX	C-421
2182.0 kHz	H-24	SIMPLEX	
2187.5 kHz	H-24	DSC SIMPLEX	

MMSI: 007350090

Appendix 3

Designator	Function	Text
System name	Code word	GALREP
	Type of report: Sailing plan Final report Deviation report	One of the following 2-letter identifiers: SP FR (on *finally* leaving reporting area) to include only **A**, **B**, **C**, **E** and **F**. DR to include only **A**, **B**, **C**, **E**, **F** and **I**.
A	Ship	Name and call sign (Name of ship, call sign, IMO No. and MMSI No.) (e.g. TAURUS/HC4019/T-04-0561)
B	Date and time corresponding to position at C, expressed as UTC	A six-digit group followed by a Z. The first two digits indicate day of the month, the second two the hours and the last two the minutes. The Z indicates that the time is given in UTC (e.g. 081340Z).
C	Position (latitude and longitude)	A 4-digit group giving latitude in degrees and minutes, with the suffix N or S, and a 5-digit group giving longitude in degrees and minutes, with the suffix W (e.g. 0030S 08805W)
E	Course	True course. A 3-digit group (e.g. 270).
F	Speed	Speed in knots. A 2-digit group (e.g. 14).
G	Name of last port of call	Name of the last port of call (e.g. Guayaquil)
I	Destination and ETA (UTC)	Name of destination and date and time group as expressed in B (e.g. Puerto Ayora 082200Z)
P	Cargo	Type(s) of oil cargo, quantity, quality and density of heavy crude, heavy fuel, asphalt and coal tar. If the ships are carrying other potentially hazardous cargoes, indicate type, quantity and IMO classification (e.g. 10,000 TN DIESEL OIL).
Q	Defects, damage, deficiencies, limitations.	Brief details of defects, including damage, deficiencies and other circumstances that impair normal navigation
T	Address for the communication of cargo information	Name, telephone number, and either fax or e-mail
W	Total number of people on board	State how many
X	Miscellaneous	Miscellaneous information concerning these ships: – Characteristics and approximate quantity of bunker fuel for tankers carrying an amount of it greater than 5000 tonnes. – Navigational status (e.g. at anchor, moving under own propulsion, no steering, limited manoeuvrability, depth restriction, moored, aground, etc.)

Appendix 4

Particularly Sensitive Sea Area (PSSA)

Point	Latitude	Longitude
A	02°30′ N	092°21′ W
B	02°14′ N	091°40′ W
C	01°14′ N	090°26′ W
D	00°53′ N	089°30′ W
E	00°35′ S	088°38′ W
F	00°52′ S	088°34′ W
G	01°59′ S	089°13′ W
H	02°05′ S	089°34′ W
I	02°01′ S	090°35′ W
J	01°32′ S	091°52′ W
K	01°13′ S	092°07′ W
L	01°49′ N	092°40′ W

Annex 15 – Baltic Sea Area Particularly Sensitive Sea Area

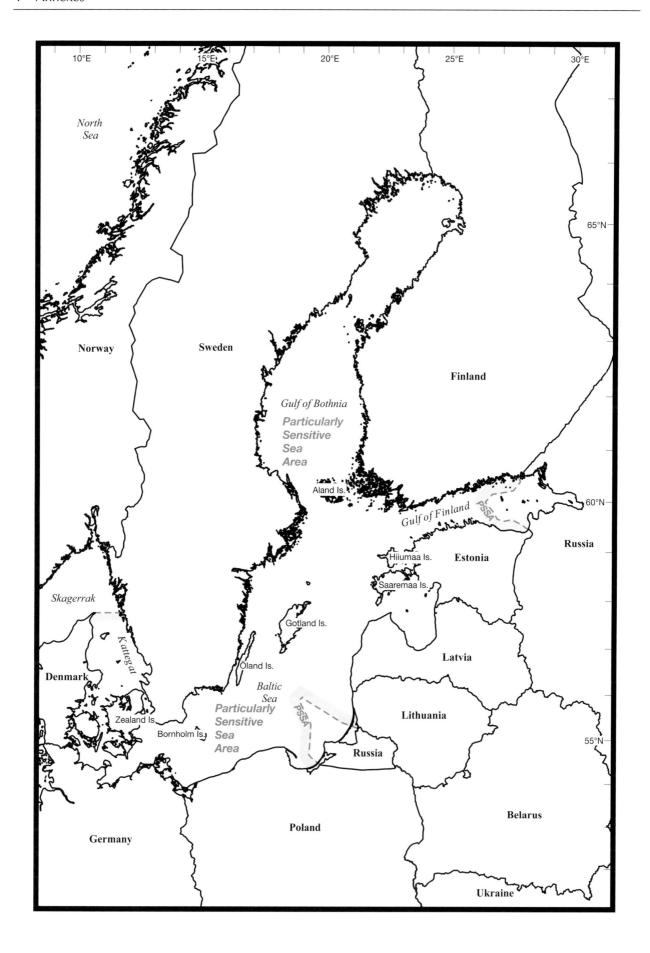

Resolution MEPC.136(53)

adopted on 22 July 2005

Designation of the Baltic Sea Area as a Particularly Sensitive Sea Area

THE MARINE ENVIRONMENT PROTECTION COMMITTEE,

BEING AWARE of the ecological, social, economic, cultural, scientific and educational value of the Baltic Sea Area, as well as its vulnerability to damage by international shipping traffic and activities in the area and the steps taken by Denmark, Estonia, Finland, Germany, Latvia, Lithuania, Poland and Sweden to address that vulnerability,

NOTING that the Guidelines for the Identification and Designation of Particularly Sensitive Sea Areas adopted under resolution A.927(22) set out procedures for the designation of Particularly Sensitive Sea Areas,

HAVING CONSIDERED the proposal from Denmark, Estonia, Finland, Germany, Latvia, Lithuania, Poland and Sweden to designate the Baltic Sea Area (as defined in paragraph 1.1 of annex 1 to this resolution) as a Particularly Sensitive Sea Area,

HAVING AGREED that criteria for identification of a Particularly Sensitive Sea Area provided in resolution A.927(22) are fulfilled for the Baltic Sea Area (as defined in paragraph 1.1 of annex 1 to this resolution),

1   DESIGNATES the Baltic Sea Area as defined in paragraph 1.1 of annex 1 to this resolution as a Particularly Sensitive Sea Area; and

2   INVITES Member Governments to note the establishment of associated protective measures defined in annex 2. The associated protective measures and their dates of entry into force are expected to be adopted by the Assembly at its twenty-fourth session in November/December 2005.

Annex 1

Description of the Baltic Sea Area Particularly Sensitive Sea Area

1 Description of the area

1.1 The Baltic Sea Area PSSA comprises the Baltic Sea proper, the Gulf of Bothnia, the Gulf of Finland and the entrance to the Baltic Sea bounded by the parallel of the Skaw in the Skagerrak at 57°44′.8 N, as defined in regulation 10(1)(b) of Annex I of MARPOL 73/78, excluding those marine areas within the sovereignty of the Russian Federation, or subject to the sovereign rights and jurisdiction of the Russian Federation as referred to in Article 56 of the United Nations Convention on the Law of the Sea. The designation of the Baltic Sea Area PSSA shall not prejudice the sovereignty or such sovereign rights and jurisdiction of the Russian Federation under international law.

2 Significance of the area

2.1 The Baltic Sea Area is a globally unique and sensitive brackish-water ecosystem. It is geologically young, semi-enclosed and shallow. The exchange of water with the North Sea is limited and slow, resulting in long residence time of water as well as low and varying levels of salinity. The climate ranges from sub-arctic to temperate and large parts of the Baltic Sea are annually ice-covered. All these factors have resulted in a marine environment with low biodiversity. Despite the low number of marine species, the area hosts a unique mix of marine, freshwater and a few true brackish-water species. The Baltic marine and coastal areas consist of globally important breeding grounds, nurseries, shelters and food sources for coastal birds and waterfowl. The diversity of coastal biotopes is high and characterized by many threatened aquatic and terrestrial species. The disappearance of single key species could seriously impede the functioning of the whole system. Hence, the Baltic marine ecosystem is considered as particularly vulnerable to man-made disturbances.

2.2 The Baltic Sea Area PSSA is vulnerable to damage by international shipping activities. The Baltic Sea Area has some of the densest maritime traffic in the world. During recent decades the traffic in the area has not only increased but the nature of the traffic has also changed rapidly. One tendency is the increase in the transportation of oil and other harmful substances by ships, which also increases the potential for water pollution. A spill could have disastrous effects on the vulnerable nature of the area such as fish spawning areas and breeding, nursery and resting areas for birds and marine mammals.

2.3 More than 2,000 ships are en route in the area on an average day, not including ferries, smaller fishing vessels or leisure craft. Of these 2,000 ships around 200 are oil tankers, some carrying a cargo of 150,000 tons.

Annex 2

Associated Protective Measures

A   Traffic separation schemes and associated routeing measures in SW Baltic Sea

The traffic separation schemes "In Bornholmsgat" and "North of Rügen" and amendments to the traffic separation schemes "Off Gotland Island" and "South of Gedser" were adopted at the twenty-fourth session of Assembly in 2005, coinciding with the designation of this PSSA. Full technical descriptions of the traffic separation schemes and their associated precautionary areas and inshore traffic zones are in part B of editions of the IMO publication "Ships' Routeing"; only chartlets of these schemes are included here. The traffic separation scheme "Off Gotland Island" was renamed "North Hoburgs Bank" at the eighty-seventh session of MSC in 2010. Many other traffic separation schemes had been established in the Baltic Sea and in the Kattegat, Sound and Belts before the designation of the PSSA, and others have subsequently been established. These other traffic separation schemes are "Off Kalbådagrund lighthouse", "Off Porkkala lighthouse", "Off Hankoniemi Peninsula", "Off Kõpu Peninsula (Hiiumaa Island)", "South Hoburgs Bank", "Midsjöbankarna", "In Norra Kvarken", "The Åland Sea", "West Klintehamn", "Off Öland Island", "On the approaches to the Polish ports in the Gulf of Gdańsk", "Słupska Bank", "Adlergrund", "Off Falsterborev", "In The Sound", "Off Kiel lighthouse", "Between Korsoer and Sprogoe" and "At Hatter Barn". Full technical details and illustrative chartlets for all of these are in part B of editions of the IMO publication "Ships' Routeing". The sections and parts that are mentioned on these chartlets are in "Ships' Routeing".

In Bornholmsgat

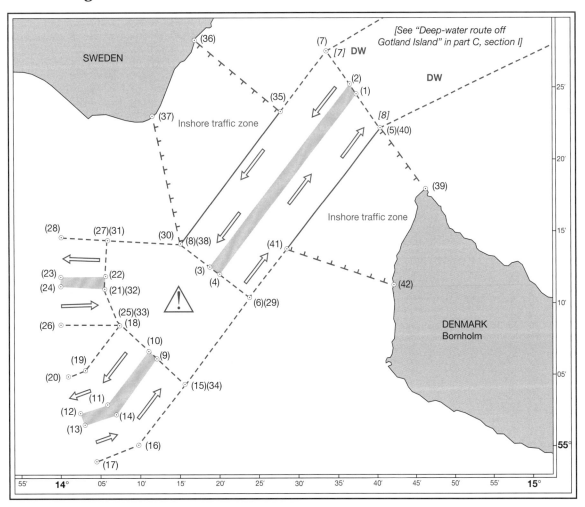

North of Rügen

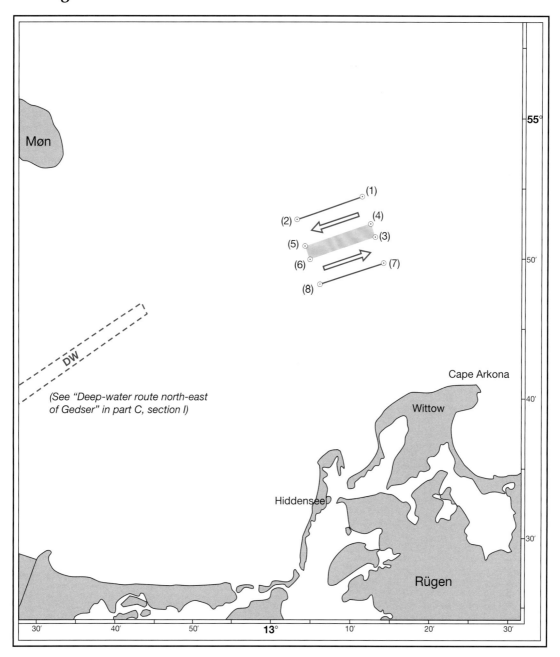

Off Gotland Island (later named "North Hoburgs Bank")

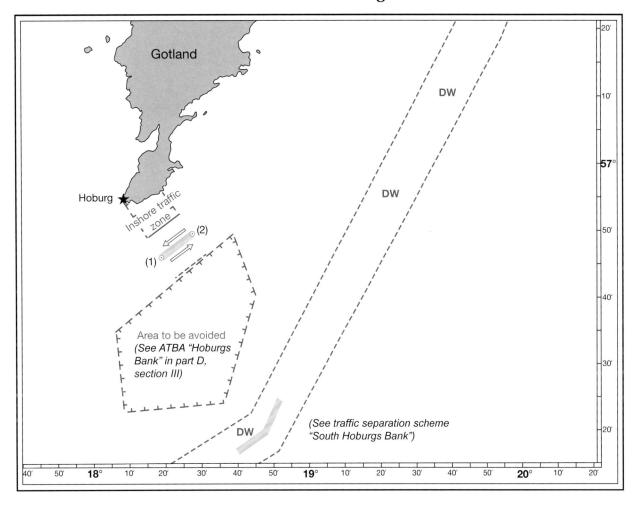

South of Gedser

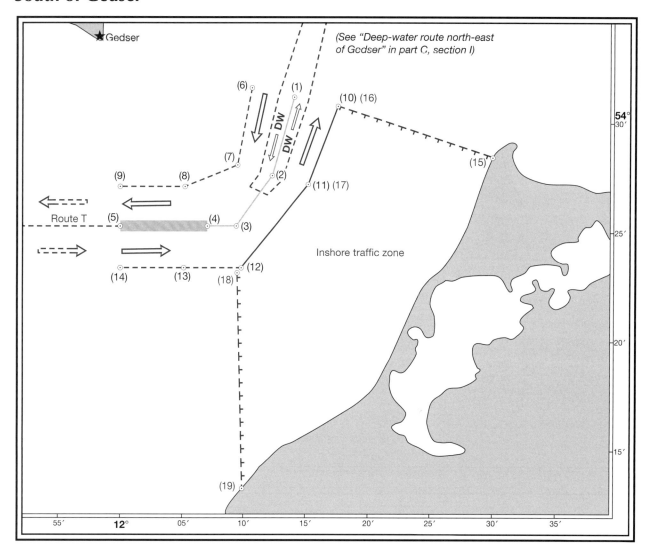

B   Deep-water route off Gotland Island

A deep-water route "Off Gotland Island" was adopted at the twenty-fourth session of Assembly in 2005. A full technical description of this deep-water route is in part C of editions of the IMO publication "Ships' Routeing"; only a chartlet of the route is included here. Other deep-water routes had been established in the Baltic Sea and in the Kattegat, Sound and Belts before the designation of the PSSA, and others have subsequently been established. These other deep-water routes are "Recommendation on navigation through the entrances to the Baltic Sea", "Deep-water route between Hatter Rev and Hatter Barn", "Deep-water route off the east coast of Langeland", "Deep-water route north-east of Gedser", "Deep-water route inside the borders of the "North Åland Sea" traffic separation scheme" and "Deep-water route inside the borders of the "South Åland Sea" traffic separation scheme". Full technical details and illustrative chartlets for all of these are in part C of editions of the IMO publication "Ships' Routeing".

Deep-water route off Gotland Island

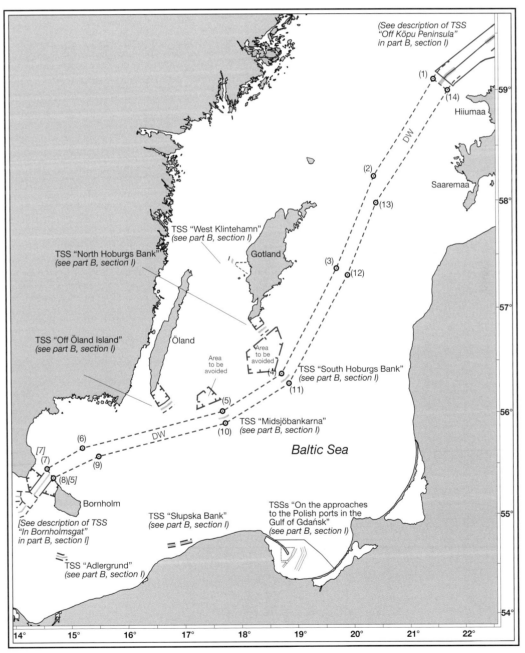

C   Areas to be avoided in the southern Baltic Sea south of the Island of Gotland

The areas to be avoided "Hoburgs Bank" and "Norra Midsjöbanken" were adopted at the twenty-fourth session of Assembly in 2005. All vessels with a gross tonnage of 500 or more should avoid the areas. Full technical descriptions of the areas to be avoided are in part D of editions of the IMO publication "Ships' Routeing"; only chartlets of the areas are included here.

In the southern Baltic Sea south of the Island of Gotland: Hoburgs Bank

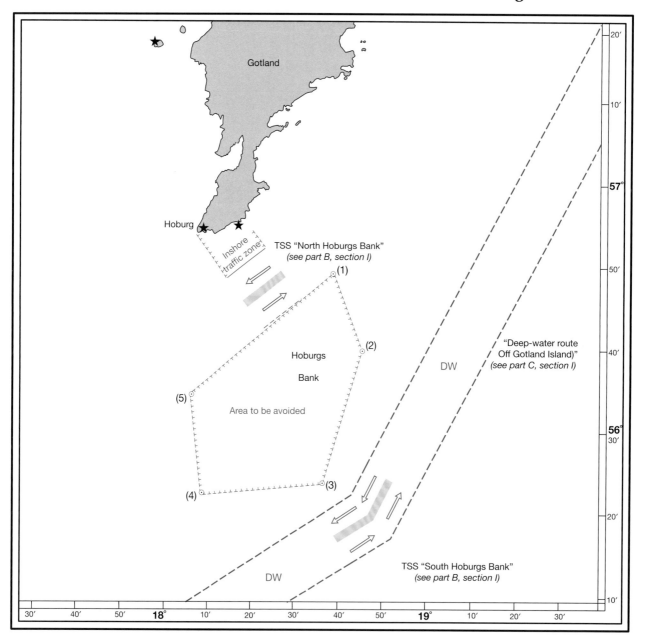

In the southern Baltic Sea south of the Island of Gotland: Norra Midsjöbanken

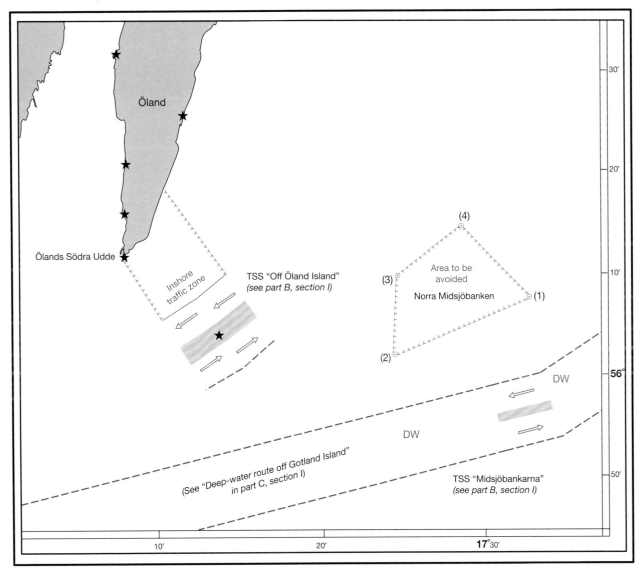

Other routeing measures or protective measures within the area of the Baltic Sea PSSA include "Recommended directions of traffic flow in the precautionary area of the separation scheme "Off Porkkala lighthouse"", "Two-way routes "In Norra Kvarken"", "Recommended two-way route leading to the Åland Sea", "Two-way route "Salvorev", north of Gotland Island", "Recommended tracks in the approaches to the Polish ports in the Gulf of Gdańsk", "Recommendations on navigation through the Gulf of Finland Traffic area", "Recommendations on navigation to the Polish ports through the Gulf of Gdańsk Traffic area" and the mandatory ship reporting systems "In the Gulf of Finland", "On the approaches to the Polish ports in the Gulf of Gdańsk", "In The Sound between Denmark and Sweden" and "In the Storebælt (Great Belt) Traffic area". Full technical details and illustrative chartlets for all of these are in parts E, F and G of editions of the IMO publication "Ships' Routeing".

Annex 16 – Papahānaumokuākea Marine National Monument Particularly Sensitive Sea Area

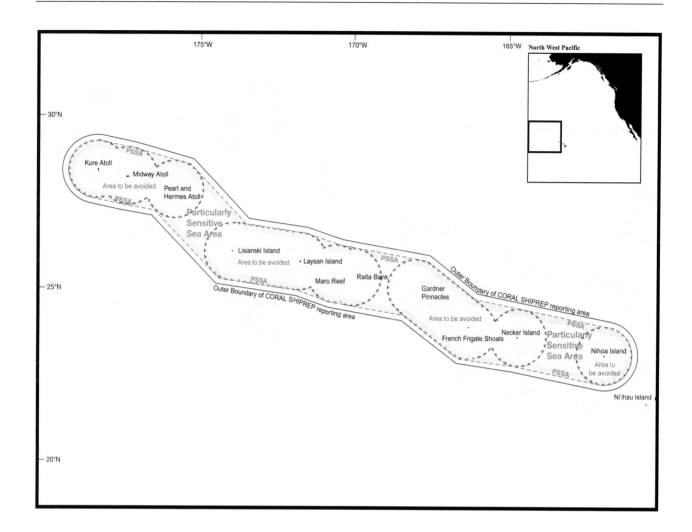

Resolution MEPC.171(57)

adopted on 4 April 2008

Designation of the Papahānaumokuākea Marine National Monument as a Particularly Sensitive Sea Area

THE MARINE ENVIRONMENT PROTECTION COMMITTEE,

BEING AWARE of the ecological, socio-economic and scientific attributes of the Papahānaumokuākea Marine National Monument, as well as its vulnerability to damage by international shipping activities and the steps taken by the United States to address that vulnerability,

NOTING the Revised Guidelines for the Identification and Designation of Particularly Sensitive Sea Areas adopted by resolution A.982(24) (PSSA Guidelines) and the Revised Guidance Document for Submission of PSSA Proposals to IMO set forth in MEPC/Circ.510,

HAVING CONSIDERED the proposal made by the Government of the United States that the Papahānaumokuākea Marine National Monument be designated as a Particularly Sensitive Sea Area,

HAVING AGREED that the criteria for the identification and designation of a Particularly Sensitive Sea Area provided in resolution A.982(24) are fulfilled for the Papahānaumokuākea Marine National Monument,

HAVING NOTED that the Maritime Safety Committee, at its eighty-third session, in considering the necessary associated protective measures, adopted new and amended routeing measures, as well as a new ship reporting system applicable to the proposed Particularly Sensitive Sea Area,

1   DESIGNATES the Papahānaumokuākea Marine National Monument described in annex 1 as a Particularly Sensitive Sea Area;

2   INVITES Member Governments to recognize the ecological, socio-economic, and scientific attributes of the area, set forth in annex 2, as well as its vulnerability to damage by international shipping activities, as described in annex 3; and

3   FURTHER INVITES Member Governments to note the associated protective measures established to address the area's vulnerability, the details of which are contained in annex 4, and request ships flying their flag that they act in accordance with such measures.

Annex 1

Description of the Papahānaumokuākea Marine National Monument PSSA

(Reference chart: United States 19016, 2007 edition; 19019, 2007 edition; 19022, 2007 edition. These charts are based on World Geodetic System 1984 and astronomic datum.)

Description of the Particularly Sensitive Sea Area for the Papahānaumokuākea Marine National Monument

To avoid the risk of damage from ship groundings and pollution damage by international shipping activities and the destruction and degradation of this unique, fragile, and pristine coral reef ecosystem, as well as of significant cultural and archaeological resources, mariners should exercise extreme care when navigating in the area bounded by a line connecting the following geographical positions which is designated as a Particularly Sensitive Sea Area:

Point	Latitude	Longitude
1	28°26'.24 N	175°10'.65 W
2	28°16'.07 N	175°00'.00 W
3	26°50'.89 N	173°30'.79 W
4	26°36'.00 N	171°37'.70 W
5	26°35'.49 N	171°33'.84 W
6	26°35'.09 N	171°30'.84 W
7	26°34'.07 N	171°27'.50 W
8	26°33'.35 N	171°25'.16 W
9	26°14'.25 N	170°23'.04 W
10	25°50'.55 N	167°57'.88 W
11	25°48'.99 N	167°48'.35 W
12	25°47'.09 N	167°36'.72 W
13	25°39'.84 N	167°26'.48 W
14	25°35'.10 N	167°19'.79 W
15	25°10'.43 N	166°45'.00 W
16	24°40'.91 N	166°03'.36 W
17	24°35'.64 N	165°34'.99 W
18	24°23'.98 N	164°32'.24 W
19	23°52'.82 N	161°44'.54 W
20	23°52'.10 N	161°41'.20 W
21	23°51'.18 N	161°37'.92 W
22	23°50'.08 N	161°34'.71 W
23	23°48'.79 N	161°31'.58 W
24	23°47'.33 N	161°28'.55 W
25	23°45'.69 N	161°25'.62 W
26	23°43'.88 N	161°22'.81 W
27	23°41'.92 N	161°20'.13 W
28	23°39'.80 N	161°17'.60 W
29	23°37'.54 N	161°15'.21 W
30	23°35'.14 N	161°12'.99 W
31	23°32'.62 N	161°10'.93 W
32	23°29'.99 N	161°09'.05 W

Point	Latitude	Longitude
33	23°27'.25 N	161°07'.35 W
34	23°24'.42 N	161°05'.85 W
35	23°21'.51 N	161°04'.54 W
36	23°18'.52 N	161°03'.43 W
37	23°15'.48 N	161°02'.53 W
38	23°12'.39 N	161°01'.84 W
39	23°09'.27 N	161°01'.35 W
40	23°06'.13 N	161°01'.09 W
41	23°02'.97 N	161°01'.03 W
42	22°59'.82 N	161°01'.19 W
43	22°56'.69 N	161°01'.57 W
44	22°53'.58 N	161°02'.15 W
45	22°50'.51 N	161°02'.95 W
46	22°47'.50 N	161°03'.95 W
47	22°44'.55 N	161°05'.15 W
48	22°41'.67 N	161°06'.54 W
49	22°38'.88 N	161°08'.13 W
50	22°36'.19 N	161°09'.90 W
51	22°33'.61 N	161°11'.85 W
52	22°31'.14 N	161°13'.97 W
53	22°28'.81 N	161°16'.25 W
54	22°26'.61 N	161°18'.69 W
55	22°24'.56 N	161°21'.26 W
56	22°22'.66 N	161°23'.97 W
57	22°20'.92 N	161°26'.80 W
58	22°19'.35 N	161°29'.74 W
59	22°17'.95 N	161°32'.78 W
60	22°16'.73 N	161°35'.90 W
61	22°15'.70 N	161°39'.10 W
62	22°14'.85 N	161°42'.37 W
63	22°14'.20 N	161°45'.68 W
64	22°13'.73 N	161°49'.03 W

Point	Latitude	Longitude
65	22°13'.47 N	161°52'.41 W
66	22°13'.40 N	161°55'.80 W
67	22°13'.53 N	161°59'.18 W
68	22°13'.85 N	162°02'.55 W
69	22°14'.31 N	162°05'.45 W
70	22°14'.37 N	162°05'.89 W
71	22°45'.18 N	164°51'.62 W
72	22°50'.26 N	165°34'.99 W
73	22°55'.50 N	166°19'.63 W
74	22°55'.93 N	166°23'.32 W
75	22°57'.41 N	166°36'.00 W
76	23°03'.75 N	166°45'.00 W
77	23°05'.48 N	166°47'.45 W
78	24°12'.69 N	168°22'.84 W
79	24°12'.69 N	168°22'.84 W
80	24°12'.70 N	168°22'.86 W
81	24°35'.77 N	170°44'.39 W
82	24°36'.29 N	170°47'.58 W
83	24°37'.18 N	170°50'.37 W
84	24°37'.76 N	170°52'.17 W
85	24°56'.23 N	171°50'.19 W
86	25°16'.61 N	174°24'.84 W
87	25°49'.84 N	175°00'.00 W
88	27°14'.76 N	176°29'.87 W
89	27°24'.95 N	177°33'.31 W
90	27°35'.87 N	178°29'.90 W
91	27°36'.64 N	178°33'.93 W
92	27°37'.53 N	178°37'.32 W
93	27°38'.60 N	178°40'.65 W
94	27°39'.85 N	178°43'.90 W
95	27°41'.28 N	178°47'.05 W
96	27°42'.89 N	178°50'.10 W
97	27°44'.66 N	178°53'.03 W
98	27°46'.59 N	178°55'.83 W
99	27°48'.67 N	178°58'.49 W
100	27°50'.89 N	179°01'.00 W
101	27°53'.25 N	179°03'.35 W
102	27°55'.74 N	179°05'.54 W
103	27°58'.34 N	179°07'.54 W
104	28°01'.05 N	179°09'.35 W
105	28°03'.85 N	179°10'.98 W
106	28°06'.74 N	179°12'.40 W

Point	Latitude	Longitude
107	28°09'.71 N	179°13'.61 W
108	28°12'.73 N	179°14'.62 W
109	28°15'.80 N	179°15'.41 W
110	28°18'.91 N	179°15'.98 W
111	28°22'.05 N	179°16'.33 W
112	28°24'.72 N	179°16'.44 W
113	28°25'.20 N	179°16'.45 W
114	28°25'.82 N	179°16'.44 W
115	28°28'.35 N	179°16'.36 W
116	28°31'.49 N	179°16'.03 W
117	28°34'.60 N	179°15'.49 W
118	28°37'.68 N	179°14'.72 W
119	28°40'.71 N	179°13'.74 W
120	28°43'.68 N	179°12'.54 W
121	28°46'.58 N	179°11'.13 W
122	28°49'.39 N	179°09'.52 W
123	28°52'.11 N	179°07'.70 W
124	28°54'.72 N	179°05'.70 W
125	28°57'.21 N	179°03'.51 W
126	28°59'.58 N	179°01'.15 W
127	29°01'.81 N	178°58'.62 W
128	29°03'.90 N	178°55'.93 W
129	29°05'.83 N	178°53'.10 W
130	29°07'.60 N	178°50'.13 W
131	29°09'.21 N	178°47'.04 W
132	29°10'.64 N	178°43'.84 W
133	29°11'.89 N	178°40'.54 W
134	29°12'.95 N	178°37'.16 W
135	29°13'.82 N	178°33'.71 W
136	29°14'.50 N	178°30'.21 W
137	29°14'.99 N	178°26'.66 W
138	29°15'.28 N	178°23'.08 W
139	29°15'.36 N	178°19'.49 W
140	29°15'.25 N	178°15'.90 W
141	29°14'.94 N	178°12'.32 W
142	29°14'.43 N	178°08'.78 W
143	29°03'.47 N	177°12'.07 W
144	29°02'.55 N	177°07'.29 W
145	28°38'.96 N	175°35'.47 W
146	28°38'.67 N	175°34'.35 W
147	28°34'.91 N	175°19'.74 W
148	28°26'.24 N	175°10'.65 W

Chartlet

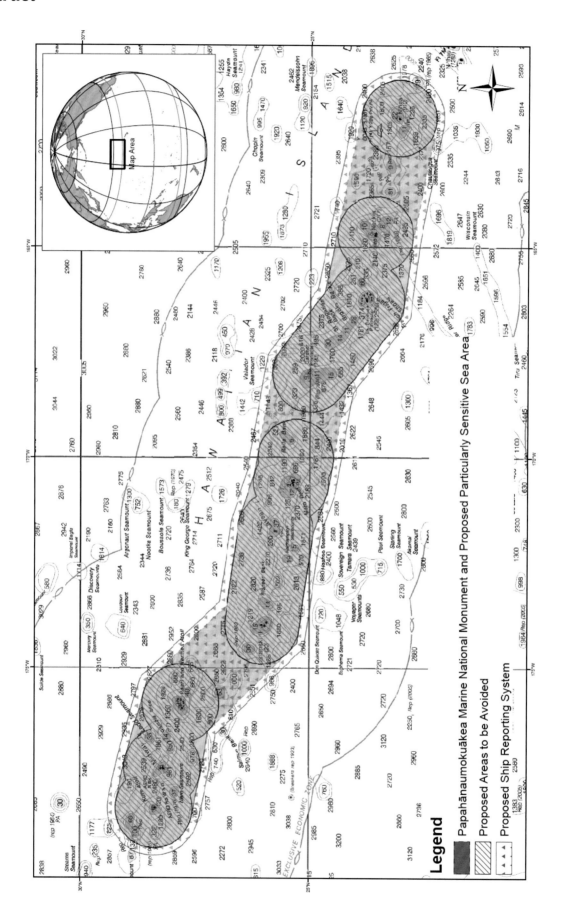

Annex 2

Ecological, socio-economic, and scientific attributes of the Papahānaumokuākea Marine National Monument PSSA

1   Ecological criteria

1.1   Uniqueness or rarity

1.1.1   The Papahānaumokuākea Marine National Monument (North-western Hawaiian Islands or NWHI) supports a unique, dynamic coral reef ecosystem, which, thanks to its relative isolation, is among the healthiest in the world (Citizen's Guide 2006). It is one of the last remaining large-scale wilderness coral reef ecosystems on the planet and the largest coral reef ecosystem in the marginal tropical seas (Cousteau 2003). Approximately one-quarter of the species found in the NWHI are endemic to the Hawaiian Island chain, which is one of the highest rates of marine endemism in the world (Friedlander et al. 2005; Citizen's Guide 2006). The proportion of scientifically non-described coral reef species (e.g. sponges, corals, algae, and other invertebrates) in this area is one of the highest in the world (Cousteau 2003). The NWHI also contain important breeding and nesting grounds for a number of species, many of which are at risk, including the critically endangered Hawaiian monk seal, the threatened green sea turtle, and 19 species of seabirds (Henderson 2001; NOAA 2004; Citizen's Guide 2006).

1.1.2   The uniqueness of this area was expressed in 2003 by ocean explorer Jean-Michel Cousteau in his *Voyage to Kure* expedition log: "These islands are a celebration of the uniqueness brought on by isolation. Along this ribbon of life, we found teeming populations of spinner dolphins and large apex predators such as reef sharks, jacks, and groupers. We encountered many of the Hawaiian endemic species of reef fish, including the rare masked angelfish and Hawaiian grouper; all perfect reminders of an intact coral reef ecosystem" (Cousteau 2003).

1.2   Critical habitat

1.2.1   Parts of the proposed area provide critical habitat for a variety of endangered or threatened species that are protected under various United States domestic laws. These species include the critically endangered Hawaiian monk seal; the endangered sperm whale; the endangered hawksbill, leatherback, and green sea turtles; the endangered short-tailed albatross; six endangered plant species; and four endangered land birds: the Nihoa finch, Nihoa millerbird, Laysan finch, and Laysan Duck, the world's rarest duck. Of these species, seven are listed in Appendix I of the Convention on Trade in Endangered Species of Wild Flora and Fauna (CITES) and nine are listed on the World Conservation Union (IUCN) Red List of Threatened Species (including three with "critically endangered" status).

1.3   Dependency

1.3.1   The ecological processes of the NWHI ecosystem are dependent on the health of its vast, diverse coral reef tracts. Often called the "rainforests" of the sea, coral reefs are vital to maintaining the biological diversity of the oceans (Citizen's Guide 2006). The pristine coral reefs of the NWHI are the foundation of a symbiotic community composed of countless millions of plants and animals dependent upon one another for survival (Citizen's Guide 2006). These reefs perform important ecosystem services, including filtering water, protecting islands from sediment deposition and storms, and providing nourishment for marine organisms.

1.3.2   Thousands of species depend on the coral reefs of the NWHI. Hawaiian monk seals, a majority of which make their home in the NWHI, are the only surviving marine mammal that is dependent on coral reef ecosystems (Citizen's Guide 2006; Cousteau 2003). The high incidence of apex predators such as sharks, jacks, and groupers also depends on the high productivity of this ecosystem. In turn, the prevalence of apex predators has a significant effect on the structuring of the fish assemblage of the area, impacting the diversity and relative abundance of species lower on the food chain. Thus, adverse impacts on these apex predators could cause populations of smaller fish to quickly become unbalanced, changing the trophic structure and order of dominance within the ecosystem (Maragos and Gulko 2002; Friedlander and DeMartini 2002; Suthers 2004).

1.3.3   Approximately 14 million seabirds, with 5.5 million nesting annually in the NWHI, rely on the coral reef ecosystem for food and other habitat needs (Naughton and Flint 2004). In turn, the ecosystem is dependent on these birds' role in the high relative productivity and diversity of the NWHI. Nutrient-rich defecation (guano) deposited by the birds on the islands and near-shore waters – which subsequently is dissolved and provides significant levels of nitrogen to the ecosystem – is thought to stimulate the prolific growths of algae found around the islands. When high levels of algal growth are combined with significant wave action, such as at La Perouse Pinnacle at French Frigate Shoals, this creates favourable conditions for the growth of other species (Maragos and Gulko 2002).

1.3.4   The ecological processes of the NWHI depend on more than just its coral reefs. Beyond the banks and steep slopes, between 1640 and 14,000 feet, the ocean floor levels out at sea bottom which contains distinct, rich habitat (Press and Siever 1986; Benoit-Bird et al. 2001). This habitat is linked to the coral reef ecosystem by a dense assemblage of small fish, shrimp, and squid that migrate from the ocean depths to near the surface in regular patterns and serve as an important food resource for many animals, including spinner dolphins, bottom fish, tunas, and billfish (Benoit-Bird et al. 2001). The importance of offshore and deepwater habitat is also evidenced by the movements and diets of Hawaiian monk seals. Although part of the seals' diet comes from shallow-water coral reef fish, the seals are known to travel over one hundred miles between islands and dive to depths of greater than 900 feet when foraging for deepwater prey, mainly bottom fish, which make up the primary part of their diet (Henderson 2001; TenBruggencate 2006). Each of these habitats is essential to the other, and the loss of one affects the operation of all the others throughout the system. Accordingly, an impact on one part of the system can threaten the entire ecosystem as well as the diversity of species that depend on the area.

1.4   Diversity

1.4.1   The NWHI support more than 7000 species of fishes, mammals, plants, coral, and other invertebrates (Bush 2006). Discoveries of species in the NWHI are continuing to be made, as demonstrated by a 2006 research expedition in French Frigate Shoals which yielded over 100 species not previously known to exist in the area and many of which may be previously unknown to science (Associated Press 2006). The rich diversity of the NWHI is in part due to the relative isolation of the area and minimal impact from humans, which is underscored by the starkly contrasting lower levels of diversity found in the marine areas of the main Hawaiian Islands (DeMartini and Friedlander 2004; Friedlander et al. 2005a; NOAA 2004b). Coral reefs are among the most highly diverse of all ecosystems on the planet; the coral reef ecosystem of the NWHI exemplifies this point.

1.4.2   Further contributing to diversity, the ecosystem of the NWHI contains a wide variety of habitats, extending from the shoreline to depths of approximately 14,000 feet. For example, within the pristine coral reefs of the NWHI, the percentage of coral cover varies widely, creating a series of interconnected but distinct types of coral reef habitats, or zones (e.g. shelf, fore reef, reef crest, back reef, and lagoon). Wave exposure is the primary factor causing zonation in the NWHI, but gradients in sediment, salinity, and temperature are also important (Friedlander et al. 2005a). As a result of this zonation, the coral reefs of the NWHI contain a variety of environmental niches and resources that support a diverse array of species.

1.5   Productivity

1.5.1   Coral reef ecosystems have the highest gross primary productivity of all ocean areas, and the proposed area contains several thousand square miles of coral reefs, indicating a highly productive ecosystem. Also indicative of the area's productivity is the high incidence of apex predators such as sharks, jacks, and groupers, which make up more than half of the total fish biomass in the NWHI. A very high replacement rate of small and mid-size fish is necessary to support an apex-predator-dominated ecosystem.

1.5.2   The productivity of the proposed area can readily be seen by comparing it to the productivity in the main Hawaiian Islands. A comparison of both biomass and trophic structure between reef fish communities in the NWHI and the main Hawaiian Islands showed that, across similar habitats, biomass was 260 per cent higher in the NWHI (Friedlander and DeMartini 2002). Productivity is especially high in the area's inshore waters, shallow lagoons, and coral reefs. For example, the lagoon in French Frigate Shoals produces nearly ten times the amount of phytoplankton as produced in the same volume of water in the open seas. The area also has extensive submerged banks, which have high levels of primary productivity due to the existence of expansive algal meadows. Furthermore, while apex predators represent only three per cent of the fish biomass in the main Hawaiian Islands, they make up 54 per cent of the biomass in the NWHI (Suthers 2004).

1.6   Spawning or breeding grounds

1.6.1   The NWHI provide critical breeding and nesting grounds for a wide variety of species. The area contains the breeding grounds for almost the entire remaining population of the Hawaiian monk seal, and serves as the seals' primary haul-out, pupping, and weaning habitat. The area also provides the breeding grounds and primary nesting sites for approximately 90 per cent of the threatened Hawaiian Islands green sea turtle population. Millions of Central Pacific seabirds also congregate on these islands to breed, including all but three of Hawaii's 22 species of seabirds, such as the grey-backed tern, short-tailed albatross, and the red-tailed tropicbird. More than 99 per cent of the world's Laysan albatrosses and 98 per cent of the world's black-footed albatrosses return to the NWHI each year to reproduce. For some bird species, the NWHI provide their only breeding site.

1.7   Naturalness

1.7.1   Because of their geographical isolation and long history of protection, the reefs of the NWHI are among the healthiest and most undisturbed coral reefs on the planet. Their naturalness is perhaps best evidenced by the relatively high diversity and productivity in the NWHI as compared with the reefs of the main Hawaiian Islands, which have experienced much greater impacts from humans, and by the fact that the NWHI is one of the world's last remaining large-scale apex-predator-dominated reef ecosystems.

1.8   Integrity

1.8.1   The area of the NWHI is a prime example of a self-sustaining ecological entity. The volcanic islands, coral atolls, shallow reefs, banks, slopes, shoals, seamounts, deep reefs, and open water form the basis for this interlocking and complex ecosystem. Its integrated nature is evidenced by the vast number of interdependent processes that connect the varied NWHI habitats, as discussed in particular in section 3.4 (Dependency) of this proposal. Examples of this include: (1) the critical link between the shallow coral reef and the deep ocean floor habitats, manifested by species that migrate regularly from great depths and are consumed by many shallower-water animals; (2) the foraging, feeding, breeding, and pupping areas of the Hawaiian monk seal range from the offshore, deepwater habitats to the land areas; and (3) the deposits of bird guano stimulate algal growth which, when combined with wave action, contributes to the growth of other species and the high productivity of the ecosystem.

1.8.2   While the NWHI are a part of the greater chain of Hawaiian Islands, there is clear evidence that the NWHI function as a distinct biological unit. The NWHI ecosystem is highly productive, diverse, and apex-predator-dominated while the ecosystem around the main Hawaiian Islands has substantially lower productivity, less species diversity, and is not apex-predator-dominated. These differences demonstrate that the NWHI function as an integral unit.

1.9   Fragility

1.9.1   The area contains several thousand square miles of coral reefs, made up of at least 57 species of hard coral and 12 species of soft coral. Coral communities are fragile ecosystems. They require a delicate balance across a range of environmental conditions in order to be healthy and grow. The health of a coral ecosystem may be threatened by changes to even one of those environmental conditions. Corals derive a substantial portion of their nutrition from symbiotic algae (called zooxanthellae) within their tissues. Because algae require light for photosynthesis, clear and clean water conditions are necessary for growth and well-being. The introduction of pollutants can be toxic to the coral.

1.9.2   The physical structure of the reef is provided by calcium carbonate, which forms the rock framework or reef "skeleton". This calcium carbonate is deposited at a rate of about one centimetre per year by the living coral animal (polyp). These polyps exist in a thin layer at the surface of the reef rock. The coral reef system of the NWHI has taken thousands of years to build and, if damaged, regeneration of the reef may never occur. If optimal conditions for regeneration exist, it would still take hundreds, and perhaps thousands, of years for a damaged area of the reef to return to its previous condition.

1.9.3   In the NWHI, transiting ships are a primary anthropogenic threat to this fragile ecosystem because of ship groundings and pollution from operational and accidental discharges. Secondary and cumulative damage may occur when dislocated coral fragments caused by groundings are tossed against healthy coral by wave action, currents, and storms.

1.9.4   The isolation of the NWHI affords both protection from and vulnerability to invasive species, which can be transferred by ships. The islands' ecosystems have evolved without the influence of outside forces, demonstrated by the high level of native and endemic species. To date, 11 non-native species have been identified in the waters of the NWHI. Non-native species can displace native species and seriously disrupt and imbalance the natural ecosystem.

1.10   Bio-geographic importance

1.10.1   The NWHI represent one of the last remaining examples of an intact apex-predator-dominated coral reef ecosystem with large top predator fish, such as sharks, in abundance. Because it is isolated, many aspects of the area represent what a completely pristine and undisturbed bio-geographic system would look like at this latitude if one still existed.

1.10.2   The area is geologically unique. The islands were created from a single plume of magma rising from a hot spot in the Earth's mantle. Built up over millions of years of eruption, high volcanic islands were formed, then carried north-westerly by the movement of the Pacific Plate beneath. Twenty-eight million years ago the last emergent feature of the chain, Kure, was located where the present Big Island of Hawaii is now located.

2   Social, cultural and economic criteria

2.1   Human dependency

2.1.1   The NWHI are of particular importance because of their significance in Native Hawaiian history and culture. The NWHI have long been considered a sacred place in Native Hawaiian traditions, and two of the islands in particular contain important archaeological sites (Kikiloi 2006). Early Polynesian voyagers, in their trans-Pacific voyages aboard large double-hulled sailing canoes, were the first humans to arrive in the NWHI, as early as 1000 A.D. Early Hawaiians lived on Nihoa for an estimated 700 years, but this occupation mysteriously ceased before Captain Cook's first landing in Hawaii in 1778 (Citizen's Guide 2006). Their early presence is evidenced by numerous sites on Nihoa and Mokumanamana (Necker), which are listed on both United States and State of Hawaii Registers of Historic Places for their cultural and historical significance. Together, the two islands have 140 recorded cultural sites, including ceremonial, residential, and agricultural sites, some of which resemble historically important Polynesian sites in Tahiti and the Marquesas (Emory 1928; Cleghorn 1988; Liller 2000; Kikiloi 2006). These sites are being studied to increase the understanding of the connection between Native Hawaiian culture and the early Polynesians.

2.1.2   Oral traditions also confirm the relationship of the islands to ancestral Native Hawaiians, and recent ethnological studies have highlighted the continuity of traditional practices in the NWHI. Native Hawaiian cultural practitioners continue to voyage to the NWHI to honour their ancestors and perpetuate these practices. In 1997, Hui Mālama i Nā Kūpuna o Hawai'i Nei, a group dedicated to the repatriation of ancestral remains, returned sets of iwi (bones) to Nihoa and Mokumanamana (Necker). In 2003, the voyaging canoe *Hōkūle'a* travelled to Nihoa so that a group could conduct traditional ceremonies. In 2004, the *Hōkūle'a* sailed to Kure Atoll, and in 2005 it took a group to Mokumanamana (Necker) for ceremonies on the summer solstice (Citizen's Guide 2006). Finally, underscoring the importance of the NWHI marine ecosystem in Native Hawaiian culture, oral traditions identify the coral polyp as the first living creature to emerge on Earth and the foundation and the building block of all other life in the sea (Friedlander et al. 2005b). It follows that ensuring a healthy, intact ecosystem in the NWHI plays an important role in perpetuating Native Hawaiian cultural traditions.

2.2 Cultural heritage

2.2.1 The NWHI are rich in underwater cultural heritage. The numerous wrecks found in the area are time capsules which capture specific elements of our seagoing past. Documents indicate that over 120 vessels and aircraft have been lost in the waters of the proposed area. These remains are representative of distinct phases of Pacific history and include Japanese junks, Hawaiian sampans, 19th century whalers, United States Navy sidewheel steamers, French sailing ships, and fighter aircraft lost during the World War II Battle of Midway. Only a handful of these sites have been located and assessed so far, but these surveys reveal resources unique to the North-western Hawaiian Islands. The wrecks of the whaling ships **Pearl** and **Hermes**, both of which ran aground in 1822, are the only archaeological remains of the South Seas whaling industry, and the oldest shipwrecks found thus far in Hawaii. The scattered remains of the **USS Saginaw**, lost in 1870, capture the United States Civil War-era technology of the "old steam navy." The wreck site of the **Dunnottar Castle**, an iron-hulled sailing ship lost in 1886, offers a rare glimpse of the days of the Tall Ships. These and many other sites are rare, representative of broad themes of maritime history, and a testimony to the uniqueness of Pacific seafaring history. Unwarranted damage or removal of submerged archaeological sites is prohibited by state and federal preservation laws, and United States Monument management agencies seek to protect these heritage resources as windows into the past.

3 Scientific and educational criteria

3.1 Research

3.1.1 This area is of high scientific interest and offers unparalleled opportunity for research. Given the fact that the NWHI are remote and rich with marine and terrestrial life, they provide one of the few areas in the world where researchers can conduct large-scale comparisons between human-impacted marine ecosystems and un-impacted marine ecosystems (Citizen's Guide; Friedlander and DeMartini 2002). Such comparisons may serve as a living model to guide restoration efforts elsewhere.

3.1.2 As further evidence of the importance of this area for research, in October 2006 an international team of biologists made discoveries in French Frigate Shoals of several new species of coral, sea stars, snails, and clams. The researchers also discovered over one hundred species never before seen in French Frigate Shoals and many of which may have been previously unknown to science (Associated Press 2006). These scientific discoveries suggest that much research remains to be done to fully understand and appreciate this complex ecosystem.

3.1.3 Research and monitoring conducted by United States federal and state agencies, academic institutions, and other organizations over the last 30 years have contributed substantially to the understanding of natural and anthropogenic factors influencing the NWHI and the interconnectedness of the physical and biological processes along the entire Hawaiian Island chain. Ongoing research and monitoring of the marine ecosystems in the NWHI will continue to provide significant insights that will benefit management not only for the NWHI but in the entire Hawaiian Island chain and marine ecosystems around the world.

3.2 Baseline for monitoring studies

3.2.1 The NWHI are one of the few marine regions on Earth where monitoring and research activities can be conducted in the virtual absence of local human habitation and activities. It thus provides ideal baseline conditions with regard to biota and environmental characteristics because it has not had substantial perturbations and is thus in a natural or near-natural condition. Remote, uninhabited, and relatively pristine in comparison to the main Hawaiian Islands and other marine ecosystems around the world, the NWHI serve as one of the few modern sentinels for monitoring and deciphering short-term and long-term responses to local, regional, and global environmental and anthropogenic stressors.

3.3   Education

3.3.1   The NWHI provide a model and rare benchmark of a healthy, intact integrated ecosystem preserved in its natural or near-natural state that may inspire Hawaiian residents as well as others to take part in ocean restoration efforts in their communities. This guiding premise led to "Navigating Change", a multi-year, interagency project which focuses on raising awareness and motivating people to change their attitudes and behaviours to better care for Hawaii's land and ocean resources. A five-part video and educational curriculum featuring the traditional Polynesian voyaging canoe *Hōkūle'a* during its 2004 expedition to the NWHI was completed in partnership with several agencies and organizations. Teacher workshops on the "Navigating Change" programme have been held since 2003 across Hawaii and an outreach coordinator leads an associated curriculum in schools state-wide. As people learn more about the NWHI, many will want to go there and experience it. Therefore, the educational message that is being sent to preserve the fragile balance of the NWHI is that people must admire it from afar. Educational activities, therefore, will focus on bringing the place to the people, not the people to the place.

Annex 3
Vulnerability to damage by international shipping activities

1   Vessel traffic characteristics

1.1   Operational factors

1.1.1   There are limited maritime activities conducted in the waters of the NWHI, undoubtedly due to the islands' remote location and harsh environmental conditions for human activities. Pursuant to the Presidential Proclamation of June 15, 2006, most domestic activities within NWHI waters are prohibited or strictly regulated. Public access to the land portions of the NWHI has for many years been allowed by permit only, except for Midway Atoll, and permits are issued only for research and Native Hawaiian cultural activities. The maritime activities in this area are primarily research and management, fishing, cultural practices, and recreation. Research activities include assessment, long-term monitoring of resources, impacts and threats from human activities, and the protection and conservation of NWHI resources. An estimated four million dollars are spent annually on research and management of the area. There are eight remaining commercial fishing permits in the NWHI, although the Presidential Proclamation and codifying regulations require closure of the fishery five years from the date of the Proclamation. Native Hawaiian cultural practitioners voyage to the NWHI to honour their ancestors and perpetuate traditional practices. Current tourism and recreational activities are limited to Midway Atoll and, under the Proclamation, a permit is now required. The extent to which ocean tourism and recreation occurs in the NWHI is unknown, but it appears to be extremely low. These activities may include wildlife watching, diving and snorkelling, charter fishing, and tour boats. Additionally, a management plan for tourism to the historic World War II location and military heritage sites on Midway Atoll is currently being developed and up to three cruise ships may visit the island each year.

1.2   Vessel types

1.2.1   Containerships, bulk carriers, tankers, freighters, and fishing vessels regularly transit the waters surrounding the NWHI. With the exception of a few small boats at Midway Atoll and Tern Island (French Frigate Shoals), no vessels have their home port in the NWHI. Research and management vessels, eight fishing vessels, vessels used by Native Hawaiians, some recreational vessels, and a few cruise ships conduct strictly regulated activities in NWHI waters (Franklin 2006; Mohri 2006).

1.3   Traffic characteristics

1.3.1   Although, due to its remoteness, the exact route of vessels through this area is unknown, it appears that most traffic passes to the north of the island chain, following the Great Circle routes to and from ports on the west coast of North America and East Asia. Other trans-Pacific ships travelling from ports in Hawaii transit at least 100 miles south of the NWHI. Occasionally, vessels transiting from the south pass within the boundaries of the proposed PSSA (Franklin 2006; Tosatto 2005; Horizon Lines 2006; Devany 2006).

1.3.2   A preliminary analysis of vessel traffic patterns within the NWHI was conducted, based on data collected by the World Meteorological Organization's Voluntary Observing Ships scheme. This scheme collects geo-referenced data from select non-research vessels that make frequent and regular crossings of all major ocean basins. While the scheme does not capture the total traffic in the area, during a 21-month study period in 2004 and 2005, approximately 132 vessels reported from within the area of the proposed PSSA: 104 of these vessels were freighters, 8 were tankers, 4 were research vessels, 2 were passenger vessels, 2 were vessels used for educational purposes, 1 was a recreational vessel, 1 was a towing vessel with a 666-foot vessel in tow, and 10 were unidentified vessels. The 132 vessels were flagged in 23 different countries (Franklin 2006).

1.4   Substances carried

1.4.1   While precise data are not available for the types of harmful substances carried on board the vessels that transit the waters of the NWHI, it is possible to identify examples of such substances from incidents that have occurred in the area. Three vessels, the **Paradise Queen II** (1998), the **Swordman I** (2000), and the **Casitas** (2005), all grounded in the NWHI and had significant quantities of bunker fuel or were carrying other types of fuel on board (Cascadia Times 2006; Shallenberger 2004). These substances are harmful to the marine ecosystem and to the terrestrial environment when washed ashore. In another incident, a container of the pesticide carbofuran washed ashore at Laysan Island (Friedlander et al. 2005).

1.4.2   Three other ship accidents occurred involving cargoes that may not be classified as "hazardous substances," but that would be harmful if released into this area of the sea. The first incident involved the **Anangel Liberty** in 1980, where 2200 tons of kaolin clay was dumped overboard to lighten the ship enough to pull it off one of the reefs on French Frigate Shoals. Fortunately, the currents on that day carried most of the clay out to sea rather than onto the reef. Had they not, the clay could have smothered coral, thus adversely affecting the ecosystem. The other two incidents involved the grounding on Laysan of fishing vessels that had evidence of rats on board. Again, fortunately, the rats did not take up residence on the nearby island; however, if they had, it would have been extremely harmful to the ecology of the area because such introduced species can become "ecosystem busters" and cripple the ecosystem within that area (Shallenberger 2004).

2   Natural factors

2.1   Hydrographical

2.1.1   The hydrography of the NWHI underscores the need for mariners to navigate with extreme caution. The chain of small islands, atolls, banks, seamounts, pinnacles, shoals, and other emergent features are remnants of volcanic islands which are eroding and subsiding beneath the ocean surface. While only the peaks of the original islands remain above the water's surface, coral growth on submerged slopes has matched the rate of subsidence (Evans et al. 2004). Due to these features, navigation in this area is dangerous and must be done with extreme caution. Water depths in this area range from the water's surface to slightly submerged banks, reefs, and other emergent features to the ocean floor at more than 14,000 feet.

2.1.2   The area of the proposed PSSA is currently covered by mostly small-scale charts, with the most recent surveys taking place since 2000 near known islands, reefs and atolls. Although modern hydrographic surveys by the University of Hawaii and satellite imagery of the area have allowed NOAA's Office of Coast Survey to correct the position of several of these features, many of the submerged banks and isolated features have yet to be updated or discovered.

2.1.3   In 2003, a mapping expedition was undertaken by NOAA and the University of Hawaii Undersea Research Laboratory. The primary objective of this project was to provide for more complete and accurate charts and survey data to support the management of the NWHI Coral Reef Ecosystem Reserve and protection of its resources. This expedition included hydrographic experts to ensure that appropriate International Hydrographic Organization quality standards were met. The hydrographic data will be applied to all affected charts by the end of 2007. Notwithstanding, large areas of the NWHI remain to be surveyed and nautical charts updated.

2.2   Meteorological

2.2.1   The north-east Trade Winds prevail throughout the year, but westerly blows can be expected during the winter. The average velocity of the winds is 12 knots, with monthly averages of 16 knots in December and 9.5 knots in August. Gales have been experienced in July and September. Occasional heavy showers of short duration also occur, cutting visibility to about 2 miles (Coast Pilot 7, 38th ed., 2006).

2.2.2   Tropical storms and hurricanes are a potential, but infrequent, threat to the shallow coral reef community structure of the NWHI. They can generate extreme wave-energy events that can damage the coral and are the primary natural force in altering and shaping coral reef community structures (Dollar 1982; Dollar and Grigg 2004). Since 1979, two hurricanes (category 2) have passed near the NWHI. The most recent significant tropical storm was Hurricane *Nele*, which passed near Gardner Pinnacles in 1985 (Friedlander et al. 2005).

2.2.3   Pacific Decadal Oscillation (PDO) events and the El Niño/La Niña phenomenon (ENSO) are two other meteorological factors that occur in the area of the NWHI. PDO events have been described as long-lived El Niño-like patterns of Pacific climate variability. They appear to persist for 20 to 30 years, compared to the 6 to 18 months for an El Niño event. The effects of the PDO are strongest in the North Pacific, while secondary signatures exist in the tropics. PDO sea-level pressure anomalies vary with low pressures over the North Pacific and high pressure over the subtropical Pacific. These pressure patterns cause enhanced counter-clockwise wind stress over the North Pacific. With regard to the ENSO, while scientists do not fully understand how one is triggered, the initial detection occurs by a rise in atmospheric pressure in the western Pacific and a drop in pressure in the eastern Pacific (Garrison 1999). This causes Trade Winds to shift direction, which subsequently causes warm water in the western Pacific to flow across the Pacific basin. This mass of warm water has a number of effects on climate and ocean conditions. For example, it can cause Trade-Wind speeds to drop, which can cause an increase in sea surface temperature (Hoeke et al. 2004). Light winds are likely the cause of recent coral bleaching in the NWHI. Increased water temperatures stress the coral, which causes it to expel the symbiotic zooxanthellae. If water temperature does not decrease and zooxanthellae do not return to the coral tissue, the coral will die.

2.3   Oceanographic

2.3.1   The NWHI are influenced by a wide range of oceanographic conditions that vary on spatial and temporal scales. Ocean currents, waves, temperatures, nutrients, and other oceanographic parameters and conditions influence ecosystem composition, structure, and function in the NWHI. Ocean currents play an important role in the dispersal and recruitment of marine life in the NWHI. Surface currents are highly variable in both speed and direction (Firing et al. 2004), with long-term average surface flow from east to west in response to the prevailing north-east Trade Wind conditions. The highly variable nature of the surface currents is due in large part to eddies created by local island effects on large-scale circulation. Marine debris accumulation in shallow-water areas of the NWHI also is influenced by large- and small-scale ocean circulation patterns. These eddies might also result in pollution from vessels accumulating in the coral, thus damaging resources.

2.3.2   Ocean waves also play an important role in the NWHI. The distribution of corals and other shallow-water organisms is influenced by the exposure to waves. The size and strength of ocean wave events have annual, inter-annual, and decadal timescales. Annual extra-tropical storms (storms that originate outside the tropical latitudes) create high-energy large wave events, from five to over ten metres, which approach largely from the north-west during the winter. During this time, the average wave power increases substantially and extreme wave events of over ten metres pound the shallow-water coral communities, thus posing a hazard to the coral reef communities and to navigation. Decadal variability in wave power is possibly related to PDO events (Mantua et al. 1997). The number of extreme wave events has been recorded during the periods from 1985 to 1989 and from 1998 to 2002, and anomalously low numbers of extreme wave events occurred during the early 1980s and during the period from 1990 to 1996 (Friedlander et al. 2005).

2.4   Other helpful information

2.4.1   There is substantial evidence that international shipping activities are causing or may cause damage to the recognized attributes of the proposed PSSA. The hazards to navigation in the NWHI are demonstrated by the large number of shipwrecks throughout the NWHI chain. Over 60 shipwrecks have occurred in the area and some of these wrecks serve as the origin of a number of the islands' names.[*] While some of these wrecks are truly historic and therefore serve as time capsules of seafaring history, there have been a number of significant maritime casualties in more recent years. In 1998, the 80-foot **Paradise Queen II** ran aground on Kure Atoll. It spilled approximately 4,000 gallons of diesel fuel and other petroleum hydrocarbons. The remaining 7,000 gallons on board the vessel were recovered during salvage operations. The 85 foot **Swordman I** ran aground on Pearl and Hermes Atoll in 2000. It was carrying over 10,000 gallons of diesel fuel and hydraulic oil and approximately $1.5 million was spent for response and removal of the vessel. In 2005, the 145-foot **Casitas** also ran aground on Pearl and Hermes Atoll, carrying over 33,000 gallons of diesel fuel on board. The vast majority of diesel fuel was salvaged and the vessel was removed from the Atoll and scuttled in an estimated

---

[*] This figure does not include aircraft or vessels that were sunk in the Battle of Midway.

$5 million clean-up and removal operation (Cascadia Times 2006; Shallenberger 2004; Biennial Coastal Zone Conference 2003).

2.4.2   The grounding of the **Anangel Liberty** on French Frigate Shoals in 1980 ploughed a channel 2–3 metres deep, 100 metres long, and 30 metres wide in the coral reef. Coral communities were damaged within 50 metres on both sides of the channel ploughed by the freighter as a result of cargo (kaolin clay) that was dumped. In 1977, the burning and sinking of the **Hawaiian Patriot** to the south of French Frigate Shoals resulted in more than five million gallons of fuel oil entering the ocean (United States Fish & Wildlife Serv. 2005; United States Coral Reef Task Force 1999). Also in 1977, **Irene's Challenge** spilled approximately 10.4 million gallons of crude oil approximately 50 miles to the north of Lisianski Island. MEPC 56/INF.2, annex 1, provides a table summarizing select incidents that have occurred between 1970 and 2006 (United States Coral Reef Task Force 1999; NOAA 2006).

2.4.3   In addition to the damage that may be caused to the NWHI by spills or releases of ships' cargoes or bunker fuel, damage may be caused by the grounding of ships on fragile coral and other sensitive habitats in the area. In the case of vessel grounding, destruction in the area of contact may be widespread and result in the scouring and destruction of coral by dislodgement and pulverization, as well as the crushing, fracturing, and removal of reef structure. Impacts may also include the scarring and abrading of nearby resources as wave action, currents, and wind move rubble produced at the initial site of the grounding. Additionally, there may be increased sedimentation with the fracturing and erosion of the reef structure, which can smother coral and other sensitive habitats (Coral Reef Restoration Handbook 2006). Damage may also be caused by subsequent vessel removal efforts, which can further crush and bury sensitive resources. A vessel that has grounded and then is abandoned can continue to damage resources as debris becomes dislodged from the vessel and from its movement at the grounding location by wind and wave action.

2.4.4   Fortunately, although damage to coral and other resources has occurred from the ships that have grounded or sunk in the NWHI, recovery and removal efforts as well as favourable weather patterns and the currents occurring at the time of these maritime casualties have so far spared the fragile NWHI ecosystem from being seriously adversely impacted (Shallenberger 2004). Without taking the necessary action to increase maritime safety, protect the fragile marine environment, and facilitate the ability to respond to developing maritime emergencies, it is reasonably foreseeable that ships will continue to run aground in the NWHI and cause physical damage to the fragile coral reef ecosystem, as well as pose a threat of severe damage to this pristine area from the release of cargo and bunker fuel. Given the remoteness of the NWHI, the low level of development on the islands, and the minimum amount of domestic maritime activity that takes place within the surrounding waters, vessels that transit the area are one of the most persistent and significant anthropogenic threats to the recognized attributes of the area.

2.4.5   Another element that increases the vulnerability of the NWHI to international shipping activities is that, although the islands span 1200 miles, most emergency response equipment is stationed in the main Hawaiian Islands, including Kaua'i, which is to the east of the NWHI. Search, rescue, and response operations have been staged from Midway Atoll, which is at the far north-western end of the island chain; however, without assistance from resources based in the main Hawaiian Islands, search, rescue, and response from Midway can generally reach only 10 miles offshore due to the limited equipment located permanently on the island. The sparse land area and fragile environment of the other islands makes it virtually impossible for them to act as staging areas for emergency response efforts. This fact, coupled with the hazardous nature of navigation throughout this area, results in the NWHI being highly vulnerable to damage by international shipping.

2.4.6   Another potential source of damage to this pristine area by international shipping activities is from the introduction of alien species. While only approximately 11 alien species have been detected in the waters of the NWHI, once established these species are extremely difficult – if not impossible – to control and eradicate from the reefs. Therefore, it is critical to keep ships that may be carrying ballast water or species on their hulls from foundering or grounding on the reefs and providing the opportunity for the introduction of alien species (Citizen's Guide 2006).

2.4.7   In addition to the threat posed by transiting ships, another stress to the environment of the NWHI is marine debris, a severe and chronic threat to the area. Ocean currents carry a wide array of marine debris to the NWHI, including derelict fishing nets and other gear, household plastics, hazardous materials, and shore-based debris, and deposit it on the reef and beaches of the island chain. The debris frequently entangles and kills coral and leads to the death of animals such as seabirds and the Hawaiian monk seal through the ingestion of material or entanglement in nets. Derelict fishing gear also poses a navigation hazard because, for example, it can get wrapped around the propeller of a vessel. In the past 10 years, United States agencies have removed over 560 tons of debris from NWHI reefs at a cost of approximately US$13.5 million (Citizen's Guide 2006; Brainard 2006).

2.4.8   The IMO measure of six existing ATBAs is already in effect. While there has been no incident in the areas of the existing ATBAs subsequent to their adoption that involves the vessels to which the ATBAs apply (e.g. vessels of 1000 gross tons and above), there have been incidents in the NWHI outside of the existing ATBAs and incidents within the ATBAs by vessels to which the ATBAs do not now apply. For instance, the **Paradise Queen II** grounded on Kure Atoll, an area which is not now included within the ATBAs. Within the ATBA surrounding Pearl and Hermes Atoll, the **Swordman I** and **Casitas** ran aground; however, these vessels were smaller than the 1000 gross ton applicability threshold of the existing ATBAs.

Annex 4

Associated Protective Measures for the Papahānaumokuākea
Marine National Monument PSSA

Expansion and amendment of the areas to be avoided "In the Region of the North-West Hawaiian Islands" and
renaming them as "In the Papahānaumokuākea Marine National Monument Particularly Sensitive Sea Area"

Amended areas to be avoided "In the Papahānaumokuākea Marine National Monument Particularly Sensitive
Sea Area" were adopted at the eighty-third session of MSC in 2007. All areas should be avoided by all ships
solely in transit. A full technical description of the areas to be avoided is in part D of editions of the IMO
publication "Ships' Routeing"; only a chartlet of the areas is included here.

In the Papahānaumokuākea Marine National Monument
Particularly Sensitive Sea Area

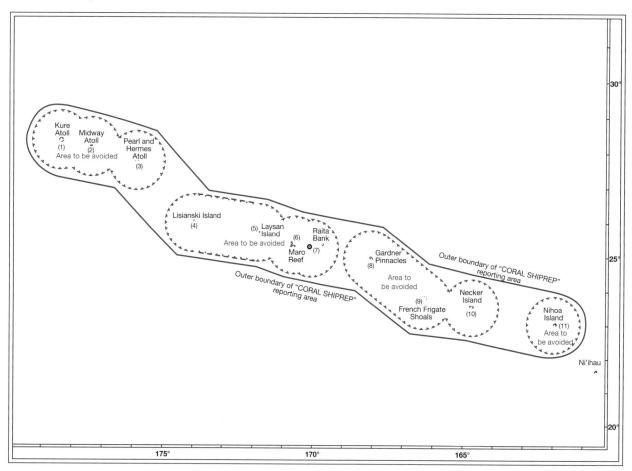

A mandatory ship reporting system "In the Papahānaumokuākea Marine National Monument Particularly
Sensitive Sea Area" was adopted at the eighty-third session of MSC in 2007. It was amended at the eighty-
fifth session of MSC in 2008 by replacing the description of geographical coordinates in the appendix. The
consolidated amended text is included here.

1   Categories of ships

1.1   Ships required to participate in the system

1.1.1   As a condition of entry to a United States port or place, all ships of 300 gross tonnage or greater, and all ships in the event of a developing emergency, and that are in transit through the reporting area, are required to participate in CORAL SHIPREP, except for sovereign immune vessels which are exempt under SOLAS regulation V/1.

1.2   Ships recommended to participate in the system

1.2.1   All ships of 300 gross tonnage or greater, fishing vessels, and all ships in the event of a developing emergency and that are in transit through the reporting area are recommended to participate in CORAL SHIPREP.

2   Geographical coverage of the system and the number and edition of the reference chart used for the delineation of the system

2.1   The geographical coverage of CORAL SHIPREP is depicted by the geographical positions in the appendix.

2.2   The reference charts that include the ship reporting area are United States 19016 (2007 edition), 19019 (2007 edition) and 19022 (2007 edition). These charts are based on World Geodetic System 1984 datum (WGS 84) and astronomic datum.

3   Format, content of reports, times and geographical positions for submitting reports, authorities to whom reports should[*] be sent, available services

3.1   Format

3.1.1   The ship report should be drafted in accordance with the format shown in paragraph 2 of the appendix to resolution A.851(20).

3.2   Content

3.2.1   The report for a ship entering the system should contain the following information:

System identifier: CORAL SHIPREP

A	Name of the ship, call sign, or IMO identification number
B	Date and time (UTC)
C *or* D	Position
E *and* F	Course *and* speed of ship
I	Destination
L	Intended route through the reporting area
O	Vessel draught
P	General categories of hazardous cargo on board
Q *or* R	Defects or deficiencies, if relevant
T	Contact information of ship's agent or owner
U	Ship size and type (e.g., length, tonnage, and type)
W	Total number of persons on board

---

[*] For those ships that are required to report, the word "should" in this text is to be read as "shall".

3.2.2   The report for a ship leaving the system should contain the following information:

System identifier: CORAL SHIPREP

A	Name of the ship, call sign, or IMO identification number
B	Date and time (UTC)
C *or* D	Position

3.2.3   A ship may elect, for reasons of commercial confidentiality, to communicate that section of the report which provides information on general categories of hazardous cargo by non-verbal means prior to entering the reporting area.

3.3   Geographical positions for submitting reports

3.3.1   Each ship should submit a full report in accordance with paragraph 3.2.1 as soon as it crosses the boundary to enter the ship reporting system.

3.3.2   Each ship should submit a report in accordance with paragraph 3.2.2 as soon as it crosses the boundary to leave the ship reporting system.

3.3.3   Further reports should be made whenever there is a change in navigation status or circumstances, particularly in relation to item Q of the reporting format.

3.4   Authority to whom reports should be sent

3.4.1   The shore-based Authority is the United States Coast Guard's Communication Area Master Station Pacific (CAMSPAC). For ships of 300 gross tonnage and greater, an e-mail address to be used for reporting through Inmarsat-C will be provided in advance of implementation of this system through Notices to Mariners. In the event of a developing emergency, ships are urged to call the United States Coast Guard 14th District. Vessels unable to report in through Inmarsat-C should report to nwhi.notifications@noaa.gov.

4   Information to be provided to ship and procedures to be followed

4.1   The CORAL SHIPREP shore-based Authority will provide critical alerts and information to shipping about specific and urgent situations and other information that may affect safety of navigation within the IMO-adopted areas to be avoided and the Papahānaumokuākea Marine National Monument Particularly Sensitive Sea Area, as well as remind ships about the existence of the IMO-adopted areas to be avoided and the necessity of navigating with extreme caution through the Particularly Sensitive Sea Area.

4.2   Navigational warnings and emergency broadcasts will be issued as NAVTEX messages or specifically directed at GMDSS-equipped vessels, using Inmarsat-C.

5   Radio communication required for the system and frequencies on which reports should be transmitted

5.1   This system will be based on Inmarsat-C and an e-mail, and ships equipped with such capabilities should report through Inmarsat-C.

5.2   In the event of a developing emergency, a ship is urged to call the United States Coast Guard 14th District at 001-808-541-2500 to request a response and assistance.

5.3   For vessels unable to communicate through Inmarsat-C, reports should be made prior to, during, or after transiting through the reporting area to nwhi.notifications@noaa.gov.

5.4   Commercially sensitive information will be kept confidential and should be transmitted prior to entry into the reporting system. Such information may be sent to nwhi.notifications@noaa.gov.

5.5   The language used for reports to the system should be English, employing the IMO Standard Marine Communication Phrases, where necessary.

5.6   Communications associated with CORAL SHIPREP are, in accordance with SOLAS regulation V/11, free of charge to affected vessels.

6   Relevant rules and regulations in force in the area of the system

6.1   International actions

6.1.1   The United States has taken appropriate action to implement the international conventions to which it is party.

6.1.2   In recognition of the fragile environment in this area and potential hazards to navigation, the IMO has adopted several areas to be avoided to protect the North-western Hawaiian Islands and has designated the area as a Particularly Sensitive Sea Area where mariners should navigate with extreme caution.

6.1.3   The United States applies its laws in accordance with international law, which includes navigational rights under customary international law as reflected in the United Nations Convention on the Law of the Sea. No restrictions shall apply to or be enforced against foreign-flagged vessels unless in accordance with such law.

6.2   Domestic actions

6.2.1   The United States has taken considerable action to ensure maritime safety and to protect the fragile environment and cultural resources and areas of cultural importance significant to Native Hawaiians in the NWHI. This area has been the subject of a variety of protective measures, including designation of this area as the North-western Hawaiian Islands Marine National Monument (subsequently renamed the Papahānaumokuākea Marine National Monument) in recognition of its fragility and to protect the many species of coral, fish, birds, marine mammals, and other flora and fauna, as well as to protect historical and archaeological heritage resources, including cultural resources and areas of significant importance to Native Hawaiians.

6.2.2   Regulations in this area, inter alia, prohibit taking, possessing, injuring, or disturbing any resource; altering the seabed; anchoring or deserting a vessel; and possessing fishing gear unless stowed. All of these activities may be allowed by permit; however, permits cannot be issued for such things as releasing an introduced species. Activities such as discharging or depositing any material into the Monument, or discharging or depositing any material outside the Monument that subsequently injures Monument resources, except discharges incidental to vessel use, such as approved marine sanitation device effluent, cooling water, and engine exhaust, are also prohibited. The United States strictly regulates entry into the Monument and, for those vessels subject to United States jurisdiction, requires the mandatory use of vessel monitoring systems on those vessels that may be allowed into the Monument for specific purposes.

7   Shore-based facilities to support operation of the system

7.1   The shore-based Authority is the United States Coast Guard's Communications Area Master Station Pacific (CAMSPAC). CAMSPAC provides maritime distress communication services and safety and weather broadcasts to commercial and recreational mariners, and also provides secure voice communications and record message delivery services for all United States Coast Guard cutters, aircraft, and shore units. Additionally, CAMSPAC is one of the United States Coast Guard's Pacific Area's (PACAREA) Continuity of Operations sites. CAMSPAC delivers contingency and inter-agency communication services for Incident Commanders by deploying a state-of-the-art transportable communications centre. CAMSPAC is the Operational Commander of the United States Coast Guard's Pacific Area Communications System, consisting of communication stations in Honolulu Hawaii, Kodiak Alaska, and remote facilities in Guam. There are approximately 150 people assigned to CAMSPAC.

7.2 CORAL SHIPREP will use Inmarsat-C communications equipment. A computer server handles and sorts incoming reports and sends the return message. Incoming reports are text messages that arrive via either internet e-mail or telex. When the ship reporting system server receives a report, the server sends the ship a specific return message. Area coordinators will monitor and update the information to the server for inclusion in the outgoing message.

8 Alternative communication if the shore-based facilities fail

8.1 NAVTEX Broadcast Notice to Mariners may be used to notify mariners of the temporary failure of the system and can provide mariners with basic information necessary to navigate safely through this area.

8.2 For those ships reporting through Inmarsat-C, the standard protocol now used for such systems will be used to re-route incoming and outgoing communications through an alternative address and it is expected that this will minimize the system's downtime, though a short delay may occur.

9 Measures to be taken if a ship does not report

9.1.1 All means will be used to encourage and promote the full participation of the ships recommended to submit reports.

9.1.2 If reports are not submitted by those ships required to report and the ship can be positively identified, appropriate action will be taken – including interaction with the flag State – in accordance with customary international law as reflected in the 1982 United Nations Convention on the Law of the Sea.

Appendix

Geographical coordinates

Ship reporting system

(Reference charts: United States 19016 (2007 edition); 19019 (2007 edition); 19022 (2007 edition). These charts are based on World Geodetic System 1984 datum (WGS 84) and astronomic datum.)

1   Outer boundary

The outer boundary of the "CORAL SHIPREP" reporting area consists of lines connecting the following geographical positions:

Starting at	(1)	29°24'.21 N,	178°06'.45 W
A rhumb line to	(2)	29°12'.16 N,	177°04'.25 W
Then a rhumb line to	(3)	28°43'.78 N,	175°13'.76 W
Then a rhumb line to	(4)	27°00'.28 N,	173°25'.37 W
Then a rhumb line to	(5)	26°44'.85 N,	171°28'.22 W
Then a rhumb line to	(6)	26°23'.95 N,	170°20'.25 W
Then a rhumb line to	(7)	25°56'.49 N,	167°32'.03 W
Then a rhumb line to	(8)	24°50'.23 N,	165°58'.56 W
Then a rhumb line to	(9)	24°02'.61 N,	161°42'.30 W
Then an arc with a 60.25 NM radius centred at	(21)	23°03'.61 N,	161°55'.22 W
To a point	(10)	22°04'.59 N,	162°08'.14 W
Then a rhumb line to	(11)	22°35'.32 N,	164°53'.46 W
Then a rhumb line to	(12)	22°47'.86 N,	166°40'.44 W
Then a rhumb line to	(13)	24°03'.30 N,	168°27'.53 W
Then a rhumb line to	(14)	24°26'.59 N,	170°50'.37 W
Then a rhumb line to	(15)	24°46'.49 N,	171°52'.87 W
Then a rhumb line to	(16)	25°07'.23 N,	174°30'.23 W
Then a rhumb line to	(17)	27°05'.50 N,	176°35'.40 W
Then a rhumb line to	(18)	27°15'.11 N,	177°35'.26 W
Then a rhumb line to	(19)	27°26'.10 N,	178°32'.23 W
Then an arc with a 60.17 NM radius centred at	(20)	28°25'.23 N,	178°19'.51 W
Then to point	(1)	29°24'.21 N,	178°06'.45 W

2   Inner boundary

The inner boundaries of the "CORAL SHIPREP" SRS reporting area are coterminous with the outer boundaries of the IMO-adopted areas to be avoided "In the Region of the Papahānaumokuākea Marine National Monument PSSA", which consist of the following:

1   Those areas contained within circles of radius of 50 nautical miles centred upon the following geographical positions:

(a)	28°25'.18 N,	178°19'.75 W	(Kure Atoll)
(b)	28°14'.20 N,	177°22'.10 W	(Midway Atoll)

    (c)   27°50′.62 N,   175°50′.53 W   (Pearl and Hermes Atoll)

    (d)   26°03′.82 N,   173°58′.00 W   (Lisianski Island)

    (e)   25°46′.18 N,   171°43′.95 W   (Laysan Island)

    (f)   25°25′.45 N,   170°35′.32 W   (Maro Reef)

    (g)   25°19′.50 N,   170°00′.88 W   (between Maro Reef and Raita Bank)

    (h)   25°00′.00 N,   167°59′.92 W   (Gardner Pinnacles)

    (i)   23°45′.52 N,   166°14′.62 W   (French Frigate Shoals)

    (j)   23°34′.60 N,   164°42′.02 W   (Necker Island)

    (k)   23°03′.38 N,   161°55′.32 W   (Nihoa Island).

2   Those areas contained between the following geographical coordinates:

		Begin coordinates		End coordinates	
		Latitude	**Longitude**	**Latitude**	**Longitude**
Area 1	Lisianski Island (N) → Laysan Island	26°53′.22 N	173°49′.64 W	26°35′.58 N	171°35′.60 W
	Lisianski Island (S) → Laysan Island	25°14′.42 N	174°06′.36 W	24°57′.63 N	171°57′.07 W
Area 2	Gardner Pinnacles (N) → French Frigate Shoals	25°38′.90 N	167°25′.31 W	24°24′.80 N	165°40′.89 W
	Gardner Pinnacles (S) → French Frigate Shoals	24°14′.27 N	168°22′.13 W	23°05′.84 N	166°47′.81 W

Literature references

Associated Press. 2006. New sea creatures found in Hawaii. 1 November 2006.

Benoit-Bird, K. J., W. W. L. Au, R. E. Brainard, and M. O. Lammers. 2001. *Diel horizontal migration of the Hawaiian mesopelagic boundary community observed acoustically.* Mar. Ecol. Prog. Ser., 217:1–14.

Brainard, Russell E. 2006. Chief, Coral Reef Ecosystem Division, Pacific Islands Fisheries Science Center, National Oceanic and Atmospheric Administration. Personal communication with Lindy S. Johnson, Office of General Counsel for International Law, National Oceanic and Atmospheric Administration. 12 December 2006.

Bush, President George W., 2006. Presidential Proclamation 8031, Establishment of the Northwestern Hawaiian Islands Marine National Monument. 15 June 2006.

Cascadia Times. 2006. *Isles of Coral: Exploring the Northwestern Hawaiian Island Coral Reef Ecosystem,* Cascadia Times, Number 58, Spring 2006.

Cleghorn, Paul. 1998. The Settlement and abandonment of Two Hawaiian Outposts: Nihoa and Necker. Bishop Museum Occasional Papers 28:35–49.

Cousteau, Jean-Michel. 2003. *Voyage to Kure* Expedition Logs. Internet website: http://www.oceanfutures.org/kure/kure_logs.php. Accessed 15 January 2007.

DeMartini, E. E. and A.M. Friedlander. 2004. *Spatial Patterns of Endemism in Shallow Reef Fish Populations of the Northwestern Hawaiian Islands.* Mar Ecol Prog Ser. 271:281–296.

Devany, CDR Mike. 2006. Chief of Operations, Marine Operations, Pacific, National Oceanic and Atmospheric Administration. Personal communication with Derek Campbell, Office of General Counsel for International Law, National Oceanic and Atmospheric Administration. 2 October 2006.

Dollar, S.J. 1982. *Wave stress and coral community structure.* Coral Reefs, 1:71–81.

Dollar, S.J. and R.W. Grigg. 2004. *Anthropogenic and Natural Stresses on Selected Coral Reefs in Hawaii.* Pacific Science, 58:281–304.

Emory, Kenneth P. 1928. *Archaeology of Nihoa and Necker Islands.* Bernice P. Bishop Museum Bulletin No. 53. Bishop Museum Press, Honolulu.

Evans, B.K., D.J. Hill, J.E. Miller, J.R. Smith, and J.B. Weirich. 2004. *Collaborative Nautical Charting and Scientific Seabed Mapping Missions: A Case Study in the Northwestern Hawaiian Islands.* IEEE Oceans 2003 Conference Proceedings, Vol. 2.

Firing, J., R. Hoeke, and R. Brainard. 2004. Surface velocity and profiling drifters track potential larval pathways in Northwestern Hawaiian Islands. Northwestern Hawaiian Islands 3rd scientific symposium, 2–4 November 2004.

Firing, June and Russell E. Brainard. 2006. *Ten Years of Shipboard ADCP Measurements along the Northwestern Hawaiian Islands.* Atoll Res. Bull., 543:347–363.

Franklin, E.C. 2006. Patterns of vessel traffic in and around the Northwestern Hawaiian Islands Coral Reef Ecosystem Reserve. Northwestern Hawaiian Islands Interagency Group Meeting, 17 January 2006.

Friedlander, A., G. Aeby, R. Brainard, A. Clark, E. Godwin, S. Godwin, J. Kenyon, R. Kosaki, J. Maragos and P. Vroom. 2005. *The State of Coral Reef Ecosystem of the Northwestern Hawaiian Islands.* In: The State of Coral Reef Ecosystems of the United States and Pacific Freely Associated States: 2005, pp. 270–311. National Oceanic and Atmospheric Administration, Center for Coastal Monitoring and Assessment.

Friedlander, Alan, Greta Aeby, Rusty Brainard, Athline Clark, Edward DeMartini, Scott Godwin, Jean Kenyon, Jim Maragos, Randy Kosaki and Peter Vroom. 2005. The Status of the Coral Reefs of the Northwest Hawaiian Islands.

Friedlander, A., G. Aeby, E. Brown, A. Clark, S. Coles, S. Dollar, C. Hunter, P. Jokiel, J. Smith, B. Walsh, I. Williams and W. Wiltse. 2005. The Status of the Coral Reef Ecosystems of the Main Hawaiian Islands.

Friedlander, Alan and Edward DeMartini. 2002. *Contrasts in density, size, and biomass of reef fishes between the northwestern and main Hawaiian Islands: the effects of fishing down apex predators*. Mar. Ecol. Prog. Ser., 230:253–264.

Garrison, Tom. 1999. Oceanography: An Invitation to Marine Science, 3rd ed. Belt, CA: Wadsworth Publishing Co.

Henderson, J.R. 2001. *A Pre- and Post-MARPOL Annex V Summary of Hawaiian monk seal entanglements and marine debris accumulation in the Northwestern Hawaiian Islands, 1982–1998*. Marine Pollution Bulletin. 42(7):584–589.

Hoeke, R.K., R.E. Brainard, R.E. Moffitt, G. Lui, A.E. Strong, and W. Skirving. 2004. The role of oceanographic conditions and reef morphology in the 2002 coral bleaching event in the Northwestern Hawaiian Islands. Northwestern Hawaiian Islands 3rd scientific symposium, 2–4 November 2004.

Horizon Lines. 2006. Personal communication with Lindy S. Johnson, Office of General Counsel for International Law, National Oceanic and Atmospheric Administration. 31 November 2006.

Kikiloi, S. Kekuewa. 2006. Reconnecting with Ancestral Islands: Examining historical relationships between kānaka maoli and the Northwestern Hawaiian Islands. Report to National Oceanic and Atmospheric Administration for the Kia'I Kai [Guardians of the Sea] Project, Kamakakūokalani, Center for Hawaiian Studies, University of Hawai'i, Mānoa. January 2006.

Liller, W. 2000. *Necker Islands, Hawai'i: Astronomical Implications of an island located on the Tropic of Cancer*. Rapa Nui Journal 14 (4), December 2000.

Mantua, N.J. 2001. *The Pacific Decadal Oscillation*. In: The Encyclopedia of Global Environmental Change, Vol. 1, The Earth System: Physical and chemical dimension of global environmental change, McCracken, M.C. and J.S. Perry (eds.), pp. 592–594.

Mantua, N.J., S.R. Hare, Y. Zhang, J.M. Wallace, and R.C. Francis. 1997. *A Pacific interdecadal climate oscillation with impacts on salmon production*. Bulletin of the American Meteorological Society, 78, pp. 1069–1079.

Maragos, J. and D. Gulko. 2002. *Coral Reef Ecosystems of the Northwest Hawaiian Islands: Interim Results Emphasizing the 2000 Surveys*. United States Fish and Wildlife Service and the Hawai'i Department of Land and Natural Resources. Internet website: http://www.hawaii.edu/ssri/hcri/files/nwhi_report.pdf. Accessed 29 December 2006.

Mercado, LCDR Carlos. 2007. Assistant Branch Chief, Incident Management Branch and D14 Small Boat Manager, United States Coast Guard, District 14. Personal communication with Derek Campbell, Office of General Counsel for International Law, National Oceanic and Atmospheric Administration. January 2007.

Metcalf, Kathy. 2006. Director of Maritime Affairs, Chamber of Shipping of America. Personal communication with Lindy S. Johnson, Office of General Counsel for International Law, National Oceanic and Atmospheric Administration. September 2006.

Miller, J.E., S. Vogt, R. Hoeke, S. Ferguson, B. Applegate, J.R. Smith, and M. Parke. 2004. *Bathymetric Atlas and Website for the Northwestern Hawaiian Islands*. Atoll Res. Bull., 543:409–422.

Mohri, Tadaatsu. 2006. First Secretary, Embassy of Japan. Personal communication with Margaret Hayes, United States State Dept. December 2006.

National Oceanic and Atmospheric Administration. 2004. Endangered Species Act Recovery Program – Biennial Report to Congress, 2002–2004. Hawaiian Monk Seal, pp. 137–140.

National Oceanic and Atmospheric Administration, Coastal Services Center. 2004a. Coastal Zone '03: Proceedings of the 13th Biennial Coastal Zone Conference, Baltimore, Maryland.

National Oceanic and Atmospheric Administration. 2004b. Northwestern Hawaiian Islands Coral Reef Ecosystem Reserve Draft Final Reserve Operations Plan. United States Department of Commerce. Honolulu, Hawaii.

National Oceanic and Atmospheric Administration, Hazardous Materials Response and Assessment Division. 1992. Oil Spill Case Histories – 1967–1991, Summaries of Significant United States and International Spills. Report No. HMRAD 92-11.

Naughton, Maura and Elizabeth Flint. 2004. *Population and conservation status of seabirds nesting in the Northwestern Hawaiian Islands*. Northwestern Hawaiian Islands 3rd Scientific Symposium, 2–4 November 2004.

Northwestern Hawaiian Islands Marine National Monument. 2006. A Citizen's Guide: Northwestern Hawaiian Islands Marine National Monument. Available at http://www.hawaiireef.noaa.gov/PDFs/Citizens_Guide_Web. pdf. Accessed 1 January 2007.

Northwestern Hawaiian Islands Marine National Monument. 2006. Northwestern Hawaiian Islands Frequently Asked Questions (Draft).

O'Hare, Donald L. 2006. Vice President, World Shipping Council. Personal communication with Lindy S. Johnson, Office of General Counsel for International Law, National Oceanic and Atmospheric Administration. 21 September 2006.

Press, F. and R. Siever. 1986. Earth, 4th edition. W.H. Freeman and Co., New York.

Shallenberger, Robert J. 2004. History of Management in the Northwestern Hawaiian Islands. Hawaiian Islands Third Scientific Symposium, 2 November 2004.

Suthers, Dan. 2004. A Predator Dominated Ecosystem: Comparing the Fish of the Northwestern and Main Hawaiian Islands. Northwestern Hawaiian Islands Multi-Agency Education Project. Internet website: http://www. hawaiianatolls.org/research/NWHIRAMP2004/features/predator-dominated.php. Accessed 15 January 2007.

TenBruggencate, Jan. 2006. *Study revises monk seals' diet*. Honolulu Advertiser, 1 December 2006.

Tosatto, Mike. 2005. Deputy Regional Administrator, National Oceanic and Atmospheric Administration, Pacific Islands Regional Office. Personal communication with Joel Paschal, Tetra Tech, Inc. 6 January 2005.

United States Coast Pilot 7, 38th Edition. 2006. Northwestern Hawaiian Islands, Chapter 14. National Oceanic and Atmospheric Administration, Office of Coast Survey.

United States Coral Reef Task Force. 1999. Coastal Uses Working Group Summary Report. November 1999.

United States Fish and Wildlife Service. 2005. Seabird Conservation Plan, Pacific Region.

Western Pacific Regional Fishery Management Council. Undated. North-western Hawaiian Islands Protected Species Zone – Closure to Longline Fishing. Available at: http://www.wpcouncil.org/protected.htm. Accessed 1 January 2007.

Annex 17 – Strait of Bonifacio Particularly Sensitive Sea Area

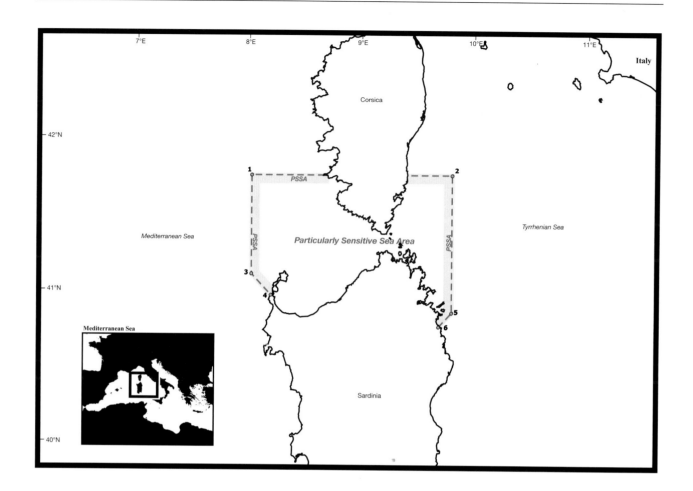

Resolution MEPC.204(62)

adopted on 15 July 2011

Designation of the Strait of Bonifacio as a Particularly Sensitive Sea Area

THE MARINE ENVIRONMENT PROTECTION COMMITTEE,

BEING AWARE of the ecological, socio-economic and scientific attributes of the Strait of Bonifacio, as well as its vulnerability to damage by international shipping activities and the steps taken by France and Italy to address that vulnerability,

NOTING the Revised Guidelines for the Identification and Designation of Particularly Sensitive Sea Areas adopted by resolution A.982(24) (PSSA Guidelines) and the Revised Guidance Document for Submission of PSSA Proposals to IMO set forth in MEPC.1/Circ.510,

HAVING CONSIDERED the proposal made by the Governments of France and Italy that the Strait of Bonifacio be designated as a Particularly Sensitive Sea Area,

HAVING AGREED that the criteria for the identification and designation of a Particularly Sensitive Sea Area provided in resolution A.982(24) are fulfilled for the Strait of Bonifacio,

HAVING NOTED that the Sub-Committee on Safety of Navigation, at its fifty-seventh session, approved the Recommendation on navigation through the Strait of Bonifacio as an associated protective measure for the application of the Strait of Bonifacio as a Particularly Sensitive Sea Area aiming at improving the safety of navigation and the protection of the marine environment,

1   DESIGNATES the Strait of Bonifacio described in annex 1 as a Particularly Sensitive Sea Area pending the final adoption of the associated protective measure for the PSSA, as set out in annex 2 to document NAV 57/15;

2   INVITES Member Governments to recognize the ecological, socio-economic, and scientific attributes of the area, set forth in annex 2, as well as its vulnerability to damage by international shipping activities, as described in annex 3; and

3   FURTHER INVITES Member Governments to note the associated protective measure established to address the area's vulnerability, the details of which are contained in annex 4, which is expected to enter into force following final adoption on a date to be circulated by the Organization to all Member Governments, and request ships flying their flag that they act in accordance with such measures.

Annex 1

Description of the Strait of Bonifacio PSSA

To avoid the risk of damage from ship groundings and pollution damage by international shipping activities and the destruction and degradation of this unique, diverse, and significant habitat and ecosystem, mariners should exercise extreme care when navigating in the area bounded by a line connecting the following geographical positions, which is designated as a Particularly Sensitive Sea Area:

  – To the north: a line linking point 41°45′00″ N, 008°01′48″ E to point 41°45′00″ N, 009°48′30″ E passing the French coast (Cap Muro to the west and Anse de Tarcu to the east);

  – On the western side: a line linking points 41°45′00″ N, 008°01′48″ E; 41°06′36″ N, 008°01′48″ E and 40°58′00″ N, 008°12′00″ E on the Italian coast; and

  – On the eastern side: a line linking points 41°45′00″ N, 009°48′30″ E; 40°41′08″ N, 009°48′30″ E and 40°45′56″ N, 009°41′42″ E on the Italian coast to the south.

The Particularly Sensitive Sea Area is bounded by the points A, B, C, D, E, and F as set out in the chartlet below.

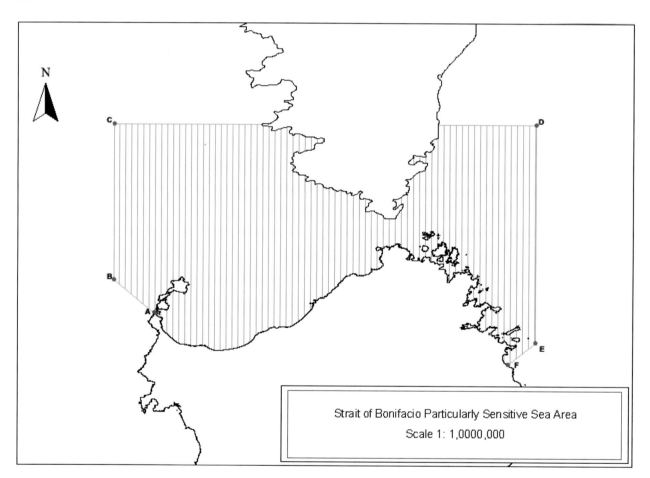

Strait of Bonifacio Particularly Sensitive Sea Area
Scale 1: 1,0000,000

Annex 2

Ecological, socio-economic, and scientific attributes of the Strait of Bonifacio PSSA

1 Ecological criteria

1.1 The ecological significance of the Strait of Bonifacio region was internationally recognized when it was granted the status of Specially Protected Area of Mediterranean Importance (SPAMI) at the sixteenth session of the Conference of Contracting Parties to the Barcelona Convention for the Protection of the Mediterranean Sea against Pollution, which took place from 3 to 5 November 2009 in Marrakesh.

1.2 The ecological significance of the French part of the Strait of Bonifacio is recognized by a number of official listings involving a total of 104,000 ha of mainly marine environment:

- Listing as a nature reserve by a decree of 23 September 1999 (80,000 ha);

- Listing as a Natura 2000 site, these being a network of European Union areas which, owing to their great environmental value, need the protection of States:

    - a Special Protection Area under Directive 79/409/EEC (Birds), "Lavezzi Islands, Strait of Bonifacio", covering 98,941 ha, designated by inter-ministerial decree of 30 October 2008;

    - three Sites of Community Importance under Directive 92/43/EEC (Habitat) concerning the conservation of natural habitats and wild fauna and flora:

      Strait of Bonifacio, Monk Islands (94,612 ha);

      Cerbical Islands and coastal strip (3698 ha);

      Pertusato/Bonifacio plateau and Lavezzi Islands (6071 ha).

1.3 The ecological significance of the Italian part of the Strait of Bonifacio is recognized by several listings, as follows:

The La Maddalena Archipelago National Park, by decree of the President of the Republic dated 17 May 1996, covering 5100 ha on land and 15,046 ha at sea;

The Asinara National Park, by decree of the President of the Republic dated 13 October 2002, covering 5170 ha on land;

The Isola Asinara protected marine area, by ministerial decree of 12 August 2002, covering 10,732 ha at sea;

The Tavolara Punta Coda Cavallo protected marine area, by ministerial decree of 12 December 1997, amended by ministerial decree of 28 November 2001, covering 15,357 ha;

Listings of Natura 2000 sites, as follows:

Six Special Protection Areas under Directive 79/409/EEC (Birds):
  Isola Asinara (9669 ha)
  Isola Piana – Golfo dell'Asinara (399 ha)
  Stagno di Pilo, Casaraccio e Saline di Stintino (1290 ha)
  Arcipelago La Maddalena (20,955 ha)
  Isole del Nord-Est tra Capo Ceraso e Stagno di San Teodoro (18,174 ha)
  Capo Figari, Cala Sabina, Punta Canigione e Isola Figarolo (4053 ha)

Twelve Sites of Community Significance under Directive 92/43/EEC (Habitat), in connection with the conservation of natural habitats and wild fauna and flora:
  Coste e Isolette a Nord Ovest della Sardegna (3731 ha)
  Isola Asinara (9669 ha)
  Isola Piana (510 ha)
  Stagno di Pilo e di Casaraccio (1879 ha)

Stagno e ginepreto di Platamona (1618 ha)

Foci del Coghinas (2267 ha)

Isola Rossa – Costa Paradiso (5409 ha)

Monte Russu (1971 ha)

Capo Testa (1217 ha)

Arcipelago La Maddalena (20,955 ha)

Isola Tavolara, Molara e Molarotto (3764 ha)

Capo Figari e Isola Figarolo (851 ha).

1.4 The European Commission approved the above-mentioned list of Sites of Community Importance by its decision of 22 December 2009 in relation to the Mediterranean biogeographical region enforceable under Directive 92/43/EEC.

1.5 The following information is taken from the declaration forms of the Natura 2000 sites mentioned above and from the biological evaluation of the Strait of Bonifacio nature reserve for the 2007–2011 management plan.

1.6 This sector is also covered by the Pelagos Agreement for the Creation of a Mediterranean Sanctuary for Marine Mammals, signed in Rome on 25 November 1999 by France, Italy and the Principality of Monaco. The aim of the agreement is to maintain a level of conservation beneficial to marine mammal populations, and to that end to monitor the cetacean populations, strengthen the application of the existing external legislation for certain types of fishing and to reduce pollution, regulate the numbers of tourists who come to observe cetaceans, and improve the information provided for the public. The bottlenose dolphin is a regular visitor to the edges of this area.

1.7 The exceptional ecological wealth of the area comprises a wide range of marine environments, including:

– inclines and rocky shallows harbouring varied fauna and flora;

– well-preserved *Posidonia* beds;

– near Figari, a rare estuary system in which areas emerge at low tide on the island.

1.8 Species and habitats whose rarity or significance are recognized at national, Community or international level find the environmental conditions ideal here.

Uniqueness or rarity

1.9 The Strait of Bonifacio area contains 37 per cent of species of Mediterranean importance (SPAMI Annex II and III, Barcelona Convention). The flora includes some 15 endemic species (Corsican or Corsican-Sardinian or Corsican/Sardinian/Balearic), with one endemic to the island of Lavezzu.

1.10 The area contains between 40 and 50 per cent of the sites for *Silene velutina*, a small endemic flower whose distribution is limited to the extreme south of Corsica and the north of Sardinia. Another protected plant belonging to the first rank in terms of floral heritage is *Limonium lambinonii*, which is endemic to Lavezzu Island.

1.11 The leatherback turtle has not been seen here since the 1960s, but the loggerhead turtle has been spotted more regularly in the Strait of Bonifacio in the past decade. In October 2001 its nests were even discovered on the beaches of Palombaggia, south of the Cerbical archipelago.

1.12 While the alga *Goniolothon byssoides* is difficult not to notice, sightings are very rare. It appears to be vulnerable, given the small number of sites where it can be found. Also, its pads detach very easily, making it highly vulnerable to trampling by fishermen and swimmers (Boudouresque et al. 1990). Verlaque (1991) noted its presence around the Lavezzi Islands.

Critical habitat

1.13   This area offers great potential for the conservation of a large number of nationally important habitats and species. Certain species (the European shag, the giant limpet *Patella ferruginea*) are present in numbers which provide the nucleus of genetically stable populations that may be considered source populations capable of providing the starting point for colonization (natural or artificial) of potential habitats, to differing degrees, depending on the manner in which the larvae and individual representatives of those species are distributed. This area of the Strait of Bonifacio is thus of vital importance for declining populations or small sub-populations of species. For example, conservation of the national gene pool of threatened meta-populations of species such as the giant limpet could allow it to be reintroduced into areas of the Mediterranean where it is now extinct.

1.14   The care of this area is also very important to marine avifauna. This is a major site for the European shag (*Phalacrocorax aristotelis aristotelis*) and for sizeable numbers of Cory's shearwater (*Calonectris diomedea*). The Strait of Bonifacio is also a main point for the passage, roosting and feeding of the Yelkouan shearwater. The whole area is a feeding ground for these species.

1.15   The European shag population does not exceed 10,000 pairs across the whole of its small area of distribution in the Mediterranean. The Strait of Bonifacio has high priority in the conservation of this species. In 2001, the nesting population of the Strait of Bonifacio represented more than 50 per cent of the French population and 7 per cent of the world population. The main problems for this species are disturbance to nesting sites, accidental capture during small-scale fishing and the disappearance of habitats owing to the expansion of tourism.

1.16   The nesting population of Cory's shearwater accounts for 40 per cent of the national nesting total. With 345 pairs, the Lavezzu Island colony is the most numerous in France. This species is on the decline owing to the introduction of allocthonous species (dogs, cats and rats), the removal of eggs from certain colonies and the development of tourism, which disturbs colonies and destroys habitat.

1.17   With around 200 nesting pairs within the perimeter of the area, the population of the highly unobtrusive storm petrel (*Hydrobates pelagicus*) represents around one third of the French Mediterranean population and between 15 and 18 per cent of the French population, including Atlantic birds. Europe's smallest marine bird (15 cm) is in steep decline in the Mediterranean, mainly owing to the introduction of predators such as the black rat (*Rattus rattus*). The colonies are now highly localized and concentrated, making them very vulnerable.

Dependency

1.18   The main ecosystems of the Strait of Bonifacio area, whether deep-sea or coastal, are closely interconnected: pelagic open-water systems, gulfs, intertidal zone, supralittoral environments, islets and lagoons.

1.19   Being an open system, the marine environment does not experience fragmentation of habitats to the same degree as the land environment. In the Strait of Bonifacio the long-protected areas of the Lavezzi, the fish confinement areas and the decreed biotopes of the Monk and Bruzzi islands shelter balanced populations which embrace all age-groups and assure the reproduction of larvae (fish, crustaceans, …) and their diffusion to more recently established nature reserves. Plankton production and the gathering of animal larvae condition the introduction of both marine and littoral trophic chains. By virtue of its geographical position and the existence of violent currents which facilitate larval distribution, the Strait of Bonifacio could play a not inconsiderable role in coastal fishing management in the north-western Mediterranean.

1.20   While the plankton-eating organisms are an indispensable resource for large pelagic species, seriolae and tuna, not to mention cetaceans (particularly bottlenose dolphins), they are also attractive to the marine birds present (European shag, Cory's shearwater, seagulls).

Representativeness

1.21 Beds of *Posidonia oceanica*, high-priority protected habitats, are widely represented. A *Posidonia* bed is a very valuable ecosystem from the biodiversity point of view, and is also very important to fishing, coastal protection and the enrichment of certain other coastal ecosystems. It is an excellent indicator of the overall quality of the natural environment. In many parts of the Mediterranean it has been seriously affected by human activities, and some beds are in serious decline. Beds of *Posidonia oceanica* are characteristic of the infralittoral stage in the Mediterranean. Those in the Strait of Bonifacio area cover more than 5,000 ha and are in excellent condition. They play a leading role in the area's productivity and provide sites for breeding, spawning and raising young.

1.22 The alga *Lithophyllum lichenoides*, found in belts in the intertidal zone, is included in annex I of the "Habitat" Directive. This species is well represented along the battered granite and limestone coasts of the Strait of Bonifacio. The oldest and largest belts are found along the cliffs at Bonifacio and in the Lavezzi Islands.

1.23 Like other algae typical of sheltered sites in the infralittoral stage, certain types of *Cystoseira* have become rare because its habitat is suffering from pollution or eutrophication or has been destroyed by coastal management. Overgrazing by sea urchins, whose predators have been partially eliminated by man, also has to be taken into account. The *Cystoseira* are very well represented in the Strait and certain species, such as *C. funkii*, are seen on rare occasions at near-surface depths (Ballesteros & Pineda, 2003).

Diversity

1.24 The number of species recorded to date in the Strait of Bonifacio is 1,745. Among the 977 species of fauna are 18 mammals, 165 birds, seven reptiles, two amphibians, 187 fish, 11 protochordates, 13 echinoderms, 262 insects, 11 arachnids, six bryozoans, 103 crustaceans, 143 molluscs, seven annelids, 23 cnidarians and 19 spongarians.

1.25 Considering the faunistic taxons as a whole, it should be noted that:

- Twenty-three animal species are of Community significance. Care of this area is particularly important for two amphibians (*Discoglossus sardus* and *Hyla arborea sarda*), the bottlenose dolphin (*Tursiops truncatus*), chiroptera, marine molluscs, the fish *Aphanius fasciatus*, the loggerhead turtle (*Caretta caretta*), the gecko *Phyllodactylus europaeus*, the lizards *Podarcis tiliguerta* and *Lacerta bedriagae* and the snake *Coluber viridiflavus*. Among the animal species of Community significance whose capture in natural surroundings and cultivation can be managed, only the red coral *Corallium rubrum* can be and is being cultivated;

- Seventy-seven taxons are listed in the "Birds" Directive (all annexes combined). Among these birds are 16 species nesting in the area (including 10 from annex I), 24 regular migrants, 30 occasional migrants and five accidental migrants;

- The taxons strictly protected under the Berne Convention (annex II) amount to 139, with 70 other species being considered as protected species whose exploitation must be regulated (annex III);

- Three migratory species are in danger of extinction, namely the Audouin's gull (*Larus audouinii*) and the loggerhead and leatherback turtles (*Caretta caretta* and *Dermochelys coriacea*), which require strict protection under annex I of the Bonn Convention. Sixty-seven other species (reptiles, mammals and birds) are considered to be in a poor state of conservation under that Convention. All these species are also listed under the Berne Convention;

- Thirty-seven rare species are listed in the three annexes of the Convention on International Trade in Endangered Species of Wild Fauna and Flora (Washington Convention), for example the peregrine falcon (*Falco peregrinus*), the loggerhead turtle (*Caretta caretta*), the bottlenose dolphin (*Tursiops truncates*), and Hermann's Tortoise (*Testudo hermanni*);

- Thirty-three species are identified as endangered or threatened under the Barcelona Protocol concerning Specially Protected Areas of Mediterranean Importance (SPAMI) (annex II) and 14 as requiring control over their exploitation. These species are also listed in the annexes to the Berne

Convention. Among the exploited species, we note two large fish: the swordfish *Xiphias gladius* and the red tuna *Thunnus thynnus*;

– There are 148 wildlife taxons protected at national level, of which the great majority comprises birds (121 species). Nineteen of these nest in the Strait of Bonifacio area. Thirteen mammals present are protected at national level: seven cetaceans, four bats, the hedgehog *Erinaceus europaeus italicus* and the weasel *Mustela nivalis corsica*. Also protected are four land reptiles, two amphibians, two marine turtles and one fish, namely the Mediterranean shad (*Alosa fallax nilotica*). Among the marine species, the needle-spined sea urchin *Centrostephanus longispinus*, the Mediterranean slipper lobster *Scyllarides latus*, the pen shell *Pinna nobilis* and the limpet *Patella ferruginea* are protected;

– In the context of the International Union for Conservation of Nature (IUCN) Red List, the leatherback turtle (*Dermochelys coriacea*), observed only a few times in the past 50 years, is classified as critically endangered and four species, the fin whale (*Balaenoptera physalus*), the loggerhead turtle (*Caretta caretta*), the dusky grouper (*Epinephelus marginatus*) and the common seabream (*Pagrus pagrus*), as endangered. Nine species are considered vulnerable, i.e. as facing a high risk of extinction in the wild. These include the gecko *Phyllodactylus europaeus*, the long-fingered bat (*Myotis capaccinii*) and certain threatened cartilaginous fish: the great white shark (*Carcharodon carcharias*), the basking shark (*Cetorhinus maximus*), the manta ray *Mobula mobular*, the liver-oil shark (*Galeorhinus galeus*), and the angel shark (*Squatina squatina*). Lastly, the status of 161 species is considered to be of concern (10 mammals, 143 birds, one amphibian, two reptiles and four fish);

– Seventy species feature in the Red Lists of the French Natural History Museum in Paris. The endangered species number 13, including the loggerhead turtle (*Caretta caretta*) and the Mediterranean slipper lobster (*Scyllarides latus*). The following are considered to be vulnerable in France: the pen shell *Pinna nobilis*, the limpet *Patella ferruginea*, the brown meagre (*Sciaena umbra*) and the nursehound (*Scyliorhinus stellaris*).

1.26   Among the floral taxons:

– Eight are included in annex I of the Berne Convention, including *Silene velutina* and *Posidonia oceanica*;

– Five algae are also included in SPAMI Annex III;

– Fifteen plant species are protected at national level, including 12 terrestrial species. The marine species include *Posidonia oceanica* and another marine phanerogam, namely the seagrass *Cymodocea nodosa*, which is also well represented in the Strait of Bonifacio;

– Four species are considered to be vulnerable by the IUCN: *Helicodiceros muscivorus*, *Drimia fugax*, *Nananthea perpusilla* and *Silene velutina*. They all enjoy protected status.

1.27   The diversity and complementarity found among the various littoral ecological compartments can be considered a major asset for this area. There are around fifty elementary habitats, with ecosystems ranging from coastal scrub to saltgrass and from lagoons to the depths of the circalittoral zone.

1.28   The coastal, littoral and salty habitats, such as the mobile and fixed dunes of the Mediterranean shores where *Crucianella maritima* is found, and halophilous scrub conceal all the floral taxons of major heritage importance.

1.29   At sea, the major "reefs" type of habitat brings together rocky habitats of the mediolitteral zone as well as all the fauna and flora of the intertidal zone. Biocoenoses of photophilous algae and coral are also integrated into this major type of habitat. All the types of *Gorgonia*, *Cystoseira* and the large bryozoans are also important elements of the area's rich heritage and require special protection against the impact of underwater activities and of global changes relating to rise in sea temperature.

Productivity

1.30 The large expanse of sea and strong currents, as well as the richness of the fish stocks, widely recognized by Mediterranean ichthyologists, give this protected marine area a major role in the dispersion of larvae throughout the western Mediterranean. That role is essential for the threatened species in a good state of preservation in the Strait of Bonifacio, such as the dusky grouper (*Epinephelus marginatus*), but also for other species of importance in the heritage and fishing contexts.

Spawning or breeding grounds

1.31 The waters of the lagoon habitats (Pisciu Cane, Testarella and Ventilègne), rich in nutritive salts carried from the drainage basins across which they pass, stimulate the growth of lagoon phytoplankton. These lagoons nourish and shelter many marine species. The dense plant growth, adapted to the complementary influences of sea and land, is home to many aquatic and avian species. These biotopes provide ideal shelter for nesting and reproduction and are an important source of food. Yellow-legged gulls, grey herons, little egrets and even young ospreys are regularly observed there. The mosaic of vegetation and the presence of smooth stretches of standing water make it possible for certain wintering or migrating Anatidae to come here on an irregular basis (mallard ducks, pintails, Northern shovellers, common teals and garganeys ...), as well as migrating shorebirds (common snipes, jack snipes, sandpipers, black-tailed godwits, little stints). Mallards, moorhens and water rails occasionally nest on Testarella lake. As mentioned above, the *Posidonia* beds play a major role in the area's productivity and provide areas for breeding, spawning and the raising of young.

Fragility

1.32 Many habitats are important, in terms of heritage, by virtue of their representativity in the Mediterranean context and the direct and indirect threats they face.

1.33 For 15,000 years man has been exerting his influence as an integral part of the ecological system of the Strait of Bonifacio. Man-induced factors (sample-captures, alteration or destruction of habitat, disturbances, introduction of species ...), whether old or more recent, direct or indirect, are exerting an increasing impact as methods of navigation and sampling techniques evolve. Those factors are responsible for the disappearance of the monk seal (*Monachus monachus*) and the reduced populations of the limpet *Patella ferruginea*, a process which has been affecting that mollusc since prehistoric times, and the grouper *Epinephelus marginatus* for 30 years.

1.34 It is also quite clear that climate change, especially the increases in air and sea temperatures, as well as fishing activities across the Mediterranean are exerting an ever-increasing influence on the overall functioning of the Strait of Bonifacio.

1.35 Increase in seawater temperature triggers significant changes in the ways that pelagic communities (tropicalization of plankton production) or benthic communities function in the north-west Mediterranean. It benefits tropical species, such as the yellowmouth barracuda (*Sphyraena viridensis*), to the detriment of certain Mediterranean species that cannot support the rise in temperature. In this regard, the spectacular rise in mortality rates since 1998 among gorgonians is cause for concern.

1.36 Man-induced activities also generate cascade effects. Such occurrences may be confined to the territory of a protected marine area or affect its periphery. Thus, the destabilization of *Posidonia oceanica* owing to increased numbers of unregulated anchorages or sediment erosion is leading to a reduction in the populations of species associated with this habitat, in particular the pen shell *Pinna nobilis*. Failure to manage household waste and the existence of open-air public landfill sites for over 30 years have brought about an increase in the population of yellow-legged gulls (*Larus cachinnans*) and a serious deterioration in the micro-insular systems of southern Corsica (destabilization of vegetation by the action of nitro-phosphates on floristic corteges, and inter-species competition between the very rare Audouin's gull (*Larus audouinii*) and the yellow-legged gull, to the latter's advantage).

1.37   Waste from purification plants undergoing repair is also likely to affect the existing habitats. Large-scale recreational use of the location also produces effluent and larger waste products, particularly plastic bags, which become mixed in with schools of jellyfish and are then consumed by loggerhead turtles and bottlenose dolphins, causing obstruction of their digestive systems.

1.38   The habitat known as "silty sands in sheltered areas (Mediterranean) biocoenosis" in the large creeks and shallow bays of Lavezzi, Cavallu, Ventilègne, Santa Manza, Porto Novo and Rondinara remains under the influence of the nutrients and pollutants which arrive from the drainage basins, bringing the risk of hypoxia or anoxia owing to the low water renewal rate. This habitat can also prove to be a good indicator of anthropization level in the drainage basins themselves.

1.39   The habitats of submerged or semi-submerged sea caves are extremely sensitive to the impact of man. The Sdragonato cave and undersea caves used in diving are areas of particular sensitivity.

1.40   In France, the belts of *Lithophyllum lichenoides* have receded in polluted areas. The situation of the algal limestone belts, like that of *L. lichenoides* at the mediolittoral level, and their porous structure make these formations highly vulnerable to surface pollution by effluents, oily film on the water and other agents. The loss of even a little salinity in the water prevents them from forming. There could also be a threat from phosphate ions and detergents (LABOREL, unpublished, in Boudouresque et al. 1990). A belt appears to take an exceptionally long time to build up (several centuries) and it is imperative to protect the existing ones (Boudouresque et al. 1990).

2   Scientific and educational criteria

2.1   Baseline for monitoring studies

2.1.1   In considering the importance of preserving the habitats and meta-populations mentioned above, their vulnerability must be assessed with caution. Long-term observation of reliable scientific indicators will help distinguish between natural cycles and genuine man-induced disturbances.

2.1.2   This area can also play a role in the transfer of ecological engineering in relation to sustainable resource management. The length of time that protection measures have been in place in southern Corsica, differences in regulations and hence in the pressures from fishing activities inside this protected area in Corsica and in Sardinia, the conservation of reference areas (areas of strict protection) and finally the long-standing acquisition of reliable scientific data are factors which can be used in establishing sustainable development models for Mediterranean coastal areas.

Annex 3
Vulnerability to damage by international shipping activities

1 Natural factors

1.1 Hydrographical

1.1.1 The hydrographical conditions in the Strait of Bonifacio are strongly influenced by the region's landscape and climate. In particular, there are frequent very strong currents (3–4 knots), largely determined by the winds. These strong currents have already, on two occasions, caused the South Lavezzi signalling buoy to shift. They derive from cyclonic and anti-cyclonic conditions and are responsible for surface changes among the Tyrrhenian and Algero-Provencal water masses. Movements originating in the Atlantic and Tyrrhenian systems, being less subject to the vagaries of the weather where water masses of permanent density are concerned, also affect the bathymetric layer between 50 m and 100 m. This situation explains (Romano, 2004), at least for surface waters, the existence of strong currents, especially as the strait between Corsica and Sardinia is characterized by a rise in depths.

1.1.2 The tides are semidiurnal with diurnal inequality, with a tidal range of less than 0.5 m.

1.2 Meteorological

1.2.1 Having a sub-humid Mediterranean climate, with temperate winters, the Strait of Bonifacio region is also particularly windy. Data recorded by the Pertusato semaphore station on the Bonifacio plateau show that the wind blows on 328 days per year (171 days of wind >16 m/s or 57.6 km/h). There is high frequency of winds of a speed faster than 8 m/s, almost exclusively from two directions: West (280°) and East (80°).

1.2.2 Given the hydrographical, topographical and meteorological conditions (shoals, strong winds and currents), the major risk to the Strait of Bonifacio area relates to accidental pollution from all forms of navigation in the Strait itself (several merchant ships have sunk in the past 30 years), and also on its periphery. The risk of collision with a bottlenose dolphin is also a threat identified by the Pelagos sanctuary for Mediterranean marine mammals.

2 Vessel traffic characteristics

2.1 In 2009, Bonifacio Trafic (the Franco-Italian service) received 2,984 mandatory ship reports. Among them were 180 abnormalities (breaches of IMO Assembly resolution A.766(18)) of which 108 were for transport of dangerous goods, amounting to 147,013 tonnes (141,867 tonnes in 2008). The offences included 55 cases of sending a mandatory report after entering the system, 19 relating to ships found to be following a route that was not recommended (down by 33% on 2008) and 108 relating to ships carrying dangerous goods (+9%).

2.2 In 2009 a total of 157 ships carrying dangerous goods passed through the Strait of Bonifacio:

- 70 containerships;
- 61 ro-ro ships;
- 13 bulk carriers;
- five chemical carriers;
- three oil tankers;
- three gas tankers;
- two ferries.

2.3   The 2,984 vessels which navigated in the Strait of Bonifacio in 2009 were distributed as follows:

European Union

Italy 831; France 371; Malta 251; Netherlands 152; Portugal 78; United Kingdom 67; Cyprus 50.

Non-EU

Turkey 100; Antigua 183; Bahamas 165; Panama 143.

2.4   The status that the Strait of Bonifacio enjoys as an international strait and the provisions of IMO resolution A.766(18) contribute to making it, although it is apart from the major shipping routes (3000 ships per year) and its dangerousness is well known, an area in which the coastal authorities are confined to the role of spectator, waiting for a maritime accident to happen.

Annex 4
Associated Protective Measures for the Strait of Bonifacio PSSA

Description of the area

The Strait of Bonifacio separates the Italian island of Sardinia from the French island of Corsica; they are only 11 km apart. The Strait takes its name from Bonifacio, the southernmost town of Corsica. It enables passage from the Sea of Sardinia in the west to the Tyrrhenian Sea in the east. Its width varies from eight to ten nautical miles and its maximum depth is 100 m.

At the eastern end lies the Italian archipelago of La Maddalena, and Cavallo island and the Lavezzi Islands, belonging to France. This is a sensitive area for navigation. In the northern part of the Strait, ships have to avoid the reefs of Perduto and the Lavezzi Islands, while in the south lie the Sardinian islands of Razzoli and Persa. Navigation is possible along a narrow three-mile-wide stretch and ships are asked to take a recommended route just over one mile wide.

Relevant rules and regulations in force in the area

The Strait of Bonifacio falls into the category of "Straits used for international navigation" regulated by the United Nations Convention on the Law of the Sea (UNCLOS), better known as the Montego Bay Convention (10 December 1982).

The maritime traffic is represented mainly by merchant ships that cross the Strait along east–west direction (several dozens of ships per day). Considering the traffic that occurs in the direction north–south, it concerns mainly passenger ships (approximately ten daily connections), is very intense and growing during the summer, especially between Bonifacio (Corsica) and Santa Teresa di Gallura (Sardinia). In addition, there are about 5000 pleasure craft crossing this area during the summer season.

Regulation applied to navigation on the Strait of Bonifacio is based on resolution A.766(18) adopted in 1993 by IMO. This text urges ships carrying hazardous materials to avoid transit along this seaway. It has been complemented by circulars SN/Circ.198 and 201 (26 May 1998) of IMO concerning "routeing measures other than traffic separation schemes" and "mandatory ship reporting systems" applicable to the Bouches of Bonifacio from 1 December 1998 at 0000 hours UTC.

France and Italy have implemented these provisions through the establishment of the rule "Bonifacio Trafic" that represents a more restrictive device; inasmuch as the French and Italian ships carrying hazardous materials are banned entirely from transit of the "Bouches de Bonifacio".

For this reason, in 1993, both Italy, with the Decree of 26 February 1993 of the Italian Ministry of Merchant Marine, and France, by ordinance of 15 February of the Prefecture of Toulon, have banned the transit of tankers flying Italian or French flag carrying hydrocarbons and other hazardous and noxious substances, as defined by international conventions in force in both countries.[*]

On the basis of these decrees, the prohibition of navigation in the Strait does not apply to merchant ships flying flags of third countries and to Italian and French ships empty or those that carry different cargoes, which, even if properly ballasted, however, represent an environmental risk factor in case of accident from the presence of fuel in their tanks. This ban has led to a reduction of marine traffic, but at the same time, it leaves the possible passage of ships flying other flags, and often these ships are in unsafe condition (especially the lack of double-hull or similar technologies) and poor maintenance.

---

[*] Particularly, the Decree n° 1/93 (signed in Toulon on 15 February 1993) of the Prefecture maritime de la Mediterranée, applicable only to French ships, prohibits in the Bouches de Bonifacio the circulation of tankers carrying hydrocarbons and ships carrying hazardous or toxic materials. The annex of the Decree lists the hydrocarbons and the substances in question, in reference to the MARPOL Convention. At the same time, the Decree of the Italian merchant marine of 26 February 1993 prohibits the movement of Italian tankers carrying hydrocarbons and ships carrying hazardous or toxic materials.

Moreover, the arrêté n° 84/98 of 3 November 1998 of the Prefecture Maritime of Toulon* (amended by the arrêté 56/2003 of the Prefecture Maritime of Toulon) disciplines the navigation in the Strait of Bonifacio to prevent accidental episodes of marine pollution.

It institutes precautionary areas at the extremities of a two-way route, and the creation of the system of monitoring of ships from a radius of 20 miles from the Strait of Bonifacio. In parallel, the Decree of the Italian Ministry of Transport and Navigation on the organization of traffic in the Bonifacio Strait establishes the same procedures contained in the Decree n° 84/98.

Furthermore, a technical agreement between Italy and France to implement the reporting system of the ships in the Bouches of Bonifacio (Bonifacio Trafic) was signed in Rome on 3 June 1999.

Moreover, in order to restrict dangerous maritime traffic through Bonifacio Strait, the *"Accordo volontario per l'attuazione di una serie di interventi finalizzati al conseguimento di più elevati standard di sicurezza ambientale in materia di trasporti marittimi di sostanze pericolose"* (Voluntary agreement to carrying out a series of interventions aimed at the achievement of higher security environmental standards concerning the maritime transport of dangerous substances) was drawn up in Italy, signed by the Italian Ministry of the Environment, Land and Sea, by the Italian Ministry of Transportation and Navigation, by Confindustria, by Assoporti, by some environmental organizations and by unions (Rome, 1 June 2001).

Inter alia, the sixth article of the agreement foresaw the commitment by companies to use, from 1 July 2001, ships carrying dangerous substances listed in Annexes I and II of MARPOL solely based on contracts that explicitly exclude the transit in the Strait of Bonifacio, against a number of other compensations by government, including the engagement in an international venue for the encouragement of a PSSA in the Strait of Bonifacio.

Particularly, the sixth article of the Voluntary Agreement provides that:

> "6.1 – Confindustria and the interested industrial sectors undertake to promote immediately the insertion in the charter party for the use of ships carrying dangerous substances listed in Annexes I and II of MARPOL 73/78 of clauses that expressly exclude the transit in the Strait of Bonifacio.
>
> 6.2 – From 1 July 2001, Confindustria and the interested industrial sectors, also on behalf of firms and associated companies, undertake to use ships carrying dangerous substances listed in Annexes I and II of MARPOL 73/78 solely based on contracts that explicitly exclude the transit in the Strait of Bonifacio.
>
> 6.3 – The government engages to act in all EU and international venues to achieve the elimination of dangerous substances traffic in the Strait of Bonifacio, starting by defining by IMO the Strait of Bonifacio as Particularly Sensitive Sea Area (PSSA). Moreover, the government engages to promote every type of voluntary adherence of the EU member and candidate states to the above-mentioned elimination of dangerous substances traffic in the Strait of Bonifacio."

In the end, by the Decree of the Italian Ministry of Infrastructures and Transport of 29 July 2008 "Definition of the control of maritime traffic area in the Bouches of Bonifacio and activation of the relevant control centre at the Harbour Office of La Maddalena", was activated the centre VTS (Vessel Traffic Services) of the Bouches of Bonifacio, whose international name is "Bonifacio Traffic" and whose headquarters is located at the area Guardia Vecchia, under the authority of the Harbour Office – Coast Guard of La Maddalena.

Existing routeing measures and mandatory systems are set out in the chartlet, below.

---

* Arrêté Prefectoral n° 84/98 de 3 novembre 1998 du Préfet maritime de la Méditerranée –"Réglementant la navigation dans les Bouches de Bonifacio en vue de prévenir les pollutions marines accidentelles".

Chart of the existing routeing measures and mandatory ship reporting system

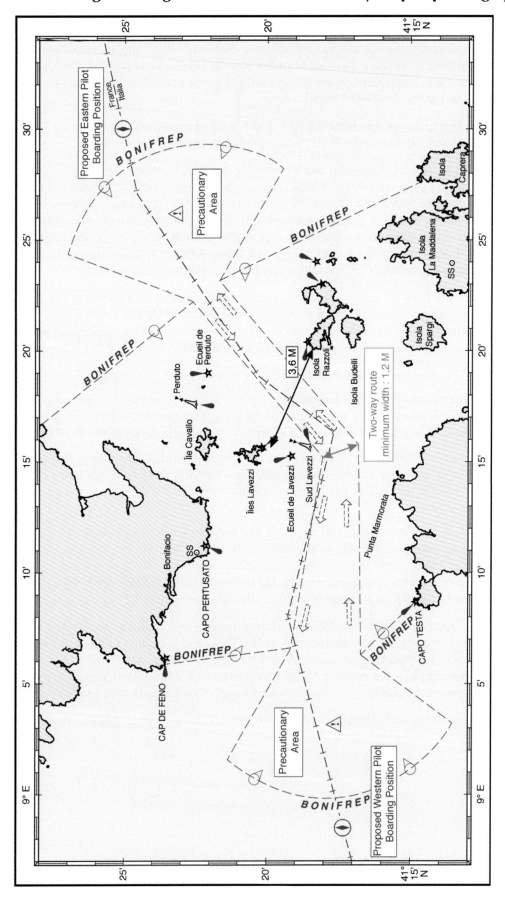

Routeing measures in the Strait of Bonifacio

A two-way route and precautionary areas at its extremities were adopted at the sixty-ninth session of MSC in 1998. Full technical descriptions of the route and the precautionary areas are in part E of editions of the IMO publication "Ships' Routeing"; only a chartlet of the route and areas is included here.

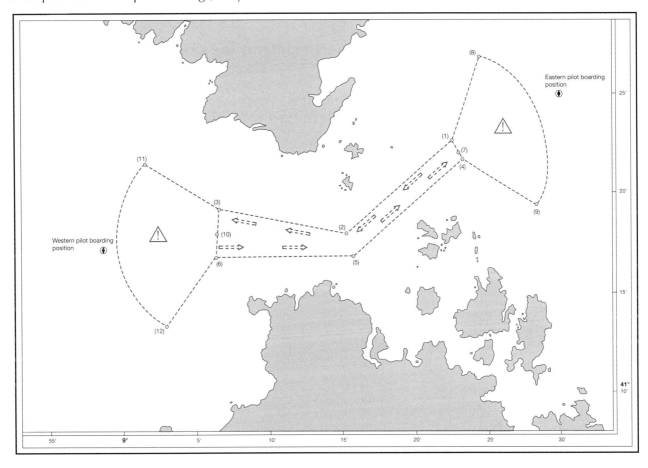

Mandatory ship reporting system in the Strait of Bonifacio

A mandatory ship reporting system was adopted at the sixty-ninth session of MSC in 1998.

In the strait of Bonifacio (BONIFREP)

1   Categories of ships required to participate in the system

Ships of 300 gross tonnage and over are required to participate in the system.

2   Geographical coverage of the system and reference chart

The reporting system covers a circular area with a radius of 20 nautical miles centred on Bonifacio. The reference chart is the French chart No. 7024 of the SHOM (Hydrographic and Oceanographic Service of the French Navy) (International chart No. 3350).

3   Format and contents of the report, times and geographical positions for submitting report, Authority to whom reports should be sent, available services

3.1   Content

The report required shall include:

- information considered essential:
    - the name of the ship, her call sign or IMO identification number (letter A)
    - time and position (letters C *or* D)
    - course and speed (letters E *and* F)
    - draught (letter O)
- additional information, if appropriate:
    - cargo (in case of transport of petroleum products, dangerous or polluting substances) (letter P)
    - defects or damage (letter Q)

In addition, in accordance with provisions of SOLAS and MARPOL Conventions, ships must report information on any defect, damage, deficiency or limitations as well as, if necessary, information relating to pollution incidents or loss of cargo. Possession of this information enables the operators to broadcast safety messages to other ship traffic and to ensure more effective tracking of the trajectories of ships concerned.

Ships shall transmit their reports on entering the precautionary areas defined in the documents about routeing measures in the Strait of Bonifacio, or when passing the following lines:

> *Eastbound:*

- A line linking the beacon of Cap de Feno in Corsica to point 41°19'.18 N, 009°06'.51 E (west end of the north limit of the two-way route)
- A line linking the beacon of Capo Testa in Sardinia to point 41°16'.75 N, 009°06'.18 E (west end of the south limit of the two-way route).

> *Westbound:*

- A line linking Pointe de Rondinara in Corsica to point 41°22'.55 N, 009°22'.38 E (east end of the north limit of the two-way route)
- A line linking Punta Galera in Sardinia to point 41°21'.58 N, 009°23'.30 E (east end of the south limit of the two-way route)

3.2   Recipient of report

The shore-based authorities are La Maddalena Coast Guard Station (Sardinia, Italy) and Pertusato Naval Signal Station (Corsica, France), common call sign: BONIFACIO TRAFFIC.

4   Information to be provided to ships and procedures to be followed

Detected and identified ships are monitored by radar, which in no way releases their master from their responsibility for safe navigation.

Following receiving a report, Bonifacio Traffic will provide:

- information on navigational conditions (status of aids to navigation, presence of other ships and their position at the moment of contact); and

- information on weather conditions.

5   Radiocommunications required for the system, frequencies on which reports should be transmitted and information to be reported

5.1   The radiocommunication equipment required for the system is VHF. Ship reports shall be transmitted by voice on VHF channel 10, back-up VHF channel 16, both permanently watched by the station. An IMO circular will provide for another back-up VHF channel, if necessary, after 1 February 1999. Use of an automatic identification system will be implemented in accordance with IMO decisions.

5.2   The report required from a ship is mentioned in paragraph 3.1 above and in the appendix "Summary". The language used shall be English or languages indicated in nautical publications.

5.3   Information of commercial confidentiality may be transmitted by non-verbal means. Detail of fax call number to be published in nautical information documents.

6   Rules and regulations in force in the area of the system

6.1   The International Regulations for Preventing Collisions at Sea (COLREGs) are applicable throughout the area of coverage of the system.

6.2   The IMO resolution A.766(18) about navigation in the Strait of Bonifacio, adopted on 4 November 1993, remains in force as far as it recommends each flag State to prohibit or at least strongly discourage the transit by certain categories of ships (operative paragraph 1). Its ship reporting provisions are replaced by those of the present instrument.

6.3   The regulation (arrêté) of the Préfet maritime for Mediterranean region n° 23/83 dated 6 May 1983 rules navigation in the approaches of the French coast in order to prevent accidental marine pollution, for ships carrying hazardous or polluting cargoes. This instrument has the following provisions:

- .1   for ships intending to enter French territorial waters, mandatory ship reporting with a six-hour advance warning. In addition to information concerning the identity of the ship, the report must specify the place and time of entry into French waters, the port arrived from and the destination, the cargo and the status of manoeuvrability and navigational capacities;

- .2   mandatory watch on VHF channel 16 while travelling through territorial waters; and

- .3   mandatory reporting of any damage occurring at less than 50 miles from the French coast.

6.4   French regulations (arrêté) of the Préfet maritime n°1/83 dated 15 February 1983 and 7/93 dated 5 March 1993 and Italian decree of the Minister of Merchant Marine dated 26 February 1993 prohibit transit through the Strait of Bonifacio for French and Italian ships carrying oil products or hazardous goods. They will remain in force.

7 Shore-based facilities to support operation of the system

7.1 Stations will be equipped with radar installations assisted by computer, covering the whole area.

7.2 Stations will be equipped with a duplicated VHF equipment.

7.3 Personnel operating the system: stations will be manned by Naval personnel on a 24-hour basis. Duty officers are qualified Senior Chief Petty-Officers.

8 Alternative communication if the communication facilities of the shore-based Authority fail

Each station will assure relief of the other one in case of failure.

Appendix

Summary

(Ship reporting system)

1 General

1.1 Vessels concerned

All ships of 300 gross tonnage and over.

1.2 Area on entering which vessels shall report

Ships shall transmit their reports on entering the precautionary areas defined in the documents about routeing measures in the Strait of Bonifacio, or when passing the following lines:

Eastbound:

- A line linking the beacon of Cap de Feno in Corsica to geographical position 41°19'.18 N, 009°06'.51 E (west end of the north limit of the two-way route)

- A line linking the beacon of Capo Testa in Sardinia to geographical position 41°16'.75 N, 009°06'.18 E (west end of the south limit of the two-way route).

Westbound:

- A line linking Pointe de Rondinara in Corsica to geographical position 41°22'.55 N, 009°22'.38 E (east end of the north limit of the two-way route)

- A line linking Punta Galera in Sardinia to geographical position 41°21'.58 N, 009°23'.30 E (east end of the south limit of the two-way route)

1.3 Reference chart

French (SHOM) chart No. 7024 (International chart No. 3350).

2 Reporting format

(In accordance with resolution A.851(20) – General principles for ship reporting systems and ship reporting requirements, including guidelines for reporting incidents involving dangerous goods, harmful substances and/or marine pollutants)

Name of system: BONIFREP

Data to be transmitted:

Heading	Information
A	Name + call sign + IMO Number
C *or* D	Time and position
E *and* F	Course and speed
O	Draught
P	Cargo (in case of transport of oil products, hazardous or polluting substances)
Q	Defect or damage (if relevant)
R	Polluting/dangerous goods lost overboard (if relevant)

In the event of defect, pollution or goods lost overboard, additional information may be requested.

3 Authority to whom the report shall be sent

Pertusato Naval Signal Station (France) – La Maddalena Coast Guard Station (Italy); common call sign: BONIFACIO TRAFFIC.

4 Communications facilities

The reports are to be transmitted on VHF channel 10 (or on channel 16 if not possible).

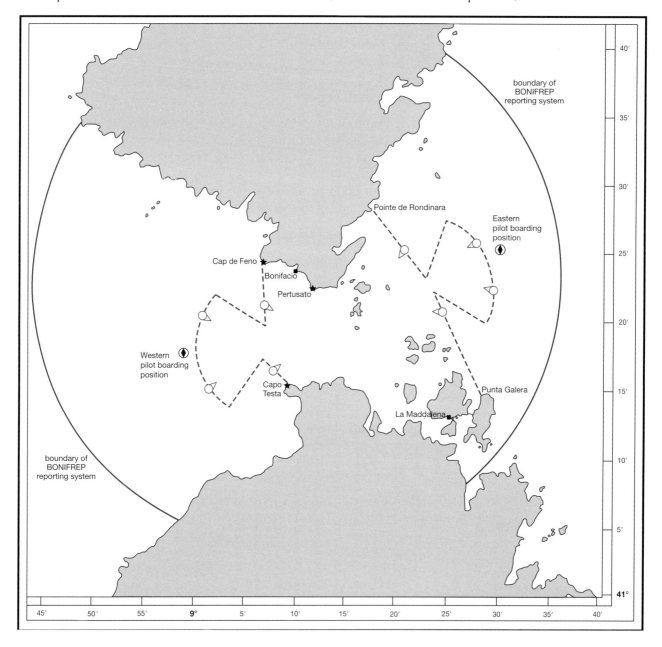

Recommendation on navigation through the Strait of Bonifacio[*]

1 Use of ships' routeing

Vessels navigating in the Strait shall exercise full diligence and regard for the requirements of the existing recommended two-way route in the Strait of Bonifacio. Due to the narrowness of the Strait, masters of vessels shall ensure that an appropriate monitoring of the ship's route is done on board in order to avoid groundings and collisions.

2 Ship reporting and navigation information

Ships of 300 GT and over entering the Strait shall participate in the mandatory ship reporting system (BONIFREP) established by the competent authorities as described in IMO's publication on Ships' Routeing (part G, section I).

3 Pilotage

Masters of vessels passing through the Strait are recommended to avail themselves of the services of a qualified pilot.

3.1 Categories of ships concerned

Ships for which the IMO Assembly recommends in its resolution A.766(18) of 17 November 1993 to Governments to prohibit or at least strongly discourage the transit in the Strait of Bonifacio: laden oil tankers and ships carrying dangerous chemicals or substances in bulk, as listed in the annex to resolution MEPC.49(31) adopted on 4 July 1991.

3.2 Description of the applicable procedure for requesting a pilot

Vessels wishing to order a Bonifacio Strait pilot should, as much as possible, send by e-mail or by fax the following information to the service named "Bonifacio Strait pilotage":

- ship's name and call sign;
- type of vessel and gross tonnage;
- draught;
- destination port/name and address of the local agent;
- boarding position and ETA.

24 hours prior to arrival, vessels should inform or confirm their ETA to the head office of the Bonifacio Strait pilotage service.

Once on Bonifacio Strait road, vessels should confirm their ETA two hours prior to arrival, calling "Bonifacio Traffic" on VHF 10.

3.3 Description of the pilotage service

The pilotage area covers the Strait and its approaches. Usually the vessels entering the Strait board their pilots out of the "BONIFREP" zone.

The boarding positions are the following (WGS 84):

- Eastern boarding position: 41°24'.80 N, 009°30'.00 E;
- Western boarding position: 41°17'.28 N, 008°58'.50 E.

---

[*] This associated protective measure was adopted at the ninetieth session of MSC in 2012.

Annex 18 – Saba Bank Particularly Sensitive Sea Area

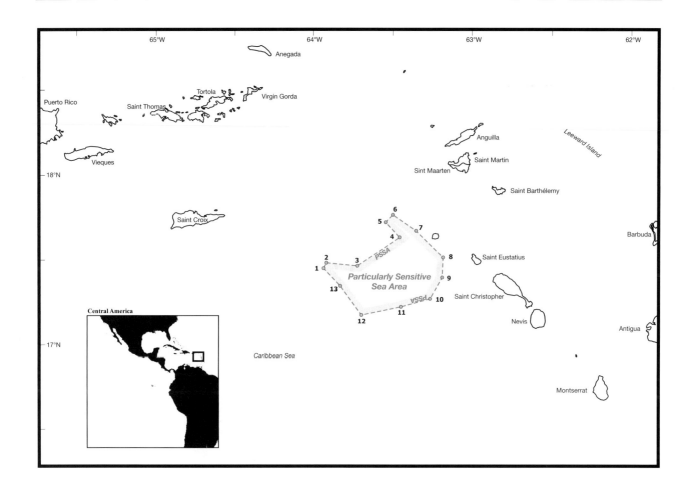

Resolution MEPC.226(64)

adopted on 5 October 2012
Designation of the Saba Bank
as a Particularly Sensitive Sea Area

THE MARINE ENVIRONMENT PROTECTION COMMITTEE,

BEING AWARE of the ecological, socio-economic and scientific attributes of the Saba Bank in the North-eastern Caribbean area of the Kingdom of the Netherlands, as well as its vulnerability to damage by international shipping activities and the steps taken by the Netherlands to address that vulnerability,

NOTING the *Revised guidelines for the identification and designation of particularly sensitive sea areas* adopted by resolution A.982(24) (PSSA Guidelines) and the Revised Guidance Document for Submission of PSSA Proposals to IMO set forth in MEPC.1/Circ.510,

HAVING CONSIDERED the proposal made by the Government of the Netherlands that the Saba Bank be designated as a Particularly Sensitive Sea Area,

HAVING AGREED that the criteria for the identification and designation of a Particularly Sensitive Sea Area provided in resolution A.982(24) are fulfilled for the Saba Bank,

HAVING NOTED that the Sub-Committee on Safety of Navigation, at its fifty-eighth session, approved the recommendation on the establishment of an Area To Be Avoided (ATBA) for ships of 300 gross tonnage and above and a mandatory No Anchoring Area for all ships as Associated Protective Measures (APMs) for the Saba Bank as a Particularly Sensitive Sea Area, aiming at improving the safety of navigation and the protection of the marine environment,

1   DESIGNATES the Saba Bank described in annex 1 as a Particularly Sensitive Sea Area, pending the final adoption by the Maritime Safety Committee of the associated protective measures for the PSSA as set out in annex 2 of document NAV 58/14;

2   INVITES Member Governments to recognize the ecological, socio-economic, and scientific attributes of the area, set forth in annex 2, as well as its vulnerability to damage by international shipping activities, as described in annex 3; and

3   FURTHER INVITES Member Governments to note the associated protective measures established to address the area's vulnerability, the details of which are contained in annex 4, which is expected to enter into force following final adoption on a date to be circulated by the Organization to all Member Governments, and request ships flying their flag that they act in accordance with such measures.

Annex 1

Description of the Saba Bank PSSA

In order to avoid the risk of pollution and damage to this unique, fragile and pristine coral reef ecosystem, and the risks to the artisanal fisheries of the area, mariners should exercise extreme care when navigating in the area bounded by a line connecting the following geographical positions, which is designated as a Particularly Sensitive Sea Area:

(1)	17°27'.06 N,	063°56'.14 W
(2)	17°29'.00 N,	063°55'.09 W
(3)	17°27'.94 N,	063°43'.32 W
(4)	17°38'.03 N,	063°27'.41 W
(5)	17°43'.35 N,	063°32'.74 W
(6)	17°45'.98 N,	063°29'.98 W
(7)	17°40'.34 N,	063°21'.10 W
(8)	17°30'.88 N,	063°10'.92 W
(9)	17°23'.80 N,	063°11'.25 W
(10)	17°16'.27 N,	063°15'.85 W
(11)	17°13'.44 N,	063°26'.89 W
(12)	17°10'.55 N,	063°41'.81 W
(13)	17°20'.85 N,	063°49'.89 W

(Reference chart: Netherlands nautical chart 2020, edition of November 2007.

Note: This chart is based on World Geodetic System 1984 datum (WGS 84).)

Chartlet

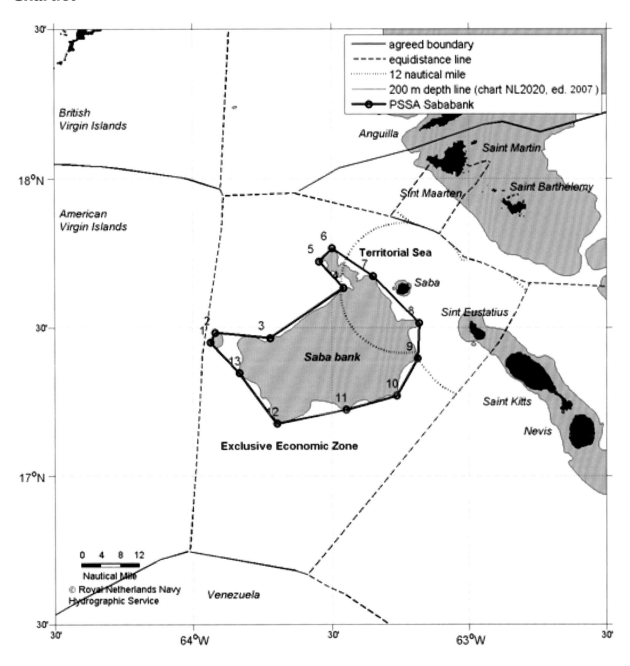

Annex 2

Ecological, socio-economic, and scientific attributes of the Saba Bank PSSA

Ecological criteria

1   Uniqueness or rarity

1.1   The reefs of the Saba Bank are far removed from land and as a consequence there is an absence of land-based influences such as elevated levels of sedimentation due to increased erosion, high nutrient concentrations caused by pollution from agricultural run-off and wastewater disposal, or sedimentation from coastal construction activities. Worldwide, reefs are in decline, from just such impacts originating from land. This unique position of the Saba Bank reefs provides a potentially greater resilience to changes in the environmental conditions, such as climate change, and it is a relatively untouched centre for recruitment and recuperation for the coastal reefs in the region.

1.2   The coral reefs of the Saba Bank, characterized by high coral cover of around 70 per cent in some places, have been determined to be among the four healthiest of the Caribbean, based on the Atlantic and Gulf Rapid Reef Assessment (AGRRA) health index, which is a compilation of many variables, including coral cover, fish populations, presence of diseases, types and cover of algae on the reef, and ratio of living coral versus dead coral.[*]

1.3   Because of its location and prevailing currents in the area, the Saba Bank is a source of larval recruitment for corals and coral-reef-associated organisms, including important fishery species such as conch (*Strombus gigas*) and lobster (*Panulirus argus*), for the entire region.

1.4   A two-week study, carried out in January 2006 by Conservation International, the former Netherlands Antilles government and the Smithsonian Institution's Museum of Natural History, to investigate the biodiversity of the Saba Bank found that the Saba Bank has the largest diversity of algae in the Caribbean. A diverse algal community is a critical food source for the herbivores on the Bank and provides shelters and habitats for fish and other invertebrate species.

1.5   Further studies, conducted in 2007, found two new species of gorgonian corals, a deep- and a shallow-water species. Since the gorgonians of the Caribbean are a well-known group of corals with only a limited number of species, the discovery of a new species in the shallowest parts of the Bank is very unique.

1.6   The Saba Bank is home to a number of species on the International Union for the Conservation of Nature (IUCN) Red List, such as the humpback whale, sperm whale, green turtle and the hawksbill turtle, yellowfin grouper, snowy grouper, Nassau grouper, queen triggerfish, yellowmouth grouper, bull shark, and tiger shark.

2   Critical habitat

2.1   The Saba Bank is a critical habitat for at least two species of sea turtles. Large areas covered in algae and areas rich in sponges provide foraging grounds for green sea turtles and hawksbill sea turtles respectively. Such feeding grounds are declining. Both of these species of turtles are listed on IUCN Red List of threatened species. The hawksbill is listed as critically endangered and the green sea turtle is listed as endangered. In addition, the Saba Bank provides critical habitat for coral species, many fish and invertebrate species, and for whales and dolphins. There are currently over 360 species of fish that have been documented on the Saba Bank and this list continues to grow.

---

[*] (Kramer, P.A. (2003) Synthesis of coral reef health indicators for the western Atlantic: Results of the AGRRA program (1997–2000). Atoll Res. Bull. (496), 1–57).

3   Dependency

3.1   The Saba Bank is formed and sustained by the growth of the corals and coral reefs on it. As such, these organisms provide habitat, food and shelter for all animals and plants living on the Bank. The high diversity of the area is maintained by the numerous feedback mechanisms characteristic for these kinds of ecosystems. As a self-sustaining ecosystem, it is highly productive and also forms an attractive feeding and nursery ground for many migratory species. The Saba Bank is the main nursery ground for fish species that are hatched in the area. The fishery on the Bank is dependent on these nursery-ground facilities and derives considerable income from them. The Saba Bank is also a source of lobster and conch larvae for the whole region down-current of the Bank.

4   Representativeness

4.1   As a submerged atoll with highly developed reefs, the Saba Bank is uniquely representative of coral reef growth processes in relatively deep water in the Caribbean, providing typical examples of deep reef structure and deep reef growthforms. The shallower parts of the Bank are representative of various high-energy hard-bottom habitats, while the deeper sandy areas provide calmer lagoon-like habitats.

5   Diversity

5.1   The reefs and other habitats of the Saba Bank have only recently been surveyed for species such as fish, gorgonians and invertebrates. Due to the vastness of the Bank, these lists are far from complete. Nevertheless, during the preliminary coral surveys 38 hard coral species were found. Similarly, the Saba Bank is rich in gorgonians, sponges, and fish species. Discoveries of new species on the Saba Bank are still made, as demonstrated by a 2006 research expedition which yielded over 200 fish species not previously known to exist in the area and over 100 species of algae, many of which were previously unknown to science.

5.2   Renowned algae experts Mark and Diane Littler consider the Saba Bank to have the highest diversity in the Caribbean with respect to marine algae. A 2007 research expedition also found two new species of soft coral. One of the new species was found in deep water (70 m), and the other was found to be common in shallow water (20 m). Since the gorgonians of the Caribbean are a well-known group of corals with only a limited number of species, the discovery of a new species in the shallowest parts of the Saba Bank was unexpected and indicative of the Bank's high diversity.

5.3   Further contributing to its diversity, the ecosystem of the Saba Bank contains a wide variety of habitats. For example, within the coral reefs of the Saba Bank, the percentage of coral cover varies widely, creating a series of interconnected but distinct types of coral reef habitats, or zones (e.g. fore-reef, reef crest, back-reef, patch reefs and lagoon). As a result of this zoning, the coral reefs of the Saba Bank contain a variety of environmental niches and resources that support a diverse array of species.

6   Productivity

6.1   As an actively growing atoll, the Saba Bank is quite productive for marine life. In many places, the corals form hills and ridges up to 20 feet high, growing fast enough to outpace destructive processes in this hurricane-prone region. The Saba Bank's productivity is also exemplified by its support of the Saba fisheries, a comparatively major economic sector which accounts for up to 7 per cent of the island's GDP.

7   Spawning and breeding grounds

7.1   Spawning aggregations of at least three species of fish are known from the Saba Bank. These species are the red hind, the queen triggerfish as well as squirrelfish. There is a worldwide general recognition that such spawning aggregations must be afforded protection. The Island Government has closed a critical red hind spawning area to fishing during the months of December to February in order to protect this important aggregation.

8   Naturalness

8.1   The Saba Bank is relatively isolated from land-based sources that generally cause the degradation of coral reefs. The Bank is close to the small island of Saba and separated from other islands by deep water. Biological surveys so far all describe the pristine conditions of the coral reefs of the Saba Bank.

9   Integrity

9.1   The Saba Bank ecosystem contains a wide variety of interconnected habitats. The diversity of habitat types enables the survival and coexistence of high numbers of marine species.

10   Fragility

10.1   Coral reefs are highly complex and diverse marine ecosystems which are very sensitive to any alteration of the environmental conditions. Due to a combination of anthropogenic and natural causes, Caribbean reefs are in decline and many of them, in this area, show decades of decrease in coral cover. The Saba Bank is relatively free from land-based sources of pollution, overfishing, and sedimentation; however, due to its high-level structural complexity and biodiversity, the Saba Bank's resilience to natural disturbances is low, and this Bank could be seriously affected by the anchoring of merchant vessels, especially by tankers.

10.2   Coral reefs require a delicate balance across a range of environmental conditions in order to be healthy. The existence of a coral ecosystem may be threatened by changes to even one of those environmental conditions. Corals derive a substantial portion of their nutrition from symbiotic algae (zooxanthellae) within their tissues. Because algae require light for photosynthesis, clear and clean water conditions are necessary for growth and well-being. The introduction of sediments increases turbidity and retards growth rates. The introduction of pollutants can be toxic to numerous parts of the ecosystem. The isolation of the Saba Bank allows protection from invasive species, which can be transferred by ships. Non-native species can displace native species and seriously disrupt and imbalance the natural ecosystem.

10.3   The physical structure of the reef is provided by calcium carbonate, which forms the rock framework or reef "skeleton". This calcium carbonate is deposited at a rate of about one centimetre per year by the living coral animals (polyps). These polyps exist in a thin layer at the surface of the reef rock. The Saba Bank coral reef system has taken thousands of years to build. If optimal conditions for regeneration exist, it would take substantial time (decades) for a damaged area of the reef to recover and fully return to its original condition.

10.4   The impact of activities like anchoring and the passage of merchant ships indisputably threatens the ecosystem of the Saba Bank. The anchors of merchant ships, and in particular the heavy anchor chains, destroy acres of coral reef as the ships swing on their anchors, waiting to load or unload at the large oil terminal of St Eustatius only 25 miles east of the Saba Bank, or just waiting for their next voyage. Regeneration of such damage will take decades, even under good conditions. Moreover, shipping traffic brings potential destruction from groundings, collisions, and pollution from operational and accidental discharges. Secondary, and cumulative, damage may occur when dislocated coral fragments caused by anchoring are tossed against healthy coral by wave action, currents and violent storms. Based on information collected from 2007 till 2009, the average number of days a ship is anchored increased from 4.5 to 7.8 days.

10.5   The Saba Bank is also vulnerable to so-called ghost traps. Ghost traps are lobster or fish traps lost by fishermen. Merchant ships crossing the Saba Bank do not notice the little buoys marking the locations of the traps and run over them. The buoys are lost or destroyed in the process, and the traps become ghost traps. This has a serious impact on the local fish stocks.

11   Bio-geographic importance

11.1   The Saba Bank has been discovered to be an atoll only recently. Its richness in terms of biodiversity is only just emerging. It is by far the largest atoll in the Caribbean, being four times the size of the next largest atoll and, as such, a unique bio-geographic object in the Caribbean.

Social, cultural and economic criteria

12   Social or economic dependency

12.1   In 2000, a year-long survey of the Saban fishery concluded that the fishery on the Saba Bank is of relatively major social and economic importance to Saba. The fishery sector generates US$1.2 million annually, or about 7 per cent of the island's GDP, and employs 8 per cent of the economically active population. The main target species of the fishery is the lobster, which accounts for 90 per cent of the catches. A management plan for sustainable fishery on the Saba Bank is in preparation and will be implemented in 2011.

12.2   The lobster fishery (lobster traps) is completely dependent on the availability of suitable habitat on the Saba Bank, (i.e. coral reefs and associated habitats which require a healthy marine environment). The destruction of the coral reefs has a devastating impact on the people and the economy of the island of Saba.

12.3   Although as yet unrealized, the extensive, healthy coral reefs on the Saba Bank and the discovery of a wreck constitute a potential for the development of dive tourism industry, which could help the economy of the island of Saba. Especially in view of the worldwide decline of coral reefs, and the fact that the Saba Bank reefs are among the healthiest of the region, the chances are considerable that this as yet untapped potential will be developed. Consequently, the conservation of a healthy marine environment on the Saba Bank is of paramount importance.

13   Human dependency

13.1   The inhabitants of the island of Saba, as well as St Eustatius, have been fishing in their small boats on the Saba Bank for generations, with written documentation going back as far as 1907.

Scientific and educational criteria

14   Research

14.1   As one of the few atolls in the Caribbean, and as an area with coral reefs that are still among the most untouched in the Caribbean, the Saba Bank is an important area for scientific research, although that potential is just beginning to be realized. In 2006, the Dutch research ship **HMS Snellius** conducted a detailed bathymetric study of a large part of the Bank. In cooperation with Conservation International, a very detailed bathymetric map of the Bank was compiled from the state-of-the art sonar data of the **Snellius**. This detailed information has been the basis for a six-month study to further investigate and classify the diverse habitat types which comprise the Saba Bank, and forms a very important resource for further research on the Bank.

14.2   This area is of high scientific interest and offers unparalleled opportunity for research. Given the fact that the Saba Bank has been relatively unexplored by scientists and is not impacted from pollution from the surrounding islands, it provides one of the few areas in the Caribbean where researchers can conduct large-scale comparisons between human-impacted marine ecosystems and unimpacted marine ecosystems.

14.3   As mentioned in paragraph 3.1.5, further evidence of the importance of this area for research was given in 2006 and again in 2007, when an international team of biologists made discoveries on the Saba Bank of two species of coral new to science and 20 new algae species that had never been described before. The researchers also recorded over 150 new fish species records for the Saba Bank, including some very rare species found only once or twice elsewhere in the Caribbean. These scientific discoveries suggest that much research remains to be done to fully understand and appreciate this complex ecosystem.

14.4   Ongoing research and monitoring of the marine ecosystems in the Saba Bank will continue to provide significant insights, not only for the Island of Saba but for the marine ecosystems around the Caribbean.

14.5   Saba Bank is one of the few marine regions on earth where monitoring and research activities can be conducted in the virtual absence of land-based human habitation and activities. It thus provides ideal baseline conditions with regard to biota and environmental characteristics because it did not have any impacts from land-based sources and is thus in a natural or near-natural condition.

15 Baseline for monitoring studies

15.1 In past years, some preliminary monitoring of the reefs of the Saba Bank took place. An Atlantic and Gulf Rapid Reef Assessment survey was completed in 1999, documenting coral cover and health, algal composition, and fish populations on three reef sites. In 2007, another AGRRA survey was completed to add to the data of the previous survey. The Saba Bank was classified as being one of the healthiest reefs in the Caribbean and, as such, forms an almost perfect baseline for comparison with other reefs in the Caribbean.

16 Education

16.1 Because baselines of human perception are bound to shift as more and more reefs become degraded, reefs like the ones found on the Saba Bank are an example of well-functioning and healthy reefs. Because the Saba Bank is in such a good condition, it offers ample opportunity for education.

Annex 3
Vulnerability to damage by international shipping activities

Vessel traffic characteristics

1   Operational factors

1.1   In addition to merchant shipping traffic, there is also a lot of traffic consisting of small artisanal fishing boats crossing the Saba Bank. In addition, some recreational traffic of sailing yachts is common in the area. Occasionally, live-aboard dive vessels operate in the area, and vessels of the Coastguard of the Netherlands in the Caribbean patrol this area. Currently there are no vessels or rigs conducting the exploration or development of oil, gas or minerals in this area.

2   Vessel types

2.1   There is a wide variety of vessels operating in this area. The main bulk of traffic consists of tankers of various sizes coming from or going to the St Eustatius Oil Terminal, 25 miles east of the Saba Bank. In addition, various dry cargo ships, as well as cruise ships, cross the Saba Bank. Smaller vessels include artisanal fishing boats and recreational yachts. Almost all of the merchant ships are trading on international voyages. Domestic traffic is limited to artisanal fishing, almost all less than 12 metres in length, and Coastguard vessels.

3   Traffic characteristics

3.1   Ship traffic is heavy in the area around the Saba Bank. Apart from the fishing boats, there are many cargo ships, tankers and cruise ships passing through the area. In 1995, St Eustatius Oil Terminal doubled its capacity to 11 million barrels and the number of visiting ships was estimated to be at least 100 a month. The port is one of the busiest tanker ports in the region. As from February 2008, the capacity has been 14 million barrels per year. It is estimated that about 200 tankers and cargo ships pass over the Saba Bank annually. An extension of the terminal in 2011 is foreseen.

3.2   Ships use the Saba Bank area mostly for passage only, but the fishermen on the Saba Bank report witnessing tank rinsing, oil spills, and the emptying of sewage tanks, and frequent sightings of anchoring on the Bank. All these activities have a severe impact on the environmental conditions of the Saba Bank, because they increase the intensity of traffic.

3.3   Some ships do not simply pass, but anchor on the Saba Bank, while waiting to load at St Eustatius Oil Terminal. Anchoring ships are both tankers and cargo ships with a draught of up to 12 m. Larger tankers avoid the Saba Bank because their draught, when loaded, is between 12 m and 20 m, which is too deep for the shallow areas of the Bank. Tankers have been seen anchoring on the Bank for a few hours to many weeks. A six-month survey of the Saba Bank in 2007 recorded a total of 21 ships anchoring on the Bank for a total of 94 anchoring days, ranging from 1 to 17 days a ship (based on visual observation). This is an under-estimation since only about half of the Saba Bank can be monitored visually from the island of Saba. As of December 2007, an Automatic Identification System (AIS) monitoring system was put in place to more accurately monitor ship movements and anchoring (coverage 50 per cent of Saba Bank).

4   Harmful substances carried

4.1   The majority of ships crossing the Saba Bank consist of tankers carrying crude oil on their way to or from the St Eustatius Oil Terminal.

Natural factors

5   Hydrographical

5.1   *Coral reef ridge* – the more than 50 km long shallow ridge on the east and south-east sides of the Saba Bank constitutes a navigational hazard for ships with a draught more than 12 metres.

5.2   The water depth of the proposed PSSA varies from 12 metres on its eastern and south-eastern edges, where the bottom drops steeply to depths in excess of 500 metres, to 20–30 metres on its southern and south-western side, where the bottom also falls steeply to great depths, to about 50 metres on the north-western side where the slope is more gradual.

5.3   The bottom topography of the Saba Bank includes everything from spectacular coral reefs to fine sand bottoms. Within this spectrum, some of the more important bottom types are: highly diverse algae meadows, coarse rubble fields, hard limestone substrate with evidence of past "karst" formations, and carbonate sand bottoms of varying degrees of coarseness.

6   Meteorological

6.1   The Saba Bank is located in the tropics, without clear wet or dry seasons. However, the Saba Bank is located in the Caribbean hurricane belt, and during the hurricane season from June to November the Bank is regularly exposed to a hurricane or a tropical storm. The area is within the Trade Wind zone with almost constant year-long eastern to north-eastern winds, except for the months of August to October when windless periods sometimes occur.

7   Oceanographic

7.1   The Saba Bank is situated in an area where surface ocean currents predominantly run east to west, although deviations both towards the north and to the south are known and even reversed currents are known to occur. It is unknown whether upwelling occurs along the eastern to south-eastern edges.

8   Other helpful information

8.1   Ship grounding and collisions on the Saba Bank have not occurred yet, but could cause great damage to the Bank's coral reefs. The grounding of large tankers or engine failure appears to be a genuine danger, because the prevailing winds and currents would carry the tanker rapidly from St Eustatius towards the Saba Bank.

8.2   The heavy ship traffic on the Saba Bank also poses a danger to the small (average <12 m length) artisanal fishing boats, which run the risk of being run over by large tankers. This risk has already caused the fishermen to avoid these traditional fishing grounds, causing a noticeable decrease of their catches.

8.3   Surveys carried out since 2007 show that anchoring on the Saba Bank has increased from an average of 4.5 days per ship till 7.8 days. The number of ships observed anchoring was 21, 20, and 24 respectively in 2007, 2008, and 2009. However, the surveys only cover about 40–60 per cent of the Bank. Most ships only anchor for a couple of days, but some may stay for as much as a month (see table 1).

Table 1: *Anchoring and ship traffic on the Saba Bank in 2007, 2008, 2009 and 2010*

Year	Anchoring ships	Total days	Average (days/ship)	Range (days/ship)	Passing ships
2007*	21	94	4.5	1–17	
2008†	20	60	3.0	1–11	54
2009†	24	187	7.8	1–33	29
2010†	20	68	3	1–14	

---

* Monitoring was mostly visual and not continuously during the year; figures indicate the minimum.

† On the basis of AIS covering 40–60 per cent of the Saba Bank.

Annex 4

Description of the area to be avoided for ships 300 GT and above and mandatory no anchoring area for all ships

An area to be avoided by ships of 300 GT and above and a mandatory no anchoring area for all ships is established in the area designated as a Particularly Sensitive Sea Area and bounded by a line connecting the following geographical positions:

(Reference chart: Netherlands 2020, edition of November 2007.

Note: This chart is based on World Geodetic System 1984 datum (WGS 84).)

(1)	17°27'.06 N,	063°56'.14 W	(8)	17°30'.88 N,	063°10'.92 W
(2)	17°29'.00 N,	063°55'.09 W	(9)	17°23'.80 N,	063°11'.25 W
(3)	17°27'.94 N,	063°43'.32 W	(10)	17°16'.27 N,	063°15'.85 W
(4)	17°38'.03 N,	063°27'.41 W	(11)	17°13'.44 N,	063°26'.89 W
(5)	17°43'.35 N,	063°32'.74 W	(12)	17°10'.55 N,	063°41'.81 W
(6)	17°45'.98 N,	063°29'.98 W	(13)	17°20'.85 N,	063°49'.89 W
(7)	17°40'.34 N,	063°21'.10 W			

Chartlets of the mandatory no anchoring area and area to be avoided

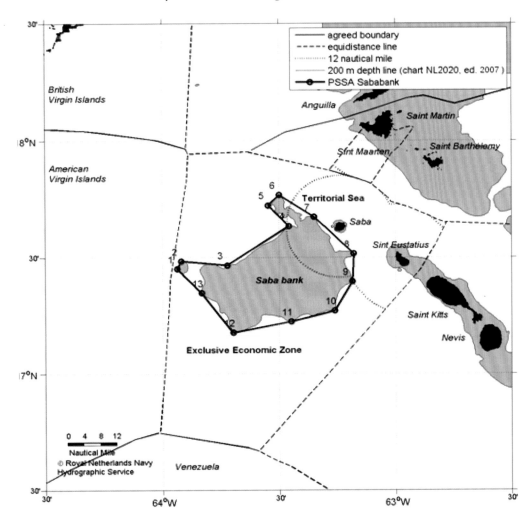

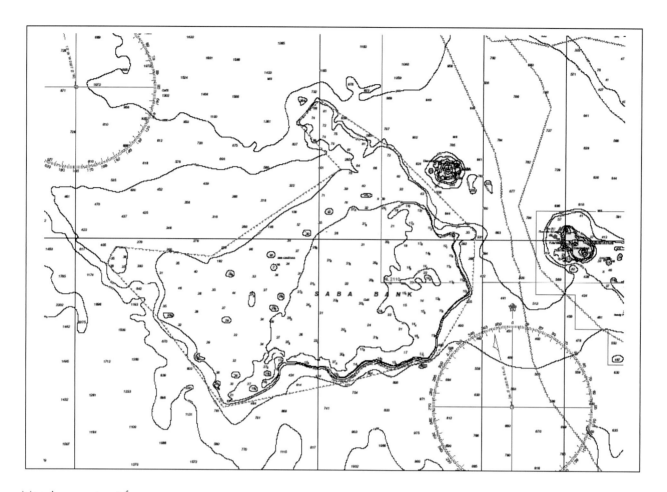

Map is an extract from:

Netherlands nautical chart no. 2020, edition of November 2007

Scale: 1:300,000

This chart is based on World Geodetic System 1984 datum (WGS 84)

© Royal Netherlands Navy Hydrographic Service

Annex 19 – Jomard Entrance Particularly Sensitive Sea Area

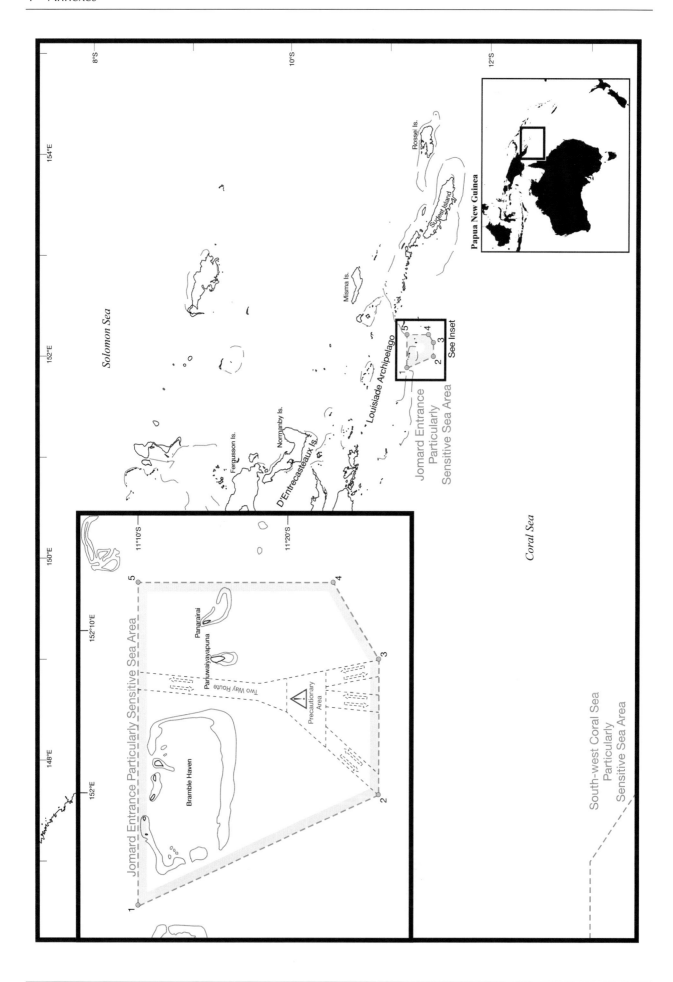

Resolution MEPC.283(70)

adopted on 28 October 2016

Designation of the Jomard Entrance as a Particularly Sensitive Sea Area

THE MARINE ENVIRONMENT PROTECTION COMMITTEE,

RECALLING Article 38(a) of the Convention on the International Maritime Organization concerning the functions of the Marine Environment Protection Committee conferred upon it by international conventions for the prevention and control of marine pollution from ships,

BEING AWARE of the ecological criteria, in particular the criteria relating to uniqueness or rarity, critical habitat, and diversity, and the social, economic, cultural and scientific attributes of the region surrounding the Jomard Entrance[*] as well as its vulnerability to damage by international shipping activities and the steps taken by Papua New Guinea to address that vulnerability,

NOTING the *Revised Guidelines for the Identification and Designation of Particularly Sensitive Sea Areas*, adopted by resolution A.982(24), as amended by resolution MEPC.267(68), (Revised PSSA Guidelines), and the *Revised Guidance Document for Submission of PSSA Proposals to IMO* set forth in MEPC.1/Circ.510,

HAVING AGREED that the criteria for the identification and designation of a PSSA provided in the revised PSSA Guidelines are fulfilled for the Jomard Entrance,

HAVING NOTED that the Jomard Entrance includes newly established routeing systems (four two-way routes and a precautionary area), adopted by the Maritime Safety Committee at its ninety-fourth session, as the Associated Protective Measures to improve the safety of navigation and the protection of the marine environment, and that these routeing systems entered into force on 1 June 2015,

1   DESIGNATES the region surrounding Jomard Entrance as defined in annex 1 to the present resolution as a Particularly Sensitive Sea Area;

2   INVITES Member Governments to recognize the ecological, social, cultural, economic and scientific attributes of the Jomard Entrance area, set forth in annex 2 to the present resolution, as well as its vulnerability to damage by international shipping activities, as described in annex 3 to the present resolution;

3   FURTHER INVITES Member Governments to note the associated protective measures established to address the area's vulnerability, the details of which are set out in annex 4 to the present resolution.

---

[*] Part of the Louisiade Archipelago at the south-eastern extent of Milne Bay Province, Papua New Guinea.

Annex 1

*Description of Jomard Entrance PSSA**

Description of the Particularly Sensitive Sea Area

To minimize the risk of damage from ship groundings and pollution damage by international shipping activities and to protect the area's unique and threatened species as well as to preserve as far as practicable its critical habitat and diversity, mariners should exercise extreme care when navigating in the area bounded by the geographical coordinates of the Particularly Sensitive Sea Area, provided below, and adhere to the Associated Protective Measures set out in annex 4.

All geographical positions are based on WGS 84. Listed numbers refer to figure 1.

No.	Latitude	Longitude
1	11°10.00′ S	151°53.00′ E
2	11°26.00′ S	151°59.90′ E
3	11°26.00′ S	152°08.24′ E
4	11°23.00′ S	152°13.00′ E
5	11°10.00′ S	152°13.00′ E

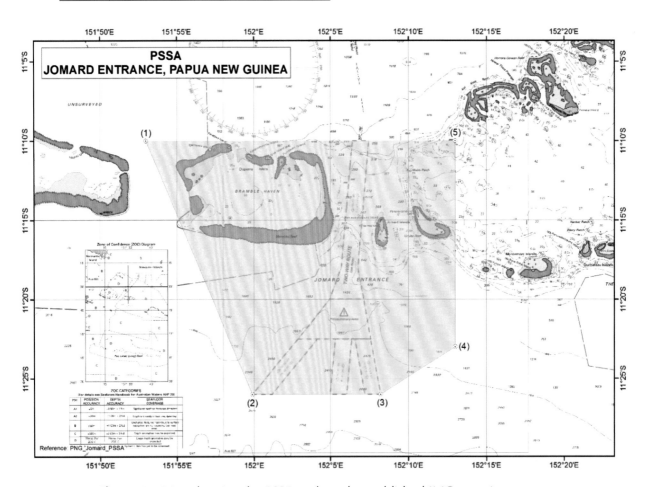

Figure 1 – *Map showing the PSSA and newly established IMO routeing systems*

---

* The text in this annex is drawn from Papua New Guinea's submission contained in document MEPC 70/8. All references from annex 2 of MEPC 70/8 are reproduced at the end of this resolution.

Annex 2
Ecological, socio-economic, and scientific criteria of the Jomard Entrance PSSA*

1   Introduction – The Jomard Entrance ecosystem

1.1   The Jomard Islands consist of two small uninhabited coral cay islands – Jomard Island (also called the Panuwaiyayapuna Island, meaning "long island") and Panarairai Island (also called Panadaludalu, meaning "island of dolphins"). The islands are located on raised reef flats and are fringed by coral reefs of significant size. The morphology of the fringing reef varies from site to site due to the different physical processes that take place on different parts of the island (e.g. wind and wave action). Without the current protection provided by the fringing reefs, the physical processes evident would ultimately erode the islands away. The fringing reef of Jomard Island also provides a significant habitat for marine species such as fish, crustaceans, corals, bivalves and other marine organisms. The marine life surrounding Jomard Island is extremely diverse in nature.

1.2   The beaches at Jomard Island are made up of fine sands and coral rubble. Ground vegetation lines the upper limits of the beach, providing stability and protection from eroding processes, while the littoral zone (intertidal zone) is home to corals that have adapted to withstand intense ultraviolet radiation, desiccation and high salinities. The reefs surrounding Jomard Island provide very good shelter for foraging and mating activities for turtles. Furthermore, these diverse reef systems support other marine species like fish, rays, clams and sea cucumbers which seek food and refuge and thrive in this healthy ecosystem. The beaches of Jomard Island and its fringing reefs accommodate a number of globally endangered species.

1.3   The terrestrial environment provides shelter for various species of birds like pigeons, crows and sea eagles. Jomard Island has been identified to have the largest turtle-nesting rookery in the southern part of Milne Bay Province. All six species of turtles that may be found in the region are currently listed in Appendix I of the Convention on International Trade in Endangered Species of Wild Fauna and Flora (CITES) as species threatened with extinction, and are also listed in Appendix I and/or Appendix II of the Convention on the Conservation of Migratory Species of Wild Animals. The IUCN Red List of Threatened Species currently lists the Loggerhead, Leatherback and Olive Ridley turtles as Vulnerable; the Green turtle as Endangered; and the Hawksbill turtle as Critically Endangered.

1.4   Bramble Haven lies to the north-west of the Jomard Islands and consists of a total of five coral cay islands, namely Punawan, Siva, Pananimunimu, Panapwa and Awanagamwana Islands. These islands are important habitat to marine fauna and flora and lie on a reef platform of approximate depth range of 2 metres to 25 metres. The southern part of this group of islands consists of moderately exposed fringing and lagoonal reefs with sand and coral bommies in the shallows and coral ridges running horizontally across the slope. These drop off into deep water. The islands harbour marine species of turtles, giant clam, bumphead parrotfish (*Bolbometopon muricatum*) and humphead (maori) wrasse (*Cheilinus undulatus*) that are on the IUCN Red List of threatened species. Green and Hawksbill turtles often utilize these areas for nesting, mating and foraging, while Loggerhead turtles transit through the region. This area is commercially exploited at a very low level. Factors that contribute toward this include the location of these islands in relation to human settlement.

1.5   As the PSSA is part of the Louisiade Archipelago, Milne Bay Province, and is also within the Coral Triangle, the critical habitat, diversity and biogeographic importance criteria are applicable throughout the PSSA. The uniqueness or rarity and fragility criteria apply particularly in the vicinity of the Jomard Islands, with the naturalness criteria particularly applicable around Bramble Haven. The social or economic dependency and human dependency criteria are also applicable in both the Bramble Haven and the Jomard Islands. Further details are provided below.

---

* The text in this annex is drawn from Papua New Guinea's submission contained in document MEPC 70/8.

2   Ecological criteria

Uniqueness or rarity

2.1   Six of the world's seven marine turtle species can be found in the waters off PNG. These include Hawksbill, Green, Leatherback, Flatback, Loggerhead and Olive Ridley. (Kinch, J., 2003). Of these, the first three are commonly found in the vicinity of Jomard Entrance. Scientific surveys and anecdotal evidence suggest that PNG has some of the largest remaining populations of these three turtle species in the world today. There is an informal tagging programme for turtle management and conservation at Jomard Islands, as the turtles have been nesting there annually for generations.

2.2   In terms of rarity, all six species of turtles that may be found in the region are currently listed in Appendix I of the Convention on International Trade in Endangered Species of Wild Fauna and Flora (CITES) as species threatened with extinction, and are also listed in Appendix I and/or Appendix II of the Convention on the Conservation of Migratory Species of Wild Animals. The IUCN Red List of Threatened Species (http://iucn-mtsg.org/) currently lists the Loggerhead, Leatherback and Olive Ridley turtles as Vulnerable; the Green turtle as Endangered; and the Hawksbill as Critically Endangered (see below).

Turtle type	IUCN Status List
Loggerhead turtle (*Caretta caretta*)	Vulnerable
Green turtle (*Chelonia mydas*)	Endangered
Leatherback turtle (*Dermochelys coriacea*)	Vulnerable
Hawksbill turtle (*Eretmochelys imbricata*)	Critically Endangered
Flatback turtle (*Natator depressus*)	Data Deficient
Olive Ridley turtle (*Lepidochelys olivacea*)	Vulnerable

Critical habitat

2.3   Fifteen marine sub-regions were identified within the Milne Bay Province by the Commonwealth Scientific and Industrial Research Organisation (CSIRO) Ocean Flagships; the Louisiade Archipelago has the largest area of reef or reef-associated (deep lagoon) habitat, with approximately 800,000 ha, representing 58% of the Archipelago (Skewes et al. 2003 and Skewes et al. 2011).

2.4   As noted above, the area provides a critical habitat for the Hawksbill, Green and Leatherback turtles. According to the IUCN, the overall global decline of the Hawksbill in particular has been in excess of 80% (Mortimer and Donnelly, 2008). In addition to these turtle species, both Bramble Haven and Jomard Island provide habitats for migratory marine and shore birds nesting sites, as well as for all giant clam species (Allen et al. 2003).

2.5   The fringing reef of Jomard Island provides a significant habitat for marine species such as fish, crustaceans, corals, bivalves and other marine organisms (UNESCO, 2016). The marine life surrounding Jomard Island is extremely diverse in nature. These habitats are sensitive to any shipping impact (e.g. oil spills, introduction of harmful marine species, marine debris and physical harm caused by groundings). Jomard Island has been identified to have the largest turtle nesting rookery in the southern part of Milne Bay Province (UNESCO, 2016).

Representativeness

2.6   The Jomard Entrance ecosystem includes pristine reefs with high species endemism that are relatively undisturbed or only commercially exploited at a very low level (see Reef Condition Index value in paragraph 2.9 below).

Diversity

2.7   Papua New Guinea (PNG) is located in the "Coral Triangle", an epicentre of rich marine biodiversity, see figure 1, and is home to 76% of all known coral species, 37% of all known coral-reef fish species, and

53% of the world's coral reefs. The area is of ecological and scientific significance and has great natural beauty and diversity, as seen in its pristine islands and reefs. Its waters host over 500 species of hard coral, 44 species of mangroves and 14 species of seagrass. PNG's Fourth National Report to the Convention on Biological Diversity (UNEP GEF 2016) notes that:

> "PNG provides one of the last opportunities for the conservation of significant areas of coral reefs in the western Pacific region of maximum marine biodiversity. Few other locations offer the combination of large areas of high-diversity reefs mostly undamaged by human activity; relatively low population size in most coastal areas; a scientific and management community that is committed to sustainable use of marine resources, and a customary land-tenure system that can be used to enhance conservation efforts."

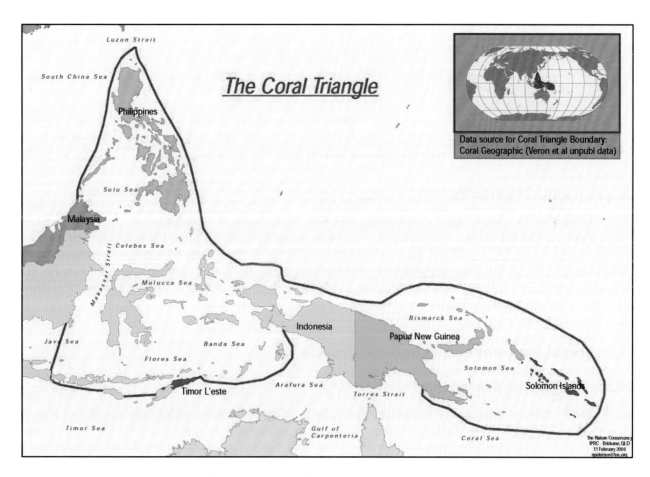

Figure 1 – *Map showing the Coral Triangle*

2.8   The Conservation International 2000 Rapid Marine Biodiversity Assessment (Allen et al. 2003) of the Milne Bay Province listed Punawan Island at Bramble Haven as the fifth most coral-diverse of the 57 sites surveyed, with 107 coral species observed. The assessment also listed both Punawan and Jomard Islands as among the best sites in Milne Bay with a rich combination of coral and fish diversity, as well as being relatively free of damage and disease.

2.9   The 2000 Assessment also assessed reef condition at 57 sites in Milne Bay Province. "Reef condition" is a term pertaining to the general "health" of a particular site as determined by assessment of key variables, including natural and human-induced environmental damage and general biodiversity as defined by major indicator groups (corals and fishes). A Reef Condition Index (RCI) value – derived from three components: coral diversity, fish diversity, and relative damage from human and natural causes – was calculated for each site. The results of this analysis indicated that the Louisiade Archipelago is included in the geographical area with the highest ranking Reef Condition Index. Overall, the RCI for the Milne Bay Province was significantly greater than the values obtained at previously surveyed reefs in other parts of the Coral Triangle.

Naturalness

2.10   The 2000 Rapid Marine Biodiversity Assessment of Milne Pay Province (Allen et al. 2003) concluded that Punawan Island at Bramble Haven was one of the six sites in the Province (from a total of 57 sites surveyed) that rated highly from an aesthetic point of view (good diversity, pristine condition, extensive cover, and good visibility). Most indicators show that Milne Bay's reefs are in remarkably good condition, especially compared to other areas in the Coral Triangle. While coral bleaching has occurred several times in limited areas of Milne Bay, this has mostly been limited to the northern areas of less than 10 degrees south.

Fragility

2.11   Jomard Island is a small coral cay island constructed on reef platforms, which have reached sea level during the Holocene. The island is fringed by a coral reef of significant size. The morphology of the fringing reef varies from site to site due to the different physical processes that take place on different parts of the island (e.g. wind and wave action). Without the current protection provided by the fringing reef, the physical processes evident will ultimately erode the island away (UNESCO, 2016).

2.12   A 2011 assessment of the coastal and marine ecosystem assets of Milne Bay found that the Louisiade Archipelago would be one of the subregions most impacted, taking into account sensitivity, exposure and weighting of ecosystem assets, climate change and human pressures (Skewes et al. 2001).

Bio-geographic importance

2.13   Milne Bay, by nature of being a series of variable island chains in close proximity to the large island of New Guinea, has led to very high levels of endemism across virtually all taxa. These islands are a part of the Woodlark and Pocklington Rises that are separated by active seabed floor spreading. The islands range from mountainous volcanic chains through to coralline, makateas, atolls and sand cays, and their associated seamounts and shelf; sunken, fringing and barrier reefs. Milne Bay has disproportionate biodiversity richness and endemism for its size (Andréfouët et al. 2006).

3   Social, cultural and economic criteria

Social or economic dependency

3.1   PNG's human population (~10 million inhabitants, 2016) has strong economic, social and cultural ties with the sea. PNG's marine resources are an important source of economic livelihood in the extensive rural portions of the country's islands and coastal areas. They support a private sector fishing industry that is a significant source of government revenue. (Asian Development Bank, 2016).

3.2   Tuna and shrimp are the major commodities comprising PNG's commercial fisheries. The 2010 tuna catch totalled 799,000 tons, while the shrimp catch has averaged about US$10.5 million in recent years. Within the PSSA, Panuwaiyayapuna and Panarairai Islands are both important sites for subsistence artisanal fishing and diving for commercially valuable resources, while Punaman Island is an important site of sea cucumbers for beche-de-mer and trochus harvesting.

Human dependency

3.3   PNG's waters are vital to the subsistence of its inhabitants and the nation's economy, with the sea acting as a "supermarket" for coastal community residents. Fish is a major source of dietary protein, particularly in island and coastal areas, evident in the relatively high annual per capita fish consumption of coastal community residents, which is estimated at 53.3 kilograms (Asian Development Bank, 2016).

3.4   Marine resource use in the Louisiade Islands is artisanal in nature, providing for subsistence needs as well as limited small-scale commercial production. Because of a lack of regularly scheduled cargo transport and the absence of refrigeration facilities, commercial harvesting primarily targets non-perishable, high-value invertebrate products. Residents of some of the smaller islands are especially dependent on income from harvesting resources such as sea cucumbers for beche-de-mer.

Cultural heritage

3.5   Traditional shell "money", locally known as "bagi", made from *Spondylus* shell is also extensively extracted and manufactured in the Louisiade Islands. These bagi flow along the Louisiade Archipelago and are eventually modified and fed into Kula Ring.

3.6   With the importance of the marine resources for islanders' wellbeing, many traditional legends, dances and hymns are linked to it. Many still ply the waters to these islands in either traditional sailing canoes or dinghies, maintaining their seamanship and navigational skills in doing so (Smaalders and Kinch, 2003).

4   Scientific and educational criteria

Research

4.1   CSIRO Division of Marine Research, PNG National Fisheries Authority and Conservation International conducted a joint marine stock assessment of the abundance of reef resources and sustainable use of beche-de-mer resources for Milne Bay in 2001. This included the islands of the Jomard Passage (Skewes et al. 2002).

Baseline for monitoring studies

4.2   Geo-referenced dive sites from the Conservation International's Marine RAP of 2000, the stock assessment mentioned in paragraph 28, ongoing turtle monitoring and tag-retrieval data held by SPREP (Secretariat of the Pacific Regional Environment Program) and Queensland National Parks and Wildlife Service as well as 2015 National Maritime Safety Authority Surveys are current baselines. Permanent transects need to be established to establish a standardized baseline.

Annex 3
Vulnerability to damage by international shipping activities

1   Vessel traffic characteristics

Operational factors

1.1   Fishing vessels, local trade vessels, local sailing canoes, tourist and recreational craft can be encountered anywhere in the Jomard Entrance area.

1.2   There are currently no existing activities or foreseeable developments of offshore exploration or exploitation of the seabed. Nautilus Mining previously held Exploration Licence Tenements in the Solomon Sea; however, these lapsed. Similarly, there are no offshore structures other than those used to provide aids to navigation in the region.

Vessel types

1.3   There is a wide variety of vessels operating in this area, including large bulk carriers, timber carriers, LNG, oil and chemical tankers, passenger ships, cruise liners and third-generation containerships.

1.4   Since July 2014, LNG has become one of the primary commodities exported by PNG. It is predicted that around 110 LNG ships will call at PNG ports each year for the first three years, with this number forecast to double by 2020. All LNG ships will use Jomard Entrance as their primary route to/from Japan, which is contracted to import around 85% of PNG's LNG. There is a second LNG project within PNG that will likely be developed in the near future.

1.5   Papua New Guinea (PNG) is experiencing significant growth in marine tourism. Cruise-industry sources reveal that up to 100 ship calls per annum are expected each year for the next five years, following which a further growth of 34% is estimated for the next five years.

Traffic characteristics

1.6   PNG is experiencing a marked increase in the volume of international ship traffic passing through its waters. It is estimated that some 9200 ships transited its waters in 2013. Many ships in ballast drift near the southern approaches to Jomard Entrance awaiting their turn to load at Australian ports. Some 90% of the ships carrying commodities exported by Australia's eastern coast ports to north Asian markets (including China, Japan and the Republic of Korea) use this most direct route through PNG's waters.

1.7   Over the last decade and a half, commodity exports have been a key driver of economic activity in Australia, driven by strong growth in demand from emerging economies in Asia. Substantial resource exports (mainly coal and Liquefied Natural Gas (LNG)) from Australian ports have contributed to increased traffic through PNG's waters. This trend is predicted to continue for some time to come.

1.8   Coal exports from the state of Queensland in Australia will be the biggest driver of increased shipping through Jomard Entrance, through which northbound ships loaded with coal from the ports of Hay Point, Abbot Point and Gladstone will traverse. The coal port of Newcastle on the central coast of New South Wales also contributes to the significant traffic through Jomard Entrance.

1.9   As an example, the number of ships calling at the Australian coal-exporting port of Abbot Point each year is forecast to grow from 172 (in 2012) to 1640 (in 2032) – almost a tenfold increase. Likewise, annual traffic from Hay Point in central Queensland is forecast to grow from 809 ships to 2380 ships in the same period.

1.10   Concurrently, strong growth in PNG's mining and resource sectors has led to it becoming one of the world's fastest-growing economies. As noted above, a variety of ship types transit PNG's pristine and reef-littered waters, the majority along well-used routes; see figure 1.

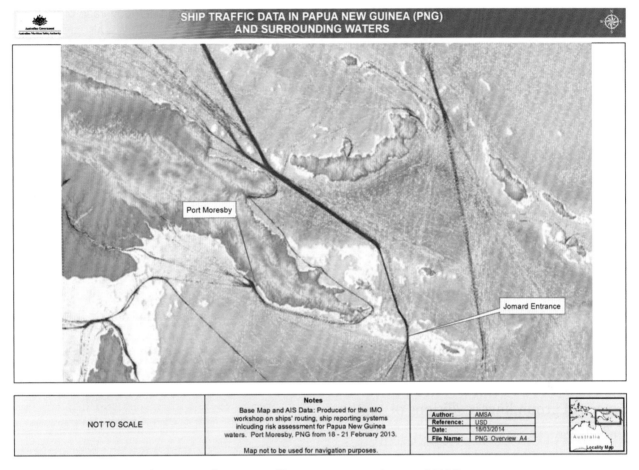

Figure 1 – *Shipping traffic patterns in and around PNG waters*

1.11   Taking into account the current and projected levels of international shipping traffic, a risk assessment conducted using the IALA Waterways Risk Assessment Program Mk2 in February 2013 found that the introduction of a two-way route could reduce the frequency of potential collisions from the one every seven years to one every 14 years – a reduction of 50% in the number of potential collisions.

Harmful substances carried

1.12   Vessels transiting Jomard Entrance are primarily bulk carriers; however, there are also significant numbers of oil, chemical/products and LNG tankers.

2   Natural factors

Hydrographical

2.1   Hydrographic surveys in the immediate area of the two-way routes are to Zone of Confidence (ZOC) B. These surveys confirm existing charted depths and depiction of reef edges, and are to be incorporated into a new 1:75,000 large-scale chart in 2014–15. Areas outside the limits of these surveys are to ZOC C. Notably, the reefs defining Jomard Entrance are fronted by deep water which considerably exceeds the maximum draught of any surface vessel which could conceivably use the route.

2.2   It is worth noting that, through extensive use by commercial shipping over an extended period of time, bathymetric surveys in the region of the two-way route have been proven as adequate for safe navigation.

2.3   Electronic Navigation Chart (ENC) coverage of the area is provided as ENC AU412152, Edition 2, at a nominal scale of 1:90,000. This was updated to include larger scale coverage to the limits shown in Chartlet 1 (see annex 4) prior to the establishment of the two-way route. Smaller-scale approach coverage of the Coral and Solomon Seas is provided by AU220150 Edition 3. Additionally, smaller-scale ENC are also available for planning. All ENC are metric and referenced to WGS 84 and Lowest Astronomical Tide (LAT).

2.4   Paper chart coverage of Jomard Entrance is available in a new chart at a scale of 1:75,000 with limits and extent as shown in Chartlet 1 in annex 4. The entrance is also depicted on existing smaller-scale charts, ranging from 1:150,000 for navigation and at smaller scales for planning. All charts are metric and referenced to WGS 84 and LAT.

Meteorological

2.5   The Jomard Passage is in a tropical-cyclone-prone zone. Though cyclone frequency is expected to decrease with climate change projections, the severity is expected to increase when they do occur. The main shipping routes are heavily exposed to prevailing south-east Trade Winds, which have a fetch of hundreds of nautical miles.

Oceanographic

2.6   Previous research has shown evidence of surface and deep boundary currents flowing around the southern end of the Louisiade Archipelago, with leakage of surface water from the Coral Sea through the Louisiade Archipelago.

3   Other information

History of groundings, collisions or spills

Groundings

3.1   Chart Aus510 shows four wrecks (visible at chart datum) on the immediate reefs in and around Jomard Entrance. In the early 2000s, several longliners ran aground in the Jomard and Bramble Haven area, with three running aground in 2000. In 2006, a bulk carrier grounded on Long Reef near Jomard Entrance, spilling oil and raw sugar. In 2011, the total loss of engine power by a containership in the same area led to the Royal Australian Navy providing assistance by way of a patrol boat (which happened to be on exercise in PNG at the time). A tow line attached to the stricken ship prevented it from grounding on nearby reefs and potentially causing reef damage and pollution of the area.

Marine debris

3.2   A marine debris survey conducted in 2012 on four islands within the PSSA – Jomard, Panarairai, Punawan and Siva – reported that marine debris is accumulating in significant amounts on these islands (Raaymakers et al. 2012). While further work would be needed to establish with any certainty the proportion of debris contributed by shipping, it is hoped that the revised MARPOL Annex V, which entered into force on 1 January 2013, will result in a reduction in marine debris from shipping within the PSSA.

Intervention and response

3.3   The length and remoteness of PNG's coastline poses major challenges to any response to an accident and containing any resulting pollution. These challenges are also compounded due to limited response capabilities in the region. As noted above, the main shipping routes are heavily exposed to prevailing south-east Trade Winds. A casualty in such circumstances will make any salvage and recovery task challenging. The closest tugs and oil spill response equipment are located at Port Moresby, which is approximately 330 nautical miles away. Therefore, it is vital to avoid incidents in the region.

Annex 4

Associated protective measures for the Jomard Entrance PSSA

Associated Protective Measures (APMs)

1   The newly established routeing systems (four two-way routes and a precautionary area) at Jomard Entrance are the APMs, as follows:

.1   a one nautical mile wide two-way route to the north of Jomard Entrance, which extends approximately 20 nautical miles from the northern boundary of the precautionary area; see chartlets, below;

.2   three 1 nautical mile wide two-way routes to the south of Jomard Entrance, each aligned with the general traffic pattern to/from ports on the east coast of Australia. The routes extend approximately 3.5 nautical miles from the southern boundary of the precautionary area; see chartlets, below; and

.3   a quadrilateral-shaped precautionary area that lies between the northern and southern two-way routes described above; see chartlets, below.

2   The two-way routes and precautionary area can be used by all ships navigating in the area.

(**Note:** These routeing systems were approved at the first session of the Sub-Committee on Navigation, Communications and Search and Rescue (NCSR 1/3/8), subsequently adopted by MSC 94 and entered into force on 1 June 2015.)

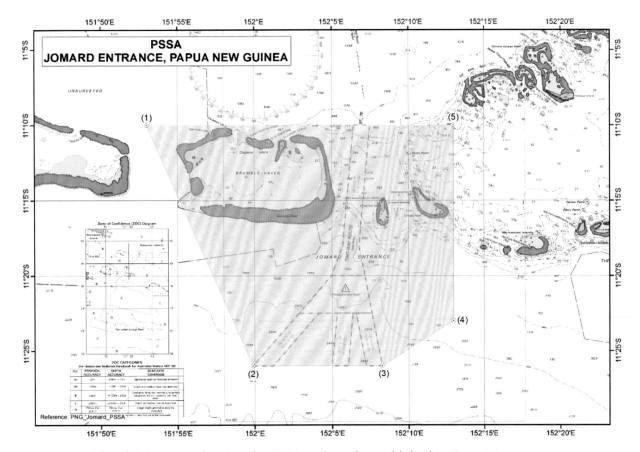

Chartlet 1 – *Map showing the PSSA and newly established IMO routeing systems*

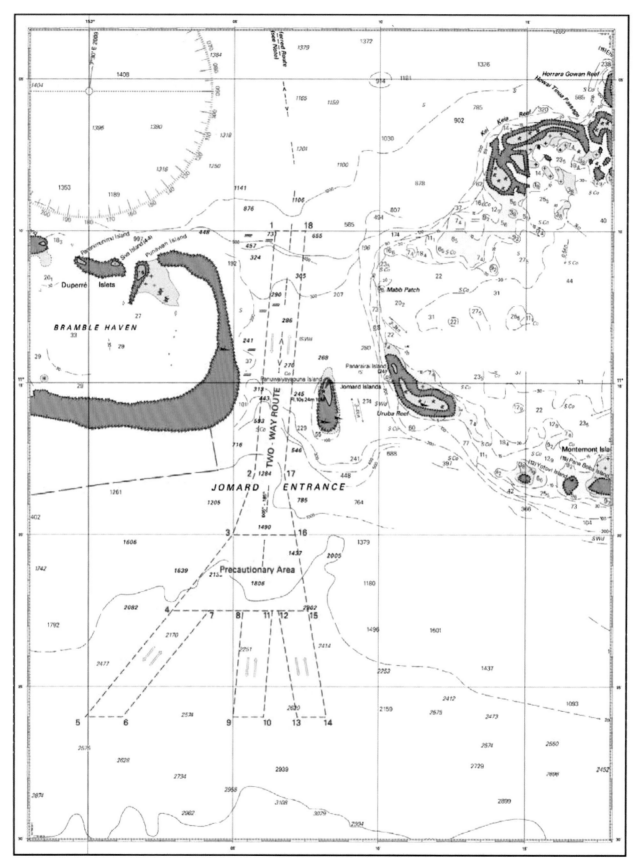

Chartlet 2 – *The four two-way routes and the precautionary area at Jomard entrance, approved by MSC 94*

References

Allen, G. R., Kinch, J. P., McKenna, S. A. and Seeto, P. (eds.). (2003). A Rapid Marine Biodiversity Assessment of Milne Bay Province, Papua New Guinea – Survey II (2000). RAP Bulletin of Biological Assessment 29. Conservation International, Washington, DC, USA.

Andréfouët S., Chauvin C., Kranenburg C. J., Muller-Karger F. E., and Noordeloos M. (2006) Atlas of Southeast Papua New Guinea Coral Reefs, Centre IRD de Nouméa, Décembre 2006, 30pp. + 10 maps.

Asian Development Bank (ADB). State of the Coral Triangle. www.coraltriangleinitiative.org/sites/default/files/resources/SCTR-PNG.pdf.

Bell. I., Kwan. D., Pita. J. and Wangunu N. (2004). Turtle Tagging and Monitoring in Milne Bay Province, December 2003. A report prepared for Conservation International, Papua New Guinea Department of Environment and Conservation and South Pacific Regional Environmental Program. Milne Bay Community-based Marine Conservation Program. PNG 01/010. 45pp.

Furnas, M., Burrage, D., Alongi, D. and Inoue, M. (1988). R.V. Franklin National Facility Oceanic Research Vessel – Research Summary, Australian Institute of Marine Science.

Hitchcock, P., Gabriel, J. (2015). World Heritage Tentative Listed Sites in Papua New Guinea – Report on a Review of the Sites. A report prepared for the World Heritage Commission.

Mortimer, J., Donnelly, M. (2008). Hawksbill turtle – Marine Turtle Specialist Group 2008 IUCN Red List Status Assessment.

Kinch, J. (2003). Sea Turtle Resources in the Milne Bay Province, Papua New Guinea: Results of a Nesting Survey (21–27/01/03) at Panayayapona and Panadaludalu Islands (Jomard Islands), with Additional Notes. Conservation International, PN. Port Moresby. 34pp.

Kinch, J. (2001). Social feasibility study for the Milne Bay Community-Based Coastal and Marine Conservation Program. A report to the United Nations Milne Bay Community-Based Coastal and Marine Conservation Program, PNG/99/ G41, Port Moresby, Papua New Guinea.

Kinch, J. (1999). Economics and environment in island Melanesia: A general overview of resource use and livelihoods on Brooker Island in the Calvados Chain of the Louisiade Archipelago, Milne Bay Province, Papua New Guinea. A report prepared for Conservation International, Port Moresby, Papua New Guinea.

Raaymakers, S., Smith, W., Limu, P., Benoma, D., Sine, R. and Blaria, E. (2012) Summary Beach Debris Report – Four islands near Jomard Passage, Louisiade Archipelago, Papua New Guinea. A report prepared for National Maritime Safety Authority, Papua New Guinea.

Skewes, T., Dennis, D., Taranto, T., Wassenburg, T., Koutsoukos, A., Polon, P., Lokani, P., Kinch, J., Seeto, P., and Sarke, J., (2002) Research for Sustainable use of Beche-de-mer resources in Milne Bay Province, Papua New Guinea. A report prepared for the CSIRO.

Skewes, T., Kinch, J., Polon, P., Dennis, D., Seeto, P., Taranto, T., Lokani, P., Wassenberg, T., Koutsoukos, A and Sarke, J. (2003) Distribution and abundance of reef resources in Milne Bay Province, Papua New Guinea: giant clams and other species. CSIRO Division of Marine Research Final Report, Cleveland Australia.

Skewes, T., Lyne, V., Butler, J., Mitchell, D., Poloczanska, E., Williams, K., Brewer, D., McLeod, I., Rochester, W., Sun, C. and Long, B. (2011). Melanesian coastal and marine ecosystem assets: assessment framework and Milne Bay case study. CSIRO Final Report to the AusAID Alliance.

Smaalders, M., Kinch, J. (2003) Canoes, subsistence and conservation in the Louisiade Archipelago of Papua New Guinea. SPC Traditional Marine Resource Management and Knowledge Information Bulletin #15.

UNEP GEF. Papua New Guinea's Fourth Report to the Convention on Biological Diversity. www.cbd.int/doc/world/pg/pg-nr-04-en.pdf.

UNESCO. Milne Bay Seascape (Pacific Jewels of Marine Biodiversity). http://whc.unesco.org/en/tentativelists/5063.

Notes